Paper

Advances in

Printing Science and Technology

Volume 3

HALFTONE PRINTING

HALFTONE PRINTING

Proceedings of the
Seventh International Conference of Printing Research Institutes
held in London, 1963

EDITED BY

W. H. BANKS

RESEARCH SUPERINTENDENT
PRINTING AND ALLIED TRADES RESEARCH ASSOCIATION
LEATHERHEAD, ENGLAND

SYMPOSIUM PUBLICATIONS DIVISION

PERGAMON PRESS

OXFORD · LONDON · EDINBURGH · NEW YORK
PARIS · FRANKFURT

PERGAMON PRESS LTD.
Headington Hill Hall, Oxford
4 and 5 Fitzroy Square, London, W.1

PERGAMON PRESS (SCOTLAND) LTD.
2 and 3 Teviot Place, Edinburgh 1

PERGAMON PRESS INC.
122 East 55th Street, New York 22, N.Y.

GAUTHIER-VILLARS ED.
55 Quai des Grands-Augustins, Paris, 6^{e}

PERGAMON PRESS G.m.b.H.
Kaiserstrasse 75, Frankfurt am Main

Distributed in the Western Hemisphere by
THE MACMILLAN COMPANY · NEW YORK
pursuant to a special arrangement with
Pergamon Press Limited

First published 1964

Library of Congress Catalogue Card Number 64–24960

Printed in Great Britain at the Pitman Press, Bath

PREFACE

SEVEN years is a significant period in the development from youth to manhood and so perhaps one might regard the 7th International Conference of Printing Research Institutes as completing a phase of its growth to maturity. It returned to its birthplace, England, for the occasion.

Some thirty-five delegates met at Sanderstead, South London, in June 1963, to read and discuss twenty-six papers on topics mostly related to halftone reproduction under the chairmanship of Dr. V. G. W. Harrison (Director of PATRA) and vice-chairmanship of Mr. Chr. W. Christensen, of the Graphic College of Denmark.

The success of a conference depends not only on the excellence of the discussion but on those concerned with its organization and in this connection must be mentioned Mr. K. N. Hoare, Miss Croxen, Miss Lubbock, Mrs. Harrison and Mr. Razzell. Finally, a special mention must be made of Mr. B. W. Blunden for his unobtrusive help behind the scenes.

W. H. BANKS

July, 1964

CONTENTS

PARTICIPANTS

Country	*Name*	*Institute*
Austria	Walter Jaschek	Graphische lehr-und Versuchsanstalt, Vienna
Denmark	C. W. Christensen	The Graphic College of Denmark, Copenhagen
	A. Frøslev Nielsen	The Graphic College of Denmark, Copenhagen
	R. Laraignou	The Graphic College of Denmark, Copenhagen
	A. Wulff	The Graphic College of Denmark, Copenhagen
	J. Reimann	Den Danske Presses Faellesindkobs-Forening, Copenhagen
Finland	R. Ginman	The Finnish Pulp & Paper Research Institute
	O. Perila	Graphic Arts Research Institute, Helsinki
France	Mme. H. Benedite	Société Professionelle des Papiers des Presse, Paris
	E. Paszkiewicz	Institut Professionelle de Recherches et d'Etudes des Industries Graphiques, Paris
Germany	J. Albrecht	Deutsche Gesellschaft für Forschung im Graphische Gewerbe, Munich
	H. Dürner	Deutsche Gesellschaft für Forschung im Graphische Gewerbe, Munich
	K. Wagenbauer	Institut für Druckmaschinen und Druckverfahren, Darmstadt
Great Britain	J. M. Adams	Printing, Packaging and Allied Trades Research Association, Leatherhead, Surrey
	W. H. Banks	Printing, Packaging and Allied Trades Research Association, Leatherhead, Surrey
	M. Graneek	Printing, Packaging and Allied Trades Research Association, Leatherhead, Surrey
	V. G. W. Harrison	Printing, Packaging and Allied Trades Research Association, Leatherhead, Surrey
	Baysung Hsu	Printing, Packaging and Allied Trades Research Association, Leatherhead, Surrey
	C. C. Mill	Printing, Packaging and Allied Trades Research Association, Leatherhead, Surrey
	Miss E. J. Pritchard	Printing, Packaging and Allied Trades Research Association, Leatherhead, Surrey
	S. R. C. Poulter	Printing, Packaging and Allied Trades Research Association, Leatherhead, Surrey
	K. Woods	Printing, Packaging and Allied Trades Research Association, Leatherhead, Surrey

Country	*Name*	*Institute*
Holland	J. F. Monroy	Stichting Instituut voor Grafische Techniek T.N.O., Amsterdam
	A. J. W. Sweerman	Stichting Instituut voor Grafische Techniek T.N.O., Amsterdam
	D. Tollenaar	Stichting Instituut voor Grafische Techniek T.N.O., Amsterdam
	Miss van der Vloodt	Stichting Instituut voor Grafische Techniek T.N.O., Amsterdam
Hungary	G. Gati	Hungarian Printing Ink Research Laboratory, Budapest
	Kálmán Lovász	Experimental Plant and Laboratory of the Printing Industry of Hungary, Budapest
Italy	G. Calabrò	Ente Nazionale per la Cellulosa e per la Carta, Rome
	I. Fabbri	Ente Nazionale per la Cellulosa e per la Carta, Rome
Norway	Otto Jansen	Norwegian Pulp & Paper Research Institute, Oslo
Sweden	G. E. Carlsson	Grafiska Forskningslaboratoriet, Stockholm
	L. O. Larsson	Tidningspappersbrukens Forskningslaboratorium, Stockholm
United States of America	M. Bruno	Lithographic Technical Foundation, Chicago, Illinois
	F. C. Myers	Graphics Division, U.S. Army Engineer Geodesy, Intelligence and Mapping, Research & Development Agency, Fort Belvoir, Virginia
	R. W. Prince	A.N.P.A., Research Institute, Easton, Pa.
	W. T. Reid	Battelle Memorial Institute, Columbus, Ohio
	W. C. Walker	West Virginia Pulp & Paper Co.
	J. A. C. Yule	Eastman Kodak Research Laboratories, Rochester
	A. C. Zettlemoyer	N.P.I.R.I. Lehigh University

CONDITIONS FOR HALFTONE PRINTING

by D. Tollenaar and P. A. H. Ernst
Stichting Instituut voor Grafische Techniek, T.N.O.,
Amsterdam, The Netherlands

SYMBOLS AND EXPRESSIONS

x Thickness in μm of the ink layer on the forme.

D Optical density of a solid print measured with respect to the unprinted surface.

D_∞ Saturation density—the optical density of a solid print if very thick ink layers are applied.

D/D_∞ Relative optical density of a solid print.

m Density smoothness, defined by the equation $D/D_\infty = 1 - e^{-mx}$.

D_h Optical density of a halftone print.

R Screen fineness in lines per cm.

a Printing area of the block $0 \leqq a \leqq 1$.

a_v Critical printing area—the minimum printing area at which complete filling-in occurs $0 \leqq a_v \leqq 1$.

c A dimensionless empirical constant of the value 0.00187.

Halftone density curve—The curve representing the optical density D_h of a halftone print as a function of the printing area a, if filling-in occurs at $a = a_v$. In this paper the shape of the curve is not essential. The approximate formula

$$D_h/D_\infty = -\frac{1}{D_\infty} \log \left\{1 + \frac{a}{a_v} + \frac{a}{a_v} \cdot 10^{-D_h}\right\}$$

has been used.

Filling-in curve —The curve representing the relative density of a filled-in halftone print as a function of the critical printing area a_v:

$$D/D_\infty = (1 - a_v)^{\frac{cR}{m}}.$$

INTRODUCTION

A PRELIMINARY enumeration of the qualifications for a good halftone impression comprises such general requirements as sufficient colour contrast, freedom from picking, freedom from filling-in if the letterpress process is used, freedom from tinting and scumming if offset is used, sufficient rendition of detail, a good tone rendition, etc. In trying to achieve all these requirements the printer finds that many of them are closely bound up with the thickness of the ink layer. At this stage it does not matter whether we choose the ink layer thickness on the paper or on the forme. The influence of the amount of

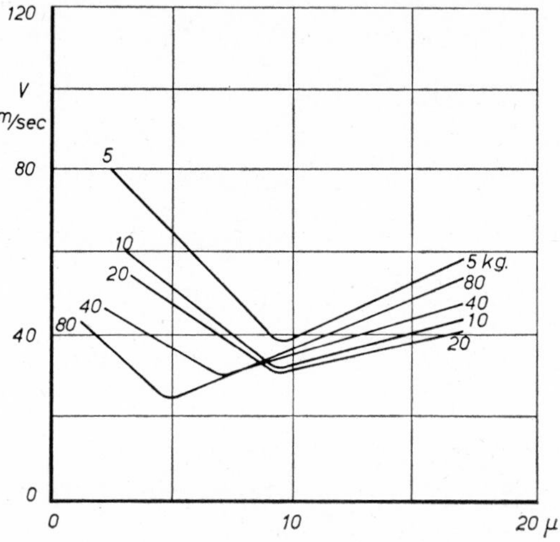

Fig. 1. Picking velocity as a function of ink layer thickness.

ink is especially clear if we consider colour contrast, filling-in of a letterpress forme and picking. It is also clear that each of these requirements calls for a definite ink layer thickness, or at least for a definite maximum and/or minimum value of the amount of ink. A minimum ink layer thickness is required for a good colour contrast and, if we leave variations in hue out of the picture, we may take the relative optical density $D/D_\infty = 1 - e^{-mx}$ as a quantitative relationship between colour contrast and ink layer thickness. Here D is the optical density of a solid print measured with respect to the unprinted surface, D_∞ is the saturation value of D which is obtained at high ink layer thicknesses and m is a "density smoothness" stating how quickly the density approaches the saturation value. In our consideration the ink layer thickness on the forme will be indicated by x.[1] With regard to the picking phenomenon Blokhuis[2] found a minimum picking speed with ink layer thicknesses between 3 and 10 μ. Below this minimum the ink layer is too thin to achieve complete contact. In thicker ink layers the splitting forces are decreasing, which is qualitatively in accordance with Stefan's law. The influence of the ink layer thickness on the filling-in of a halftone block has been studied by Laseur[3,4]. As long as filling-in is absent, the density of the print increases with the printing area of the block in accordance with the Murray–Davies equation or its revised formulation.

Fig. 2. Printing areas of a halftone block.

This means that for a definite ink layer thickness the highest density is reached when the entire surface transfers its ink layer, that is when the surface area *a* takes the value 1. As soon as filling-in occurs this highest density is reached at lower values of *a*. From this point on the density remains constant and solid prints are obtained from halftone blocks with critical printing areas which decrease with increasing ink layer thicknesses. The printer will have to

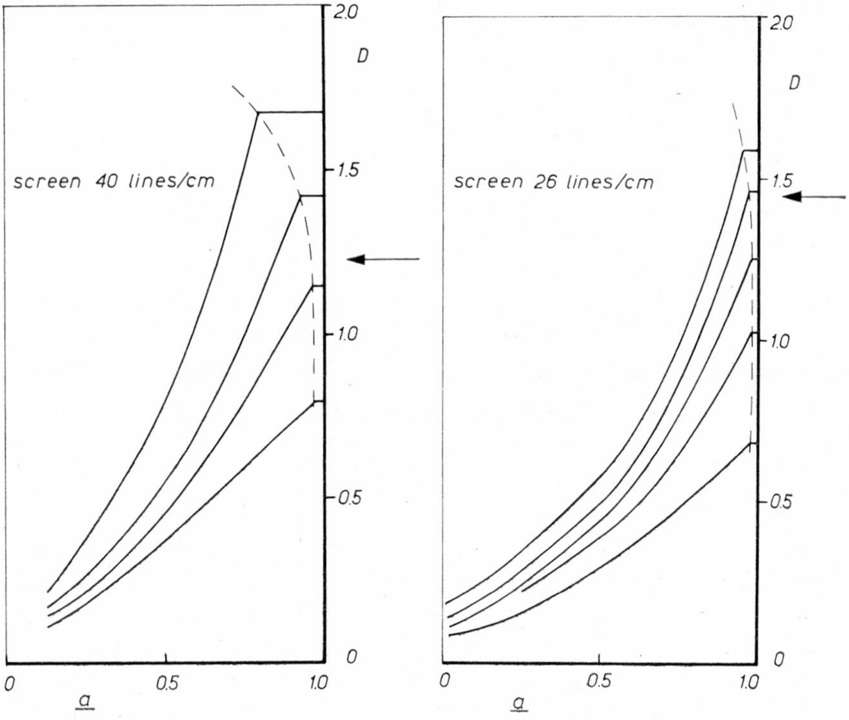

Fig. 3. Density of the print as a function of printing area.

The relationship (6) can be illustrated by means of a three-dimensional diagram with the axes D/D_{∞}, a_v and R (Fig. 5).

EXPERIMENTS

In order to test formula (5) it was necessary to make numerous impressions with different screens and different printing areas. Seven screens with R-values

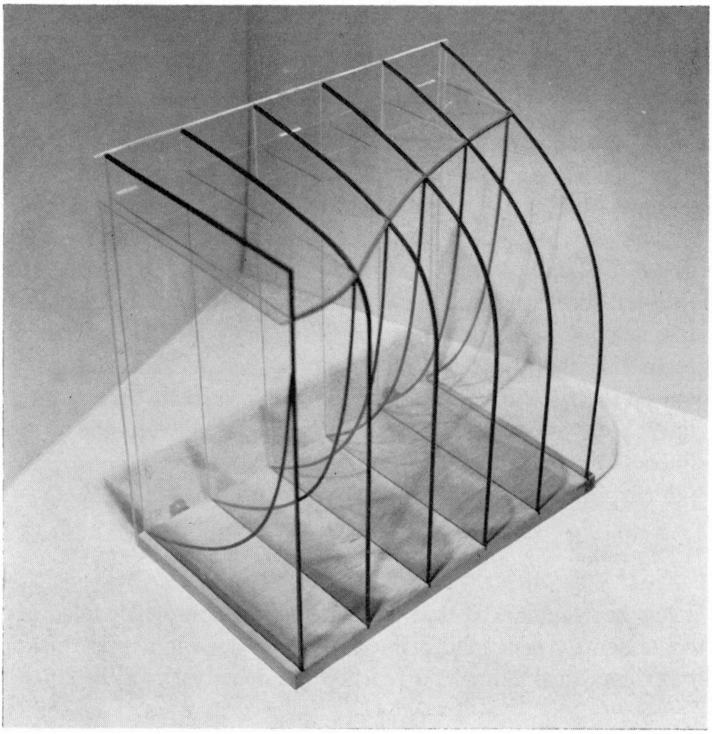

Fig. 5. Model of the relation between density, screen fineness and critical printing area.

of 12, 20, 30, 40, 48, 60 and 90 lines per cm were used to make step-wedge blocks. Each block contained nine printing areas assessed by microscope measurements. The blocks were assembled in one forme together with a solid block and this forme was used in a letterpress (Original Heidelberg Cylinder) to make impressions on nine paper surfaces ranging from cast-coated papers to newsprint. Two commercial block illustration inks were used. The ink layer thickness was measured on an ink roller close to the forme by means of a device similar to the instrument described by Shinn[5] and Medwedjew[6].

In Fig. 6 a schematic diagram of this apparatus is given. The transparent roller *A* is in rolling contact with the ink roller *I*. A light beam from the source *B* is chopped and reflected by the mirror *C* through the ink layer on *A* and received by the photocell *D*. The alternating current is amplified, rectified and measured as a direct current by the ammeter *G*. The instrument was calibrated for each of the two inks on the inking apparatus of the IGT-tester where a known volume of ink could be applied to a roller surface of known magnitude. On each paper 100 numbered impressions were made with increasing ink layer thicknesses. At 6–10 recorded levels of ink layer

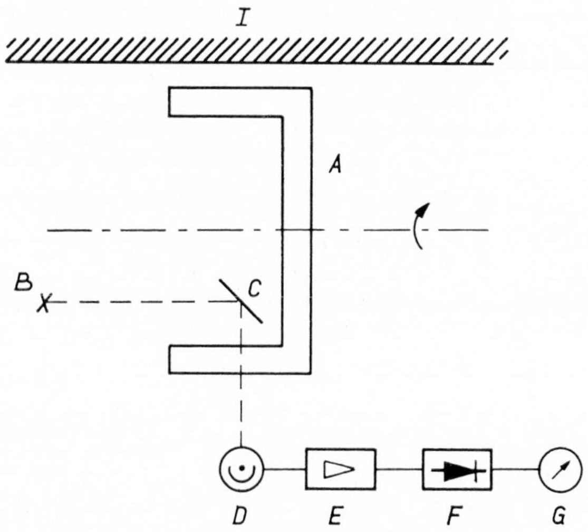

Fig. 6. Measurement of the ink layer thickness on printing rollers.

thickness a print was sampled for density measurements on the solid. Seven density measurements on each print produced data to calculate the 95 per cent confidence level for the mean density value of the solid. Figure 7 shows the 95 per cent confidence levels for the nine densities obtained on Foudrinier Bristol paper and the density curve calculated by means of the relationship $D = D_\infty(1 - e^{-mx})$. In this combination of paper and ink $D_\infty = 1.98$ and $m = 0.30$.

The parameters m and D_∞ taken from press impressions differ from the values obtained from the proof printing apparatus. This is not surprising since ink transfer, printing speed and pressure are different. However, there seems to be a high degree of correlation between press results and the measurements on the proof printing apparatus. In Figs. 8 and 9 the regression lines between the two m-values and between the two D_∞ values are shown.

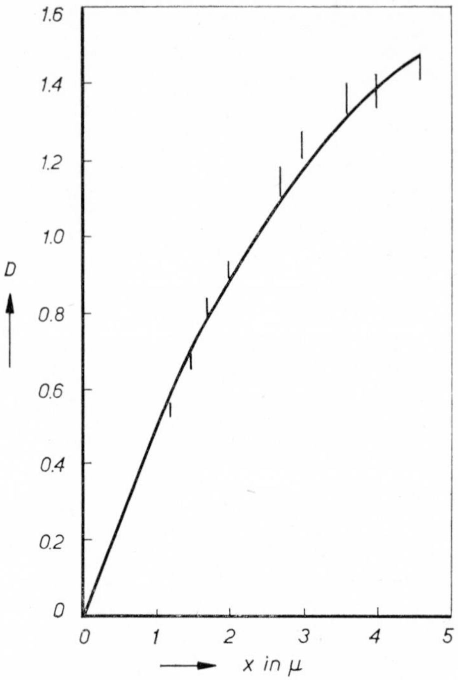

Fig. 7. Density curve for wood-free Foudrinier Bristol paper.

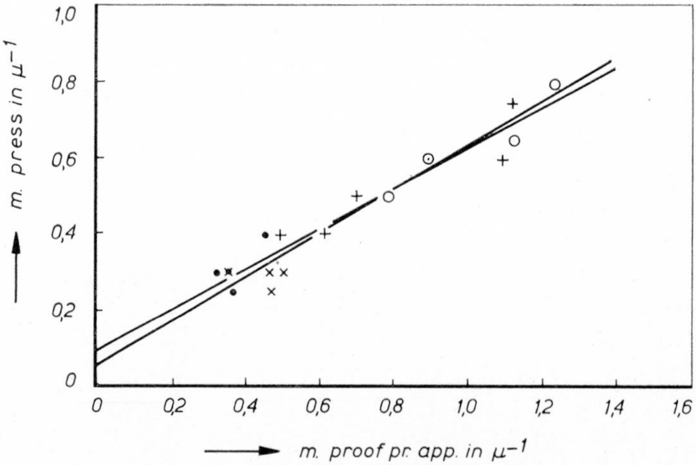

Fig. 8. Regression lines for the *m*-values calculated from press impressions and from impressions on the proof printing apparatus.

\+ coated paper, ink *A*
O coated paper, ink *B*
× uncoated paper, ink *A*
● uncoated paper, ink *B*

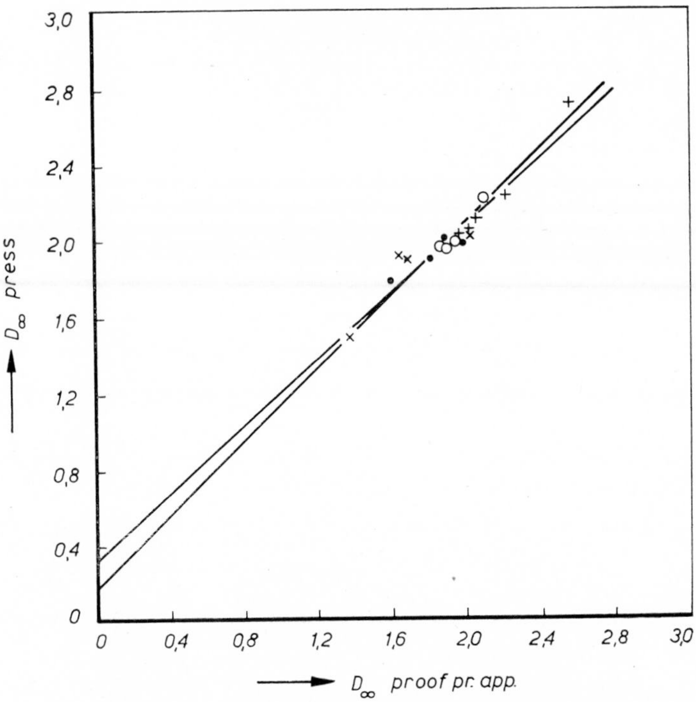

Fig. 9. Regression lines for the D_∞ values calculated from press impressions and from impressions on the proof printing apparatus, see legend Fig. 8.

In both cases the correlation coefficient was +0.96. The regression lines are:

$$1\ m_{\text{press}} = 0.54\ m_{\text{proof}} + 0.08$$

$$2\ m_{\text{proof}} = 1.71\ m_{\text{press}} - 0.04$$

$$1\ D_{\infty\text{press}} = 0.87\ D_{\infty\text{proof}} + 0.34$$

$$2\ D_{\infty\text{proof}} = 1.05\ D_{\infty\text{press}} - 0.20$$

These relations seem to hold equally well for both inks on coated and uncoated papers. It may be expected that similar relationships can be found for other presses.

MEASUREMENT OF THE CRITICAL PRINTING AREAS

In our first attempt to develop an objective method of measurement the densities D_h of the nine steps in the printed stepwedges have been plotted against the corresponding printing areas. The halftone density curves so obtained sometimes provided a sharp indication of the printing area where filling-in started. An example of this method of assessing a_v is given in Fig. 10, where the density curve intersects the level of constant solid density at $a_v = 0.92$.

In many cases, however, this method could not be used. The halftone reproduction curve very often levels off towards the solid density and an

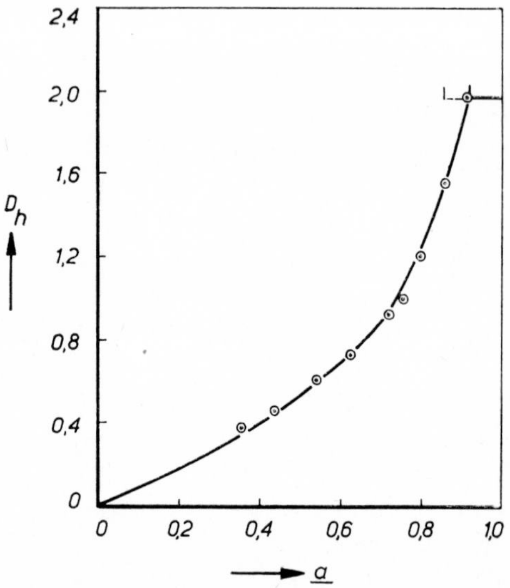

Fig. 10. Halftone density curve on wood-free chromo. Filling-in at critical printing area $a_v = 0.92$. Limits of critical printing area by visual examination: $0.86 < a_v < 0.92$. Screen width 20 lines/cm.

extrapolation of this curve becomes very uncertain. Therefore we had to abandon the objective measurement of the critical printing areas and had to resort to a method of visual examination of the prints. Generally the critical printing area could be fixed at one step in the printed step-wedge. Especially on rough papers these visually assessed limits did not coincide with any reasonable extrapolation of the halftone density curve (Fig. 11). In these cases the filling-in effect becomes obvious and troublesome before a complete filling-in of all the holes occurs. Seventeen combinations of paper surfaces and inks have been used for the measurement of the critical printing area. Together with the seven screen widths, the nine printing areas and the four ink layer thicknesses a total of 4284 printed halftones were obtained. In Table 1 the seventeen combinations of paper surface and ink are summarized.

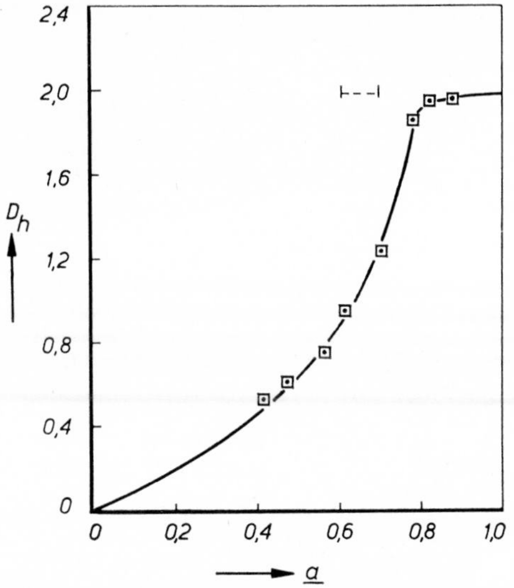

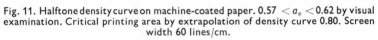

Fig. 11. Halftone density curve on machine-coated paper. 0.57 $< a_v <$ 0.62 by visual examination. Critical printing area by extrapolation of density curve 0.80. Screen width 60 lines/cm.

TABLE 1

Code	Description of paper	Side	Ink	D_∞	m in μ^{-1}
1	Wood-free writing	1	*A*	1.88	0.30
1		2	*A*	1.90	0.30
2	Wood-free duplicator	1	*A*	1.48	0.25
2		2	*B*	1.77	0.25
3	Wood-free machine-coated art . .	1	*A*	2.10	0.50
6	One-sided chromo	1	*A*	2.22	0.40
6		1	*B*	1.98	0.50
7	Wood-free one-sided chromo . .	1	*A*	2.70	0.40
7		1	*B*	2.21	0.60
8	Foudrinier Bristol	1	*B*	1.89	0.30
8		2	*B*	1.98	0.30
12	Wood-free halftone	1	*A*	2.02	0.30
12		2	*B*	2.00	0.40
17	Art.	1	*B*	1.96	0.65
17		2	*A*	2.02	0.60
18	Cast-coated	1	*A*	0.24	0.75
18		1	*B*	1.95	0.80

Table 2 shows the upper and lower limits of a_v for the different screens printed on halftone paper with the ink layer thickness of $x = 3.2\ \mu$. From these limits the upper and lower limits of the factor c could be calculated, using formula 6:

$$c = \frac{m}{R} \frac{\log D/D_\infty}{\log (1 - a_v)} \tag{6}$$

In Fig. 12 the upper and lower limits of c are shown for some of the 248 filling-in observations. It would be possible to obtain a frequency distribution

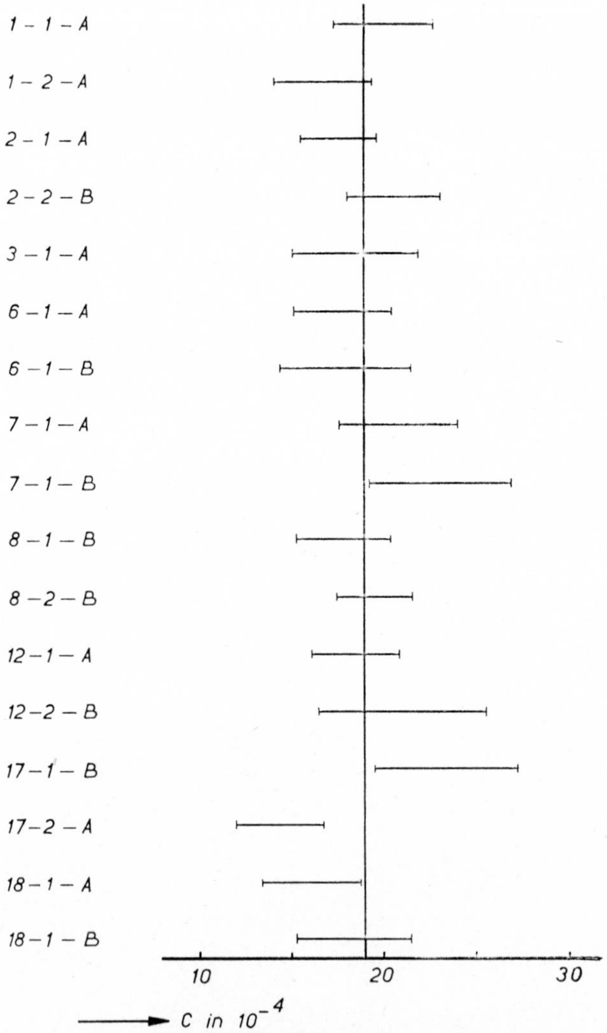

Fig. 12. Representation of the upper and lower limits of the constant c calculated for seventeen cases of filling-in.

TABLE 2

Paper 12, Side 2, ink *B*

$D_\infty = 2.00$

$m = 0.40\ \mu^{-1}$

$x = 3.2\ \mu$

Screen lines/cm	a_v		c	
	Upper limit	Lower limit	Lower limit	Upper limit
20	1.00	0.92	0×10^{-4}	25.6×10^{-4}
30	0.92	0.85	17.2	23.2
40	0.81	0.74	20.0	24.4
48	0.77	0.72	18.8	21.6
60	0.79	0.71	14.0	18.0
90	0.59	0.41	16.4	27.6

of *c*-values directly from these upper and lower limits of *c* by dividing the ranges between the limits in equal intervals and assuming that all intervals of *c*-values had equal probabilities of realization. This method would introduce all the errors of *m*, *D* and D_∞ in the statistical evaluation. Therefore, we preferred to divide the ranges between the upper and lower limits of a_v into equal intervals, to calculate the *c*-values for each a_v interval and make a frequency distribution of these calculated *c*-values. In this way equal probabilities were attributed to the a_v intervals. This distribution curve, shown in Fig. 13, is skewed with a sharp maximum at $c = 18.4 \times 10^{-4}$. The skewness can be expected since the a_v intervals contribute asymmetrically to the population of *c*-values.

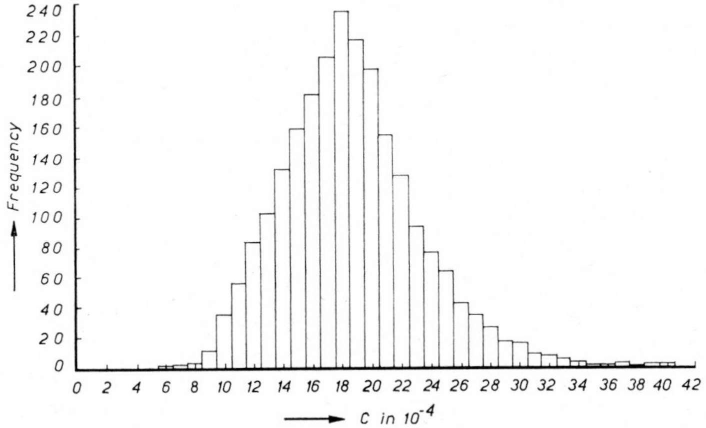

Fig. 13. Frequency distribution of c-values. Mean value c = 0.00187.

DETERMINATION OF THE SCREEN FINENESS

Equation (6) can be rewritten as follows:

$$R = \frac{m}{c} \frac{\log D/D_\infty}{\log (1 - a_v)} \tag{7}$$

In this expression the ratio

$$\frac{\log D/D_\infty}{\log (1 - a_v)}$$

represents the compromise between the acceptable density and the acceptable amount of filling-in. If the requirement of high density outweighs the requirements of a clean print with little filling-in, then this ratio takes a high value and a high screen number will be accepted. It is somewhat surprising to see to what extent a high density is desired at the cost of clean printing. Critical printing areas of 0.8 are not at all unusual even in impressions on smooth paper and on rough papers the values of a_v are still lower. The conclusion is that for better impressions coarser screens should be used.

From equation (5) we can calculate the radius of the holes that will be filled-in at each relative density. Let r be the radius of a hole in the surface of the forme with screen number R. Then the printing area is $a = 1 - \pi r^2 R^2$, and if the hole is just filled-in:

$$1 = a_v = \pi r^2 R^2 = (D/D_\infty)^{\frac{m}{cR}}$$

or

$$r = \frac{1}{R} \sqrt{\frac{1}{\pi}} \sqrt{(D/D_\infty)^{\frac{m}{cR}}} \tag{8}$$

Equation (8) shows that if screens with different screen numbers are printed with equal ink layer thicknesses the coarse screens will be filled-in earlier. However, in the range of screen numbers that are in practical use the differences are not very large. Only the very coarse screens show any appreciable differences in size of the filled-in holes.

CONCLUSIONS

The screen number to be used in a letterpress printing procedure is proportional to the m-value. The proportionality factor

$$\frac{1}{c} \frac{\log D/D_\infty}{\log (1 - a_v)}$$

depends on the requirements of density and amount of filling-in. As a practical approach to the use of the m-value for the selection of the screen number R it is possible to standardize proportionality factors for different families of papers if printed in a standardized way.

Halftone reproductions often show too much filling-in because the requirement of high contrast cannot be reconciled with clean printing if fine screens are used. In those cases the use of coarser screens could give much better results.

An alternative solution would be a deliberate reduction of the printing area in the shadows. The use of vignetted contact screens offers the possibility of making halftone blocks with built-in corrections for filling-in.

REFERENCES

1. D. TOLLENAAR and P. A. H. ERNST, *Advances in Ptg Science. Tech. Vol. II.* Pergamon Press, London, 214 (1962).
2. G. BLOKHUIS, *Int. Bull. for the Printing and Allied Trades* **73,** 64 (1956).
3. G. M. W. LASEUR, *IGT-Nieuws* **11** (7), 97 (1958).
4. J. F. MONROY, Papier und Druck, *Druck und Reproduktion* **9,** 125 (1960).
5. D. L. SHINN, *U.S.P.* **2,** 951, 416 (16 Oct. 1956).
6. E. M. MEDWEDJEW, Papier und Druck, *Druck und Reproduktion* **9,** No. 1, 2 (1960).

DISCUSSION

BAYSUNG HSU: In an equation like your proposed equation (3), normally c is determined from the slope of the straight line obtained from a plot of $m \log D/D_\infty$ against $R \log (1 - a_v)$. You appear to calculate c for each individual experimental point, thereby obtaining a frequency distribution of c. But it is possible to have a set of experimental points, which on the whole do not obey equation (3), yet give rise to the type of distribution of c as shown when c is calculated individually for each point.

TOLLENAAR: If we are talking about "a distribution of c" it seems to me that we are accepting equation (3) which defines the factor c or at least takes it as a basis for discussion. We may find different distribution functions for c if the raw material obtained by equation (3) is treated with different statistical methods. The sharp maxima in the c distribution given by only slightly different values in two treatments, seem to indicate that the picture given by equation (3) is a reasonable one.

YULE: The constant c varies over a wide range—from 6 to 40×10^{-4}. Is this due to variations in the printing process, to experimental error, or to the fact that the equations are over-simplified and do not represent the actual relationships accurately enough?

TOLLENAAR: The great spread is mainly due to the fact that we had to pin down the critical printing area to one step in the grey-scale. This results in finite contributions to the c distribution over a wide range. If the critical printing area could be assessed within narrower limits the spread would probably be less.

ALBRECHT: Since the m-value is correlated with the printed area is there a correlation between the m-value and the Chapman smoothness?

TOLLENAAR: We find a pretty good correlation but the m-value gives direct access to density which is not so easily obtained when using other smoothness factors.

WALKER: I note in your curves of density versus relative printing area, a horizontal portion after filling in at the critical printing area. Is this constancy of density strictly compatible with the mechanism you presented with the ink from the printing area spreading into the open dots over the paper surface during impression? If this were the mechanism, one might expect a slight continued increase in density with increasing printing area beyond the critical point.

TOLLENAAR: I agree that there should be a slight increase. However, in the region of high printing area the relative increase in the amount of ink on the forme, or amount of transferred ink, is small and consequently the rise in density can be disregarded.

PASZKIEWICZ: The conclusions of such work are surely dependent on the shape of the etched dot. Thus a plate etched conventionally might be expected to behave differently from one electrochemically etched.

TOLLENAAR: I would expect that the differences in the condition of the printing plate would be reflected in a shift of the *c* value because the a_v values would be different. Our *c* values have been evaluated for regular etching which was controlled before printing.

BAYSUNG HSU: Do you agree that the filling-in process depends on the flow properties of ink? If this is so, the constant *c* may vary with the ink used.

TOLLENAAR: The flow properties of the ink are reflected in the *m*-values and so they affect *R* and not *c*.

ZETTLEMOYER: The discussion so far seems to imply that the density is constant across the print including the filled in area. Could variations from constancy help in understanding the mechanism of filling in? We know the appearance of fill-in from rubber plates is different from that shown by metal plates. Does such non-uniformity affect your analysis in any way?

TOLLENAAR: I expect that the differences in roughness of a wide range of papers would affect the filling-in mechanism more than the composition of the plates. I must draw your attention to the concept that the *m*-value takes care of the influence of flow phenomena on density. In fact the *m*-value is only a descriptive factor, not an explanatory one. The heterogeneity is not very important since we are dealing with mean values of densities. Only in the transfer of their ink films may we expect some deviations.

BRUNO: Does this approach have application to lithography and dry offset?

TOLLENAAR: The characteristics of the blanket would be very important as it introduces directional effects, but it should be possible to extend these considerations to offset. There is "filling-in" or dot spread in offset which is similar to the "filling-in" in letterpress.

WALKER: You mentioned a basic mechanistic picture behind the treatment you have presented here. If there is time, I am sure we would all be interested in a brief outline of this basic mechanism. Such thinking is, of course, the most interesting aspect of such a study.

TOLLENAAR: If *R* is the number of lines per centimetre and *r* the radius of the hole, *x* the ink layer thickness transferred to the paper per unit of printing area and *b* the overall thickness after filling-in, then $1 - \pi r^2/R^2 = b/x$.

This simplified concept can be visualized as an extension of ink along the surface of the paper over the border line of the shadow dot.

Of course, this picture is complicated by roughness effects and flow effects. It is assumed that these effects are reflected in the descriptive factor *m*.

THE OPTIMUM TONE RENDERING IN HALFTONE REPRODUCTION PROCESSES

by J. A. C. YULE

Research Laboratories, Eastman Kodak Company, Rochester, New York

Abstract—When the density range of the reproduction process is lower than that of the original, some compression of the scale is necessary. A knowledge of the optimum tone-reproduction curve is needed in the design of contact screens and for the choice of methods of contrast control. Sets of halftone prints, varying in highlight and shadow contrast, but with constant highlight and shadow density, were prepared by a modification of the Person process; and the variations were analyzed by the method of principal components. The prints were evaluated for picture quality and reproduction quality.

A straight-line tone-reproduction curve, plotted in terms of Munsell value, would represent uniform compression of the visual tone scale. In the pictures studied, the preferred reproduction was slightly darker in the middletones than this would indicate. On the other hand, when the reproductions were evaluated for picture quality without comparison with the original, a lighter print was preferred. The most accurate reproduction, even of a top-quality print, therefore does not necessarily lead to the best picture quality in the reproduction. In evaluating the prints for reproduction quality, observers gave much more weight to accuracy of reproduction than to picture quality. Reproductions should, therefore, be examined first in the absence of the original. The present work assumes a unique relationship between density of original and density of reproduction in a given picture; but for the best possible reproduction, this axiom must be abandoned, thus allowing for effects like that of unsharp masking.

INTRODUCTION

IN 1947, Spencer[1] in the 15th Hurter and Driffield Memorial Lecture, gave an excellent analysis of the reasons for the poor tone rendering so frequently encountered in the reproduction of photographs, where the loss of shadow, and especially highlight, contrast is so common. Now, 16 years later, with special contact screens, masking methods and scanners in common use, it is easier to obtain good tone rendering and the question therefore arises as to what is the optimum. It should be admitted at the outset that we do not have a final answer to this question, but in the course of studying it, we have reached some tentative conclusions and have become aware of many features of the problem which were new to us.

At first glance, the answer to this question seems obvious. In reproducing a good original, we want to produce a facsimile reproduction, whose density at every point is equal to that of the original. This relationship would be represented by a 45-degree straight line, as in Fig. 1, Curve A. However, in most cases, the maximum density of the reproduction is limited by the solid ink density, and the optimum tone rendering with this limitation is the chief subject to be discussed here.

When the maximum density of the reproduction is limited, the scale must be compressed. For example, if the range of densities in the original is 0.0–1.7

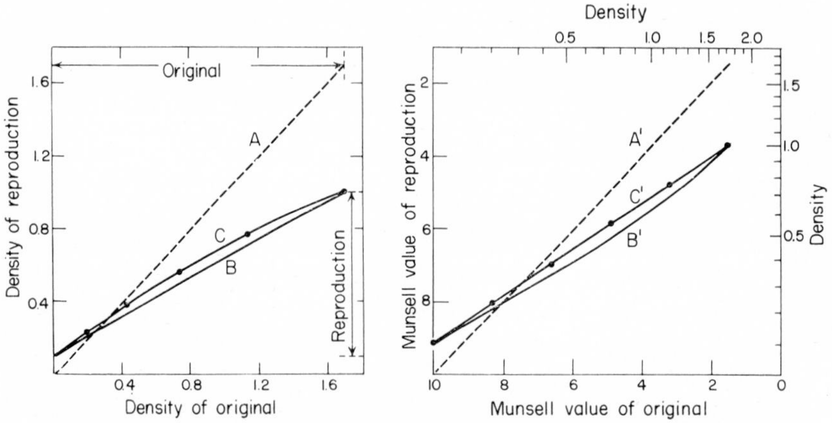

Fig. 1. Hypothetical tone-reproduction curves. Curves *A* and *A′*, facsimile reproduction; Curves *B* and *B′*, straight-line reproduction in terms of density, with limited maximum density; Curves *C* and *C′*, straight-line reproduction in terms of Munsell value. —●—●— Points which appear equidistant visually.

and that in the reproduction is 0.1–1.0, one obvious solution is to aim for a straight-line reproduction, as shown in Fig. 1, Curve *B*. However, this would not represent a uniform compression of the visual tones, because density is not quite proportional to the visual effect of darkness. With a straight-line reproduction, in terms of density, the highlights would appear slightly more flattened than the shadows.

Since the Munsell scale of values[2] is uniformly spaced as regards the visual impression, a straight-line reproduction, in terms of Munsell value (Fig. 1, Curve *C′*), would appear to be uniformly compressed when the reproduction is compared with the original.[3] It has often been assumed, without experimental evidence, that this would represent the best compromise. If the Munsell value plot, Curve *C′*, is replotted on a linear scale of density, Curve *C* is obtained, which is slightly curved. The chief object of this work was to find out whether such a curve, i.e. Curve *C*, does represent the best compromise for average subjects. Another alternative which has been suggested is that the contrast in the middletones should be maintained at the expense of highlight and shadow contrast.

The difference between the straight-line density reproduction and the straight-line Munsell-value reproduction is not great, but it is significant, especially when much compression of the scale is needed. Perhaps a more serious disadvantage of the density plot is that by expanding the shadows, compared with the visual effect, the curve gives too much prominence to that part of the scale. This is indicated by the points marked on Curve *C*, which appear equidistant in terms of the visual effect.

METHOD OF INVESTIGATION

The method of investigation was as follows: Several black-and-white negatives of subjects of different types were chosen, a series of continuous-tone prints were made from them, and the best of these were identified. A series of halftone prints with a maximum density of 1.3 were also made from each of these negatives with highlight and shadow dots of normal size but varying in highlight and shadow contrast. (Continuous-tone prints were used for one scene.) To produce the halftone prints, a highlight positive, a shadow positive, and a full-scale positive were made from the negative; and halftone negatives were made by combinations of exposures from these three positives. Because of the difficulty of controlling ink density accurately in printed reproductions, photographic rather than photomechanical prints were made from these halftone negatives. Twenty observers were asked to evaluate these prints, and their judgments were averaged. The prints were judged in two ways; on their own merits (without a reference print) and as a reproduction of the best continuous-tone print. They were not, of course, actually made from the continuous-tone print, but this would not affect the preferred density relationships. The terms, "reproduction" and "original," have been used for convenience throughout this paper in referring to the prints which were being compared, although one was not actually made from the other. Plotting the density of the preferred "reproduction" against that of the "original" gives the preferred tone-reproduction curve, which is what we are trying to determine.

One of the subjects was studied more completely than the rest. Halftone prints of three maximum-density levels were made, and their tone-reproduction variations were analyzed by the method of principal components. With this subject, the halftone prints were also evaluated as reproductions of two of the inferior continuous-tone prints. In evaluating the prints as reproductions, both accuracy of reproduction and aesthetic quality were taken into account. Evaluations of the accuracy of reproduction without regard to aesthetic quality were also made.

The second part of the paper consists of a discussion of some other aspects of the tone-reproduction problem which arose during this work. Some of the tone-reproduction work of Jones, Nelson, and Simonds is also reviewed.

PREPARATION OF THE PRINTS

The continuous-tone prints were made on Kodak Polycontrast Paper, an exposure series being made at three contrast levels. The halftone prints were made as follows:

Three positives were made from the original negative, using a Kodak Register Printing Frame, with special precautions to ensure accurate register.

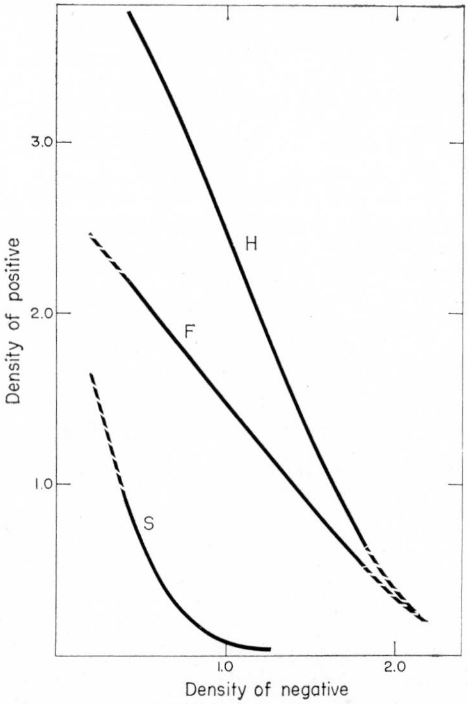

Fig. 2. Characteristics of the highlight positive (*H*), the full-scale positive (*F*), and the shadow positive (*S*) used in making the halftone prints of the picnic scene.

Kodak Separation Negative Film, Type 2, developed in Kodak Developer D–11 for 5 min at 68°F ($\gamma = 2.3$), was used for the highlight positive; Kodak 33 Positive Film, developed in D–11 (1:1) for 3 min ($\gamma = 1.0$), was used for the full-scale positive; and Kodalith Contact Film, developed in D–11 for 2 min ($\gamma = 4.2$), was used for the shadow positive. The characteristics of the positives, for the picnic scene, are shown in Fig. 2. A no-screen exposure could have been used for highlighting instead of the highlight positive, but this would not have been so convenient.

The halftone negatives were made on Kodalith Ortho Film, Type 3, and developed for an extra long time ($3\frac{1}{2}$ min in Kodalith Super Developer), to minimize adjacency effects. A vacuum board was used with two independently controlled vacuum channels, to permit the interchange of the positives without disturbing the contact between the screen and the Kodalith Film.

In making the halftone negatives, a Kodak Magenta Contact Screen (Positive), 133 lines/in. was used. Four combinations of exposure were chosen which would give highlight and shadow dots of the same size: first, the full-scale positive alone, if necessary with a yellow or magenta color-compensating filter to control contrast; second, the highlight positive and a flash exposure; third, successive exposures to the highlight and shadow positives; fourth, the full-scale positive with a magenta filter (Kodak Wratten Filter No. 30) and a flash exposure. The effects produced by these combinations are summarized in Table 1. The resulting curves are shown in Fig. 3.

TABLE 1. CHARACTERISTICS OF EXPOSURE COMBINATIONS

Types of exposure	Result		
	Highlight contrast and middletone density	Shadow contrast	Curve, Fig. 3
Full-scale positive	low	high	N
Highlight positive (magenta filter) + flash	high	very low	HMF
Highlight and shadow positive ..	medium	high	HS
Full-scale positive (magenta filter) + flash	medium	low	NMF

It was found necessary to use the highlight positive with the magenta filter, to increase the highlight contrast, which indicates that Kodalith Contact Film would have been preferable for this positive as well as for the shadow positive.

Once the exposure times needed for each of these combinations to produce highlight and shadow dots of normal size were established, they would be combined in various proportions to control the highlight and shadow contrast of the halftone negative. For example, increasing proportions of the second combination added to decreasing proportions of the first would give a series of negatives with increasing highlight contrast and decreasing shadow contrast. A similar series could then be made with the addition of a constant proportion of the third combination, and this series would have flatter middletones. The first set of negatives (those of the picnic scene) were, however, made by a much more haphazard system, which did not produce such a uniform series. In any case, it is quite difficult to obtain smoothly graduated series of negatives if the difference between adjacent negatives is small. Some negatives were included with intentional variations in highlight- and shadow-dot size, to help in evaluating the effect of small, unintentional variations in

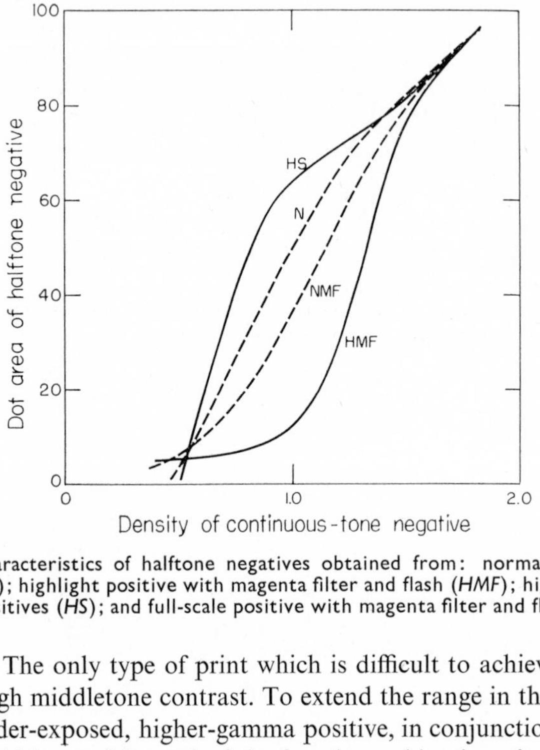

Fig. 3. Characteristics of halftone negatives obtained from: normal, full-scale positive (*N*); highlight positive with magenta filter and flash (*HMF*); highlight and shadow positives (*HS*); and full-scale positive with magenta filter and flash (*NMF*).

these factors. The only type of print which is difficult to achieve in this way is one with high middletone contrast. To extend the range in this direction, a somewhat under-exposed, higher-gamma positive, in conjunction with a flash exposure, could be used instead of the fourth combination given in Table 1.

The halftone prints were made on Kodabromide Paper, F–4, for the 1.8 maximum density, and Kodabromide, E–2, for the 1.3 and 1.0 maximum densities. The latter paper has a degree of gloss similar to that of printing ink on coated paper. The maximum density was controlled by the exposure time. Although an ink density of 1.3 is characteristic of good monochrome printing, ink densities as low as 1.0 are often encountered. The high-density prints were included to obtain more information about the relationship between maximum density and quality.

The method described here gives good control of the tone scale, but it would be simpler to use a scanner with adjustable tone rendering, such as the

Fairchild Variable Response Unit. One disadvantage of the present method is that, since the continuous-tone print was not used in making the halftones, details of tone rendering due to the curve of the continuous-tone paper might not be present in the halftone prints. For example, some highlight detail might be completely missing from the "original" and yet be present in the "reproduction".

For one scene (still life), continuous-tone instead of halftone prints were used, to see whether the results would be any different with the type of tone-reproduction curve which they give. In this case, the prints were made by successive exposures through a highlight, shadow, and full-scale negative, which were made from an intermediate positive as in the Person process.[4]

QUALITY JUDGMENTS

Three types of quality judgments were to be made in evaluating these prints, defined here as picture quality, reproduction quality, and accuracy of reproduction. The *picture quality* refers to a judgment of the print on its own merits, without reference to any original print of which it might be a reproduction. No doubt the judgments of picture quality include some estimate of how closely the print resembled the original scene, but this was not asked for in the instructions. The *reproduction quality* is intended to correspond to the basis on which commercial reproductions are evaluated. It is difficult to define, since it involves both the accuracy of reproduction and the picture quality. It is up to the observer to decide how much weight to put on these two aspects of the print, and this no doubt depends on the exact wording of the instructions. It was found that in the evaluation of these prints for reproduction quality, accuracy was given much more weight than picture quality. The *accuracy of reproduction* refers only to how closely the print matches the original, disregarding its picture quality completely.

The quality judgments were obtained by methods suggested by Nelson and Simonds, of the Kodak Research Laboratories (private communication), based on the work of Guilford[5]. The most complete information about print quality was obtained by asking the observers to arrange all the prints in the order of quality, and then assign quality ratings to them. This was done for the picture-quality ratings of the picnic scene, but it proved to be too laborious and time-consuming for general use. A simpler method is that of paired comparisons, in which the prints are compared two at a time, the observer being asked which he prefers. If he considers them equal, he is asked to pick one of the two at random. The difference in quality between the two is estimated from the degree of unanimity in the choices. Not every possible pair is compared, a satisfactory result being obtained by using about twice as many pairs as there are prints. Pairs which differ so much in quality that the choice would be unanimous are avoided. A still simpler method, used in the case of the continuous-tone prints, in which there were three exposure series of different contrast, was to ask the observer to select the best print in each series and then to select the best of these three. This method gives the least information about the relative quality of the prints, and is not satisfactory unless they form a regular, uniformly spaced array.

The instructions to the judges were as follows:

Evaluation of Picture Quality

"The prints to be judged differ in tone reproduction, maximum density, and surface texture. Please arrange them in order of your preference, from most pleasing to least pleasing. Ignore any color differences, pinholes, scratches, and other physical defects. After arranging the prints in order, please assign a quality index to each print. An index of 100 would represent optimum reproduction. An index of 0 would represent a blank sheet of paper. The best print in this group may or may not (in your opinion) have an index of 100."

For some of the scenes, these instructions were modified in accordance with the paired-comparison method.

Evaluation of Reproduction Quality by Paired Comparisons

"You will be given a reference print which is considered to have been chosen for use as an illustration in a printed article or an advertisement. The other prints represent a variety of printed reproductions, among which a choice is to be made. They will be presented to you in pairs, and in each case you are asked to choose the one which you consider to be the most satisfactory reproduction. If both appear equally good, choose one at random. The aim is to produce a reproduction with which the customer would be the most satisfied, not only for accuracy of reproduction, but also for pleasing quality. Both of these factors should be taken into account in evaluating the prints. Ignore any color differences, pinholes, scratches, and other physical defects. Also ignore the fact that the reproductions may have been made from a different negative with a slightly different pose."

Evaluation of Accuracy of Reproduction by Paired Comparisons

"You will be given a reference print of high maximum density, and a number of other prints of low maximum density will be presented to you in pairs. From each pair, please choose the one which matches the reference print most closely. If both appear equally good, choose one at random. In making this choice, please disregard the aesthetic quality of the print. The print which resembles the reference print most closely should be chosen even if it is less pleasing. Ignore any color differences, pinholes, scratches, or other physical defects."

Most of the observers who judged the prints had had experience with the evaluation of halftone reproductions. It would be interesting to repeat the judging, using a jury composed of those directly concerned with quality control in production, and also of the customers for whom the printing is done. It has been found, however, that the average rating by experts usually corresponds quite closely to that of less skilled observers, although the range of preferences is greater among the latter.

ANALYSIS OF PRINT CHARACTERISTICS

The picture quality of a reproduction depends not on its relationship to the original print but on its relationship to the original scene. Insofar as picture quality enters into the evaluation of a reproduction, it is desirable to know the relationship of the prints to the original scene, in addition to the relationship of the reproductions to the originals. The relative luminance of areas in the original scenes can be established from density measurements of the negative if the characteristic curve of the negative material is known and a correction for flare is made. Flare is determined by including a black box in the scene. The luminance values can also be checked by direct visual readings taken from the scene itself.

The curves of the best continuous-tone photographic prints are given in Fig. 4. It would be interesting to use a subjective brightness scale for these

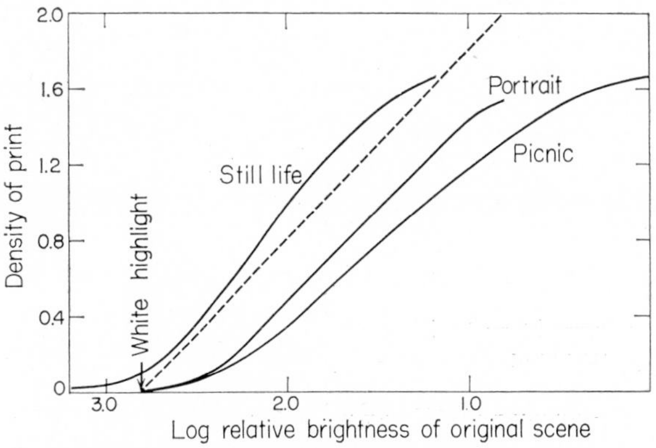

Fig. 4. Characteristics of the best continuous-tone glossy prints of three subjects.

curves similar to the Munsell scale. However, the Munsell scale does not apply here (at least for the outdoor scenes) because of the high intensity of illumination (about 1000 ft-c). No subjective brightness data are available at this level. The curves have been shifted laterally so that a fully lighted white object falls at the point indicated by the arrow. The 45-degree broken line indicates the curves that would be obtained if the brightness ratios in the scene were reproduced in the print. As is well known from the work of Jones and Nelson[6], such a print usually appears much too dark. Fully lighted objects would appear in the print at their original densities, but in the optimum print they are much lighter than this. This is not true of the still-life picture, in which a darker print was necessary to maintain the modelling in a white vase and to retain the sparkle in the catchlights—but even in this case the optimum print had a toe on the curve.

To establish what types of variation were present in the halftone prints, the prints of the picnic scene were analyzed by the method of principal components. An analysis of this sort also makes it easier to understand the relationship between curve shape and print quality, especially when several types of variation are present.

The application of the method of principal components to tone-reproduction problems by Morris and Simonds[7,8] was described to this group at an

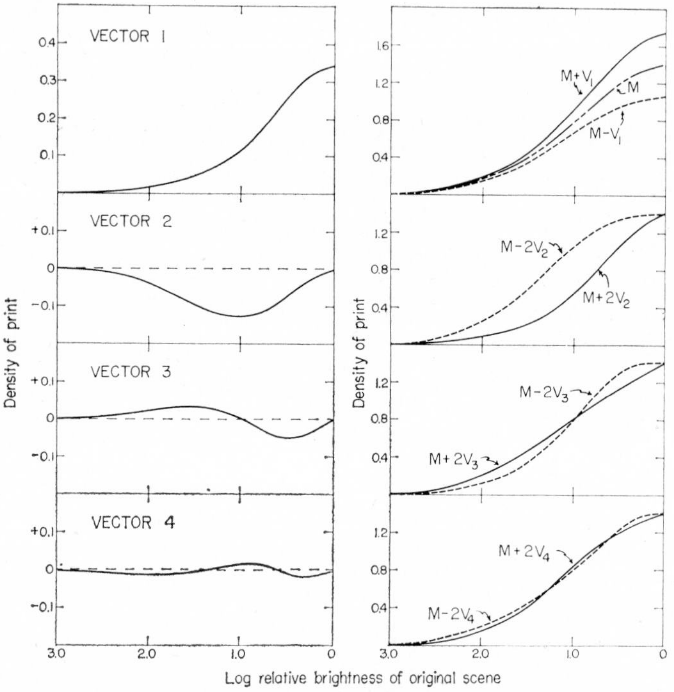

Fig. 5. Variation in tone rendering of the halftone prints of the picnic scene: left, the four vectors; right, the mean curve M modified by the four vectors V_1–V_4.

earlier conference.[9] In this method, a set of curves were analyzed into a mean curve and a small number of component curves, known as principal components or characteristic vectors. Any of the original curves can be synthesized by adding to the mean curve various proportions of the principal components. In order to do this, the ordinates of the principal-component curves are multiplied by coefficients (or "scalar multiples") and added to the ordinates of the mean curve.

The principal components or vectors for the picnic-scene prints are shown at the left of Fig. 5. The form of these vectors depends, of course, on the characteristics of all the steps in the process by which the prints were made.

The variations in the shape of the curve produced by adding or subtracting each vector from the mean curve are indicated on the right. The computation was carried out in such a way that all the variation in maximum density (the last step of the scale) was included in the first vector. The others are zero in the last step. This is accomplished by multiplying the last-step densities by 100 in the data supplied to the computer. In this way, the effect of maximum density on quality could be easily separated from the effect of curve shape.

Vector 2 controls the darkness of the middletones. A large proportion of this vector corresponds to light middletones, low highlight contrast, and high shadow contrast. Vector 3 affects the contrast of the middletones, and a high proportion of it means high highlight and shadow contrast and low middletone contrast. The most important feature of Vector 4 is the contrast in the extreme shadows. Vector 4 represents a minor variation in curve shape which did not appear to affect the quality.

Since the prints had been made at three levels of maximum density, Vector 1, which contains all the maximum-density variation, was approximately constant within each of these three groups. For each of the three density levels, the scalar multiples for Vectors 2 and 3, which contained nearly all of the remaining variation, could therefore be plotted against each other, as in the square portion of Fig. 6, to show the way the characteristics of the individual prints varied. Each point represents a print, and the position of each point indicates whether the print in question was light or dark, flat or contrasty. The identification number of each print is indicated above, and the picture quality below, each point on the graph. The quality ratings have all been corrected for the slight unintentional variations in maximum density. These quality ratings are for the prints judged on their own merits, not as reproductions of another print. The optimum, for the medium-density prints, is in the neighborhood of -0.6 and -0.8 for the scalar multiples of Vectors 2 and 3, respectively.

To locate the optimum more accurately, the quality can be plotted against each scalar multiple, for prints which are near optimum in the other scalar multiples. This has been done in the two curves at the bottom and left of Fig. 6 for the medium-density prints. For each of the prints on these curves, there is a corresponding point on the square portion of the graph. The three graphs are arranged in this way to show the relationship between them.

The optimum for Vector 2 is clearly established by the curve at the bottom, but although the prints covered quite a wide range of middletone contrast (Vector 3), this was not wide enough to establish the shape of the curve on the left very clearly. The effect of middletone contrast on quality is surprisingly small—smaller, apparently, than the effect of varying the contrast in ordinary photographic prints, where lowering the contrast lowers the density range and raising it causes loss of highlight and shadow detail. Of course, it is

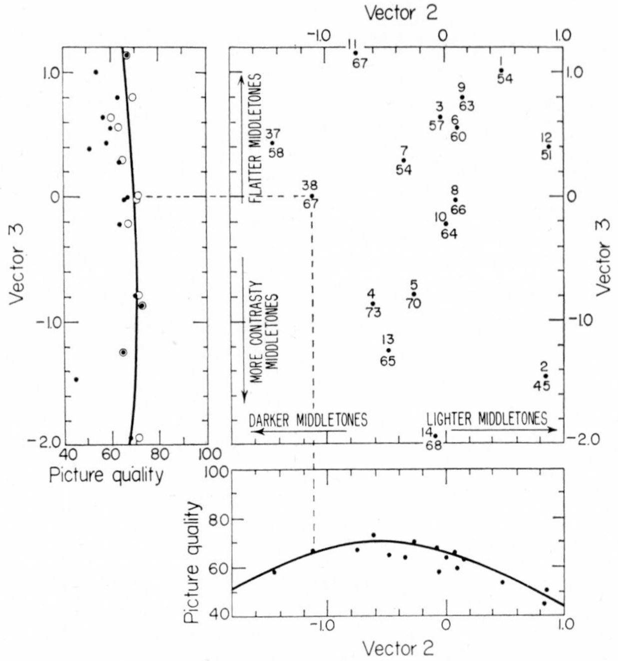

Fig. 6. Relationship of print characteristics to quality for 1.3 D_{max} prints of the picnic scene. Each point represents a print. Numbers above the points represent the print identification number, and the numbers below represent the quality rating. —●— Quality values adjusted for variation due to Vector 1 (D_{max}). —○— Quality values also adjusted for variation in Vector 2.

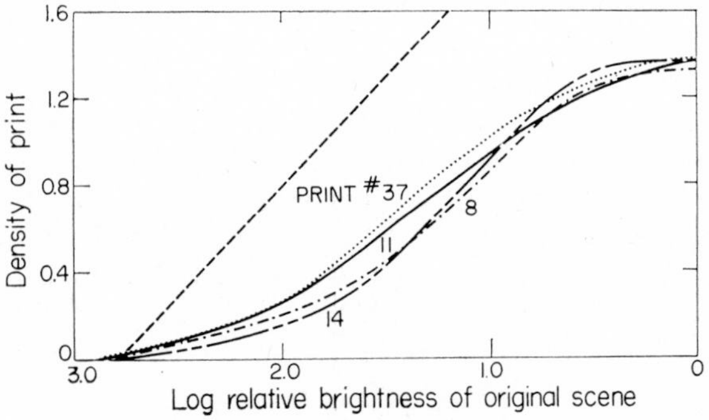

Fig. 7. Curves showing range of 1.3 D_{max} halftone prints of the picnic scene chosen as best by different observers: a light print (8), a dark print (37), a flat print (11), and a contrasty print (14).

necessary to examine the original prints to get a clear idea of the amount of variation represented here, but it can be estimated by referring to Figs. 5 and 7.

The flatness of these curves is largely due to the wide variation of preference among different individuals. Prints as different as Nos. 8, 11, 14, and 37 were picked as the best by at least one out of twenty observers. The curves of these four prints are shown in Fig. 7.

Since curves such as those of Fig. 6 are approximately parabolic, the relationship of picture quality to the scalar multiples conforms quite well to

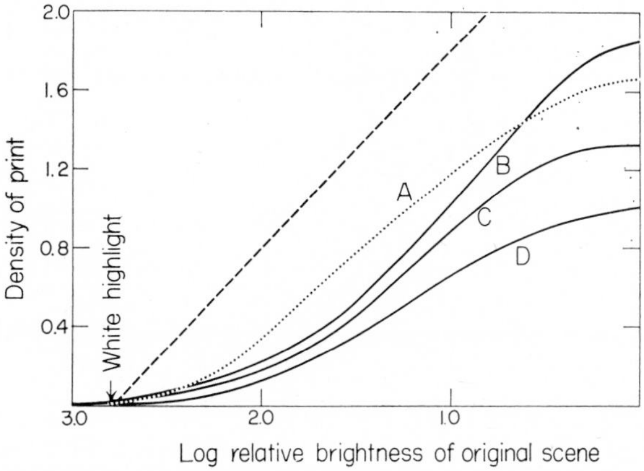

Fig. 8. Characteristics of prints of the picnic scene with highest picture quality: A, normal photographic print; B, C, D, halftone prints with highlight and shadow contrast adjustment, and maximum densities of about 1.0, 1.3, and 1.8.

a second-order equation, whose coefficients can be established by the method of least squares. This provides another method of establishing the characteristics of the optimum print. The curves of the best prints of maximum density 1.0, 1.3, and 1.8 are given in Fig. 8. The 1.8 curve is the average of two curves of equal quality rating. The ratings of the best prints are 51, 73, and 80, respectively. The quality, of course, is quite low for the prints of low maximum density. As already mentioned, the optimum photographic print is lighter than is indicated by the 45-degree line. The optimum halftone print for this subject is even lighter than the optimum continuous-tone print, probably because the process used for the halftone prints made it possible to reduce the highlight contrast without complete loss of detail in the extreme highlights. For a sunlit scene, the lightness of the preferred print helps to compensate for the relatively weak print-viewing illumination, and gives a more sunlit appearance. The reason for preferring a light print even in indoor scenes is not so obvious.

Jones and Nelson found that, at the shadow end of the scale, the curve of the optimum continuous-tone print usually had a shoulder, and this was true of this scene. The optimum high-maximum-density halftone print, however, had a very short shoulder, and this print was preferred to the optimum continuous-tone print by a majority of the judges, in spite of the loss of detail caused by the halftone pattern. Evidently, the photographic materials used did not suit this subject perfectly, so that the best continuous-tone print was not ideal. This print represents a compromise, at the shadow end of the scale, between high shadow density and high shadow contrast; and, at the highlight end of the scale, a compromise between highlight detail and light middletones. The shadow contrast can be increased by lowering the print exposure, but the shadow density is then too low, and there is a tendency to lose detail in the extreme highlights. These limitations do not apply to the halftone prints made by the method used here.

THE OPTIMUM REPRODUCTION CURVE

Up to this point we have been considering the quality of the halftone prints judged on their own merits without comparison with a continuous-tone print. We are, however, more concerned here with their merits as reproductions of a continuous-tone print.

Three continuous-tone prints of the picnic scene were chosen as originals—the best, a lighter one, and a light, contrasty one. The halftone prints of 1.0 and 1.3 maximum density were evaluated as reproductions of these, to determine the characteristics of the best reproduction. In two cases, the set of prints did not cover adequately the range of tone rendering close to that of the best reproduction. The other four are plotted in Fig. 9. Since the gray-scale characteristics did not exactly correspond to those of the picture area, owing mainly to developer adjacency effects, the gray scale was used to establish the detailed shape of the curve, whereas its exact position was established from points in the picture. The points indicated in Fig. 9 were measured in the picture area, and the lower curve is an average of the three 1.0-maximum-density reproduction curves, for the three originals. Similar curves (for reproduction of the best print, at a maximum density of 1.3 only) are given for the portrait, in Fig. 10, which contained important shadow detail in the form of a black sweater, and for the still-life scene, for which continuous-tone reproductions were used. It will be seen that for all these subjects, the optimum reproduction curves are nearly straight on the Munsell-value plot on the right, being perhaps slightly darker in the middletones. The density plots, as might be expected, are more curved. There is no indication of a toe on the curve, even for the still-life scene, where the minimum density of the reproductions (0.07) was higher than that of the original. The kinks in the curves are due to unintentional differences in curve shape between the continuous-tone and halftone prints, and should be disregarded.

The evaluation of these "best reproductions" included both the accuracy and the quality of the reproduction. To determine how much weight was

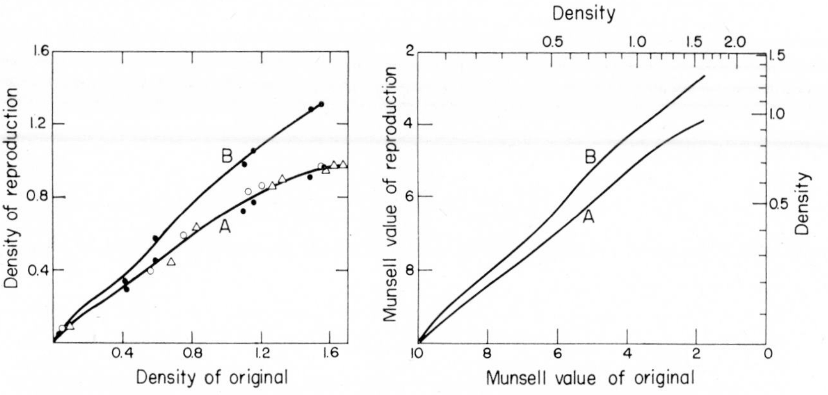

Fig. 9. Tone rendering of the best reproductions with a D_{max} of 0.97 (Curve A) and 1.26 (Curve B) of three prints of the picnic scene: —△— reproduction of the best print; —○— reproduction of a lighter print; —●— reproduction of a light, contrasty print. *Left*, with linear density scale; *right*, with linear Munsell-value scale.

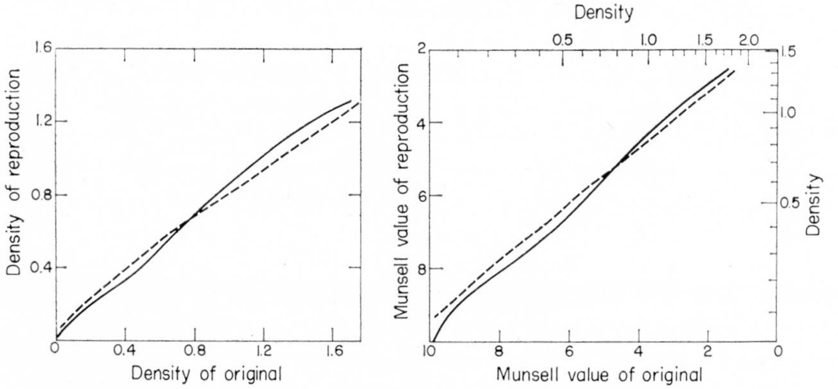

Fig. 10. Tone-reproduction curve of the best 1.3 D_{max} reproduction of the best continuous-tone print of the portrait (————) and the still-life scene (— — —).

given to quality rather than to accuracy, some prints were judged for accuracy alone. Several of the high-maximum-density halftone prints were selected and the 1.30 and 1.0 prints which matched them most closely were determined. A halftone print was used for the original in this case because its tone-reproduction curve was more like that of the low-density reproductions, so that accidental differences in curve shape would not distort the results. The "most accurate reproduction" curves, shown in Fig. 11, are the same shape as the "best reproduction" curves of Figs. 9 and 10, within the limits of experimental error, if allowance is made for the fact that the maximum densities of the originals used for Fig. 11 were slightly higher.

There are several possible reasons why the optimum Munsell-value curves are not quite straight. The viewing conditions and the optical conditions for density measurement may not correspond to those used to establish the Munsell scale; these conditions may have a different effect on the appearance

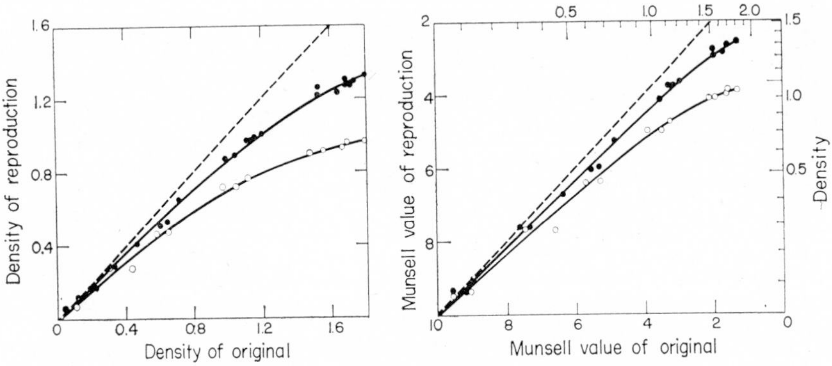

Fig. 11. Characteristics of the most accurate low-density reproductions of several high-D_{max} glossy prints.

or the density of glossy and matte prints (the original being glossy); the optimum low-density reproduction curve may be preferred because it corresponds more closely to the familiar appearance of a scene viewed through a slight haze or a dirty window, and thus appears more natural; or the curve may be a compromise between uniform compression of the scale of values and accurate reproduction of absolute values. The most accurate reproduction of values would be represented by a 45-degree straight line going up to the maximum density, with a horizontal line for the rest of the curve. This would, of course, represent a complete loss of shadow detail.

In reproducing a live scene, a toed curve is preferred to a 45-degree straight line. If this were preferred because of the limited density range of the print, one might expect that the same would be true in reproducing the original print at a still lower density range. However, the need for a toe is probably connected with the conversion of a full-scale three-dimensional scene, often brilliantly lighted, to a small print, and once this has been done, no additional toe is needed in making a reproduction of the print. The present results give no indication that maintaining the middletone contrast and flattening the highlights is preferred, although the picture quality of such a reproduction would be higher, at least with the picnic scene. Possibly a different result would have been obtained if the prints had been judged by art directors, more skilled in evaluating reproductions, but experience indicates that the average preference of experts is about the same as that of others, the difference being that their preferences are more consistent.

The fact that all these curves are so consistent is reassuring, since it indicates that the precision of the work is adequate in spite of the rather small number of observers and the incomplete range of prints. In every case, prints closer to a straight line on the density plot were rejected as inferior reproductions.

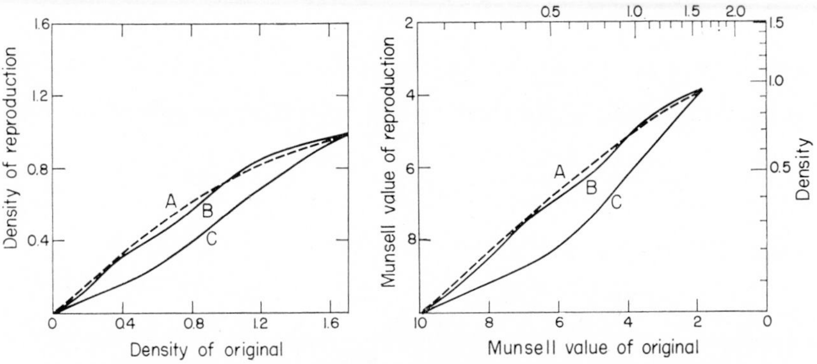

Fig. 12. Relationship of 1.0 D_{max} prints to the best continuous-tone print of the picnic scene: *A*, the most accurate reproduction of this print, predicted from Fig. 11; *B*, the best reproduction; *C*, the 1.0 D_{max} print with the highest picture quality.

The "best reproduction" turns out to be surprisingly different from the halftone print with the best picture quality, as shown in Fig. 12. *B* is the curve of the best reproduction of the best continuous-tone print, whereas Curve *C* represents the 1.0-maximum-density print with the highest picture quality. The reason for this is evidently that, as already mentioned, the best continuous-tone print of this subject falls far short of optimum tone-rendering being too dark in the middletones. Lighter prints were rejected because of loss of highlight detail and low shadow density. Such losses did not occur in the halftone prints, even when the tone scale was adjusted to give light middletones.

The "most accurate reproduction" curve, derived from Fig. 11, is also given in Fig. 12, Curve *A*. Since the best reproduction (Curve *B*) is practically the same as the most accurate reproduction, and very different from the most pleasing print (Curve *C*), it appears that reproductions, when compared directly with the original, are evaluated almost entirely for accuracy rather than for picture quality. If this is true, it would be advisable always to look at a reproduction first without the original, remembering that the final viewer of the reproduction will have no original with which to compare it.

ADDITIONAL ASPECTS OF THE PROBLEM

Time did not permit us to study the tone reproduction required in other important situations such as the reproduction of transparencies; reproduction on paper which is darker than the highlights of the original; and the reproduction of originals of lower density range than the full scale of the reproduction process. However, in the course of this and other work on tone reproduction, many related aspects of the problem have come up, and the remainder of the paper consists of a discussion of some of these other aspects. These are the detailed shape of the tone-reproduction curve, the compromise required between picture quality and accurate reproduction, the number of variables available for controlling the shape of the tone-reproduction curve, and local variations in tone reproduction.

A. Details of the tone-reproduction curve

It is common practice to speak of the tone rendering of a picture as if it consisted of three parts—highlights, middletones, and shadows. According

Fig. 13. Photomicrograph of chain-dot formation produced by the Kodak Gray Contact Screen (133 lines per inch).

to this, high highlight contrast would mean dark middletones, for example. The present experimental work was carried out on this basis. This may be sufficient to establish the best shape for the tone-reproduction curve, which is, no doubt, a smooth curve, but of course it does not tell the whole story.

The shape of the toe is of particular importance, although the experiments described here indicate that there should be no toe at all on the tone-reproduction curve. The other important requirement is that there should be a smooth curve. "Jumps" in the tone scale are likely to occur at three points: in the extreme highlights and shadows, and where the dots join up. Such jumps make it impossible to produce smooth vignettes. The jump where the dots join up can be minimized by the use of a slightly unsymmetrical dot pattern[10] (a chain-dot formation), as in the Kodak Gray Contact Screen, 133 lines per inch (Fig. 13). This divides the jump into two smaller jumps which are almost imperceptible. Jumps in the highlights or shadows occur when it is impossible to hold very small dots, so that dots smaller than a certain size disappear completely. These, as well as the jump in the middletones, become more pronounced with finer screens.

The opposite effect, complete loss of detail at the ends of the scale, can also be very undesirable. This is usually due to misjudgment of the exposure or development of halftone negatives, which is critical because the scale comes to an abrupt end at zero and 100-per cent dot area. Small highlight and shadow areas containing no important detail can be dropped out in this way, but this is a matter which calls for expert judgment.

The phrase "highlight contrast" sometimes refers to the contrast (and hence the detail) in the extreme highlights, and sometimes to everything lighter than the middletones. The variation of highlight contrast in the present series of prints (corresponding to Vector 3) was of the latter type. Unless this distinction is kept in mind, much confusion can result. For a more adequate treatment, the highlight region should be subdivided into two sections.

B. Picture quality versus reproduction quality

We have established that the best reproduction of the best available original does not always lead to the best picture quality in the reproduction. Should we aim for the best reproduction, the best picture quality, or something in between? Obviously, this will depend to a large extent on the requirements of the particular situation, and especially on whether the customer has requested that the deficiencies of the original should be corrected. Before discussing this further, we shall consider the form of the curve relating reproduction quality and picture quality to print characteristics.

In a series of prints varying in a single characteristic such as darkness, a single observer's ratings of their picture quality will be quite erratic but will roughly form a bell-shaped curve. A second observer's ratings will form a similar bell-shaped curve, with its maximum probably at a different place. The average ratings of a large number of observers (picture-quality curve, Fig. 14) will form a wider, rather flat-topped curve which, for purposes of computation, can be approximated by a parabola. The highest point (A) on this curve is considered to represent optimum picture quality, but it should be remembered that this just represents an average preference, and that those observers whose preferences differ from the average are entitled to their opinion. The wide range of preferences is surprising at first, and this is why it is necessary to average so many observers to locate the optimum precisely. On the other hand, because of this wide range and because of the difference between different subjects, not much is gained by great precision. For example, in the medium-density picnic prints, the print which had the highest-average quality rating was picked as the best by only two out of twenty observers. Thirty observers are considered desirable for obtaining an accurate quality rating, but thirteen to twenty were used in this work (a) because extreme accuracy did not mean much in this study for the reasons just mentioned, (b) because in this exploratory work it was considered more important to investigate as wide a variety of prints as possible, (c) because the same people evaluated both the print and the reproduction, which led to good accuracy in the relationship between the two, and (d) owing to personnel and time limitations.

The average reproduction-quality curve has a more clearly defined peak than the picture-quality curve because there is less disagreement in evaluating

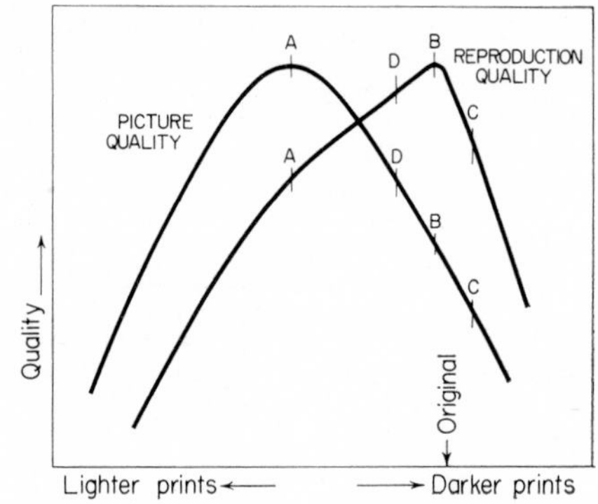

Fig. 14. Probable form of relationship of reproduction quality and picture quality to a characteristic of the print, when the tone rendering of the original is not optimum: *A*, highest picture quality; *B*, highest reproduction quality; *C*, excessively dark print; *D*, intermediate print.

similarity than in evaluating aesthetic quality. The observers were asked to consider picture quality as well as similarity when evaluating the prints as reproductions, but Fig. 12 indicates that picture quality played a very minor role in the evaluation.

There was not a wide enough variety of prints nor a sufficient number of observers to establish the shape of the reproduction-quality curve, but it is probably similar to that given in Fig. 14. This represents the case of the picnic scene where the original to be reproduced was darker than the optimum. The "best reproduction" is at *B* and is similar to the original—possibly a little lighter—and prints which are closer to the optimum picture quality (toward the left) are rated lower as reproductions. But the reproduction quality falls off still more rapidly (toward the right) for prints which are even darker than the optimum picture.

If the original is of good quality, the customer will probably be best pleased with a reproduction which has the highest reproduction quality, which will closely match the original. On the other hand, the final viewer of the reproduction has no original for comparison, and will be affected only by the picture quality of the reproduction. Moreover, a slight error in aiming at optimum reproduction quality may result in a reproduction at *C* on the steep right-hand slope of the curve, which is low in both reproduction quality and picture quality. In most cases, therefore, it is probably best to aim at a reproduction at *D* which is slightly below optimum reproduction quality but is a better picture. In other words, since you cannot reproduce the original exactly, try to lean in the direction of a better picture rather than a worse one.

Another way of looking at this is to say that in designing the reproduction process, the errors of the reproduction process should be fully corrected and, in addition, the errors of the original should be partially corrected, to a very limited extent. This statement applies particularly to the reproduction of color photographs, whose errors are usually far greater than those of black-and-white prints because of dye deficiencies. The question comes up frequently in color photographs when there is a separate correction step in the process. It is true that color correction rather than tone correction is involved here, but the reasoning is similar. It has often been erroneously stated that the object of the correction process is to correct for the deficiencies of the original, and color-reproduction theories based on this idea have actually been worked out.

This mistake is possible since the original process often has characteristics quite similar to those of the reproduction process, in which case the solution is similar in both cases. The fallacy becomes obvious when the reproduction of a painting is considered. In this case, the original is presumably free from errors, but the color correction required in the reproduction process is about the same as that required in reproducing a color photograph.

Three types of variations must be considered in designing the reproduction process. First, there are the consistent errors of the process used for making the original. As already mentioned, it is advisable to include a very small partial correction for these in the design of the reproduction process. Secondly, there are the errors of the reproduction process itself, and these should be corrected as completely as possible. This usually involves improving the highlight contrast to produce a tone-reproduction curve like those shown in Fig. 11. A somewhat low density range is usually unavoidable. Thirdly, there are the variations from print to print due to poor technique or differences in subject matter. These should as a rule be disregarded except on special request from the customer, who, for example, often likes to have the pictures which are to appear on a single page evened up. It is best to perfect the reproduction process as far as possible and standardize it, rather than to adjust it according to the characteristics of every original. Adjustments for originals of varying density range are, of course, desirable.

C. Degrees of freedom

In order to appreciate the type of control available in the system used here and in ordinary photographic prints or photo-mechanical reproductions, the number of variables available is important. In any reproduction process, there are a limited number of variables that can be used to control tone reproduction, the object being to keep the other factors constant. In making a Kodachrome transparency, for instance, the only variable affecting tone reproduction is exposure, and no adjustment in contrast is available to allow for the difference between long- and short-range subjects. In choosing the exposure, a compromise is therefore made between loss of highlight detail on the one hand, and dark middletones and loss of shadow detail on the other.

In making a photographic print, the exposure of the negative is adjusted, but this is not usually for the purpose of varying the tone reproduction to suit the subject. Likewise, the development of the negative is usually standardized, and changing it would only mean that a different grade of paper would have to be chosen. So these can hardly be regarded as effective degrees of freedom. In making the print, however, there are two degrees of freedom (exposure and contrast), whereas there are four things that we should like to control, namely: highlight and shadow density, and highlight and shadow contrast. Middletone density and contrast are fixed by the choice of these four. Since we have only two degrees of freedom, we cannot control these four factors independently, and the best print is a compromise. For example, good highlight contrast is obtained at the expense of high highlight density and dark middletones.

In the case of a halftone reproduction, it is usual to aim for a certain highlight- and shadow-dot size. Two degrees of freedom are needed for this, which are often the flash and the detail exposure. Variation of development time does not count as an extra degree of freedom, because its effect is the same as that of changes in exposure.

The use of an additional, no-screen exposure provides an extra degree of freedom, by means of which the highlight contrast and the middletone density can be adjusted, the highlight- and shadow-dot sizes being kept constant by adjustment of the other two exposures.

In the present work, a supplementary exposure through a highlight positive took the place of the no-screen exposure, and an additional degree of freedom not usually available was obtained by making a supplementary exposure through a shadow negative. The fourth combination (Curve NMF), Fig. 3, cannot be regarded as providing an additional degree of freedom since it is intermediate between two of the other curves. Thus, the four degrees of freedom necessary for adjusting the highlight and shadow contrast while maintaining the highlight and shadow density constant were available. This does not mean that all combinations of highlight and shadow contrast were obtainable. Some combinations were outside the range of the positives used. Moreover, the exact curve shapes obtained will also depend on the characteristics of the positives.

D. Non-Jonesian tone reproduction

As in non-Euclidean geometry, much can be learned by abandoning one of the axioms which was assumed to be true throughout L. A. Jones's classic work on tone reproduction[6]. The axiom in question is that in a given picture there is a unique relationship between the brightness or density of the original subject and the density of the reproduction. We are not concerned here with erratic variations due to unevenness of development, etc., but with the fact that the optimum density at a given point in the reproduction depends not only on the density at the corresponding point in the original but also on that of the neighboring areas. This problem could be investigated theoretically with the help of modern computers, if some assumption were made about the visual sensitivity to brightness differences of points at various distances from each other. Practical work with unsharp masking and with scanners of the LogEtronics type has shown big improvements in reproduction quality when these adjacency effects are properly controlled, although very objectionable effects are produced when the conditions are not properly adjusted. It should be remembered that the optimum tone-reproduction curve discussed in this paper implies the absence of such effects and so does not represent the best possible reproduction. These adjacency effects can also be troublesome, because when they occur, it is no longer possible, by measuring the highlight and shadow densities of the original, to predict accurately the exposures required to produce the desired highlight- and shadow-dot sizes; and small highlight areas in which it is necessary to hold a highlight dot are often dropped out. Such effects are characteristic of lith-type developers, but they also occur with continuous-tone developers to a greater extent than is commonly realized.

CONCLUSIONS

In order to arrive at an optimum tone-reproduction curve for average work, it would be necessary to study many more scenes, using prints which cover the range more adequately. This work has raised questions rather than answered them, and the methods used could be greatly improved if it were continued, but perhaps it is sufficient to justify certain tentative conclusions.

1. In making a reproduction of limited maximum density, the most accurate reproduction, apart from aesthetic considerations, was a little darker in the middletones than would be indicated by a straight-line reproduction in terms of Munsell value, and considerably darker than indicated by a

straight line in a density plot. There was no indication that a toe on the reproduction curve would be desirable.

2. In comparing a reproduction with an original of good quality, accuracy of reproduction was given far more weight than the picture quality of the reproduction, so that the curve for the best reproduction was practically identical with the curve for most accurate reproduction. It should be noted, however, that S. Levine (private communication) working with the Fairchild Variable Response Unit, by means of which the tone-reproduction curve can be controlled at will, concluded that a straight line on a density graph is the best compromise. The reason for the discrepancy is not known.

3. The best continuous-tone prints that can be made by straightforward methods may depart considerably from optimum tone rendering, being too dark in the middletones for one of the subjects used here. Consequently, the best reproduction of the best print was also too dark and was by no means the best halftone print that could be made.

4. It follows from 2 and 3 that where picture quality rather than reproduction quality is desired, reproductions should be evaluated without a reference print before being compared with the original.

Obviously, there is no single, optimum tone-reproduction curve. The choice depends on the subject and on the person making the choice. In practice, however, a compromise must be used. Sometimes this compromise is imposed by the lack of flexibility of the process, but even where flexibility exists, it cannot be fully made use of because of the difficulty of predicting the treatment required for a given subject. It appears to be best to perfect the process as far as possible, then to standardize it, and to keep the variations from subject to subject to a minimum.

ACKNOWLEDGEMENTS

I should like to thank Miss J. Newkirk for her assistance in the experimental work, many members of the Laboratories for judging the prints, and Mr. C. N. Nelson and Mr. J. L. Simonds for supplying the negatives and for furnishing information on the methods which they have developed for studying tone reproduction.

REFERENCES

1. D. A. Spencer, Tone rendering in the reproduction of photographs. *Phot. J., Section B* **87B**, 94–104 (1947).
2. Tentative method for specifying color by the Munsell system. ASTM Pamphlet D-1535-58T (1958).
3. W. L. Rhodes, Tone and color control in reproduction processes. *Proc. 6th Ann. Tech. Meeting of TAGA (Technical Association of the Graphic Arts)*, 48–64 (1954).

4. A. PERSON, *Bildmässige Leica-Photos durch Tontrennung nach dem Person–Verfahren*, H. Bechhold Verlagsbuchhandlung, Frankfurt-M., 2nd Ed., 1935.
5. J. P. GUILFORD, *Psychometric Methods*, McGraw-Hill, New York, 1936.
6. C. E. K. MEES, *The Theory of the Photographic Process*, pp. 910–969, Macmillan, New York, 1954.
7. J. L. SIMONDS, Analysis of the variability among density-log exposure curves of black-and-white negative films by the method of principal components. *Phot. Sci. and Eng.* **2**, 205–209 (1958).
8. J. L. SIMONDS, A quantitative study of the influence of tone-reproduction factors on picture quality. *Phot. Sci. and Eng.* **5**, 270–277 (1961).
9. J. A. C. YULE, Variation of tone reproduction in halftone processes. *Printing Inks and Color* (Proc. 5th Intern. Conf. of Printing Res. Institutes, Bethlehem, Pa., June 8–13, 1959), W. H. Banks, ed., Pergamon Press, New York, 1961, pp. 48–66.
10. R. E. MAURER, A study of dot shapes for contact screens. *Proc. 15th Ann. Tech. Meeting of TAGA (Technical Association of the Graphic Arts)*, 51–64 (1963).

DISCUSSION

ZETTLEMOYER: Would you get the same preferred curve for coloured prints? This question, of course, brings up the importance of the undertone of the black ink and any effect due to colour of the paper.

YULE: The preferred curve for multicolour prints is related to colour correction. Without colour correction, a more contrasty print is preferred, since it has higher colour saturation. With colour correction, the preferred tone rendering is about the same as for black and white. Monochrome reproductions with a coloured ink or a coloured paper may possibly require different tone rendering from black-and-white prints, since the colour saturation may perhaps affect the apparent strength of a tone, but we have not investigated this.

BRUNO: What effect would the tone of the black (brown or blue) have on the ideal tone reproduction?

YULE: I should not expect the rather small differences in the colours of "black" inks to make a significant difference. However, it is true that in the case of light sources, a cold light appears duller than a warm light of equal luminosity, so there is a possibility of a slight difference in preferred tone rendering between a cold and a warm black.

GRANEEK: I would like to ask a question about the use of subjective assessments in this investigation. Such methods can, in general, often be fraught with difficulties. I would be interested to know whether it was necessary to resort to statistical analysis of the results or whether there was sufficient agreement among observers to produce clear answers in most cases.

YULE: No statistical analysis of the significance of the results was made, but it was evident from inspection of the results that there was sufficient agreement to produce clear answers in the cases given in the paper.

A statistical analysis of the relationship between picture quality and curve shape was made. A second-order equation was derived expressing the quality as a function of the first three scalar multiples. However, this was not done for reproduction quality and accuracy.

HARRISON: You mention that in reproducing a live scene, a toed curve is preferred to a 45-degree straight line and this may be due to the conversion of a full-scale three-dimensional scene to a small print. Have any comparisons been made with stereoscopic pairs of prints in which, if this assumption is true, the need for a toe could be expected to be less?

YULE: I do not know of any tone-reproduction work with stereoscopic pairs. Another factor may be the difference between the angle subtended by a small print and by a live scene which completely surrounds the observer.

WOODS: Were the densities quoted measured with a purely objective densitometer? If so, to what extent would the very high gloss of the original and the lesser glossy finish of the print, produce an apparent density difference; probably accounting for the darker mid-tones in Fig. 12?

YULE: The densities were measured with a Densichron densitometer whose readings correspond quite closely to standard diffuse reflection density measurements. It is true that this does not correspond to ordinary viewing conditions, and this is a possible cause of the darker middletones of Fig. 12. However, originals usually are more glossy than reproductions, and their densities are measured in this way, so the curves would nevertheless be applicable to practical printing conditions.

SOME NOTES ON THE SENSITOMETRY OF LITH MATERIALS

by A. J. W. Sweerman, W. M. du Pont and F. G. Scheulderman
Stichting Instituut voor Grafische Techniek, T.N.O.,
Amsterdam, The Netherlands

1. INTRODUCTION

The light-sensitive properties of films can be described by a curve relating log "exposure" and the density after development.

Such curves are only valuable for practical use if the physical circumstances during use and experimental determination of the curve are not too different, unless it is certain that the discrepancies are of no consequence.

For example it is known that a sensitometric curve determined by long exposure times say 1–10 sec has little meaning for use with flash exposures.

Such a difference between physical circumstances during testing and practical use also appears when normal sensitometric curves are determined for lith materials.

In halftone photography the density variation of the screen determines the result rather than the image tone. It is known that the very steep gradation of lith films is partly a consequence of the accelerated action of an unstable oxidation transition product of hydroquinone.[1]

The influence of diffusion and agitation will be different for a steep density gradient as occurs in halftone dots or for a small density gradient as usual with a gray wedge. It is also possible that conclusions from the normal sensitometric curves, which are large in size compared with a halftone dot, are of no value for lith films when used for halftone photography.

2. EXPERIMENTAL

Two somewhat different screening and methods of judgment were applied:

2.1. In the first method, exposures through a normal contact screen were made. As criterion the "reproduced density range" was used, by which is understood the difference in corresponding original densities at which the halftone negative presents a sufficiently dense highlight and shadow dot. It is thus assumed that if the sensitometric curve is steeper, the density differences in the contact screen will be more noticeable.

Because the density gradient of the highlight compared with the shadow tones is greater on the screen negative than the positive, the printing down quality of the highlight dots is judged on the screen negative and that of the shadow dots on the screen positive (Fig. 1). 18 films from 8 different manufacturers were proved, series 1 with a contact crossline screen 50 l./cm and

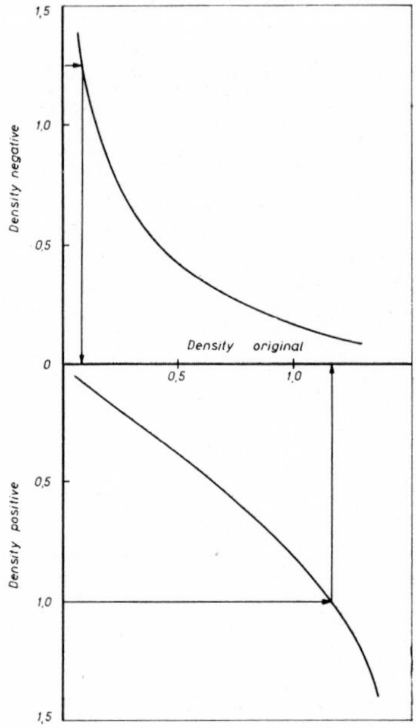

Fig. 1. Showing how the reproduced density range is measured. A requirement is that the halftone positives are made by a standard method.

series 2/3 with a contact line screen 50 l./cm. The development was $2\frac{1}{4}$ min in Kodalith 20°C. The comparison of the results of series 1, 2 and 3 is shown in Fig. 2 and 3. From Figs. 2 and 3 a reasonable agreement between the series 1, 2 and 3 appears. (The reproduced density range with the contact crossline screen appears to be about 0.1 greater than with the contact line screen.)

The accuracy can be further improved if instead of a reflection original as was used in series 1, 2 and 3, the exposures are made in contact with a transparent gray wedge and the exposed film strips are developed simultaneously. The reproduced density range was judged empirically on the positives. Some results of three chosen films (with a high, middle and low reproduced density range in series 1, 2 and 3) are compiled in Table 1.

Photomicrographs Figs. 7 and 8 illustrate the line or dot quality of halftone exposures on these films. The accuracy appears now to be so improved that other causes of variations could be found. (The standard deviations dropped

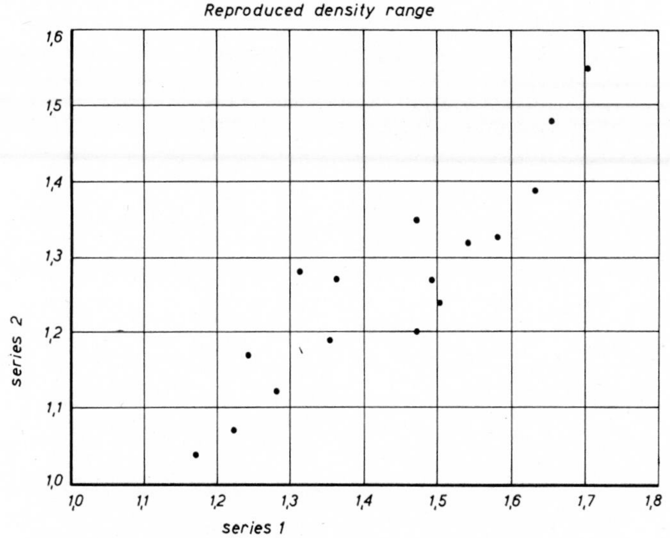

Fig. 2. Comparison of the reproduced density range, series 1 and 2.

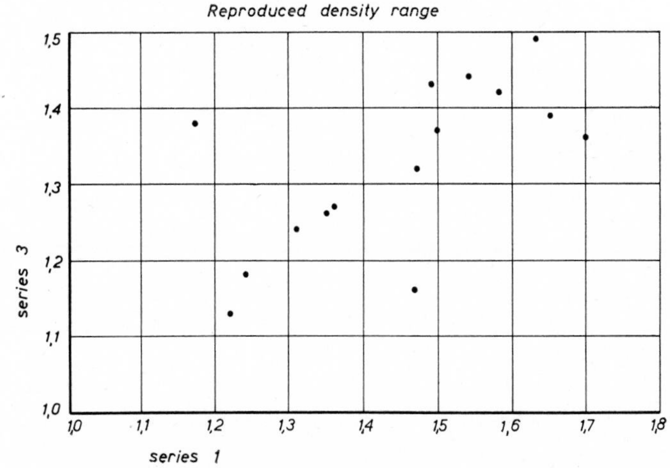

Fig. 3. Comparison of the reproduced density range, series 1 and 3.

from 0.07 to less than 0.02.) For example, slight developer variations caused by storage conditions have mainly influenced the film speed. Whereas from the normal sensitometric curves of the films 14, 15 no difference appears, the

TABLE 1. REPRODUCED DENSITY RANGE

Original contact screen	Reflection gray scale line 50 l./cm		Transparent gray wedge			
	series 2	series 3	line 50 l./cm		crossline 50 l./cm	crossline 44 l./cm
Film no. 14	1.32	1.44	1.30	1.28	1.47	1.38
Film no. 15	1.24	1.37	1.24	1.20	1.38	1.29
Film no. 9	—	1.06	1.12	1.10	1.28	1.20

halftone exposures show an obvious difference (Fig. 4). Film 9 proved to have indeed a less steep gradation, according to the lower reproduced density range.

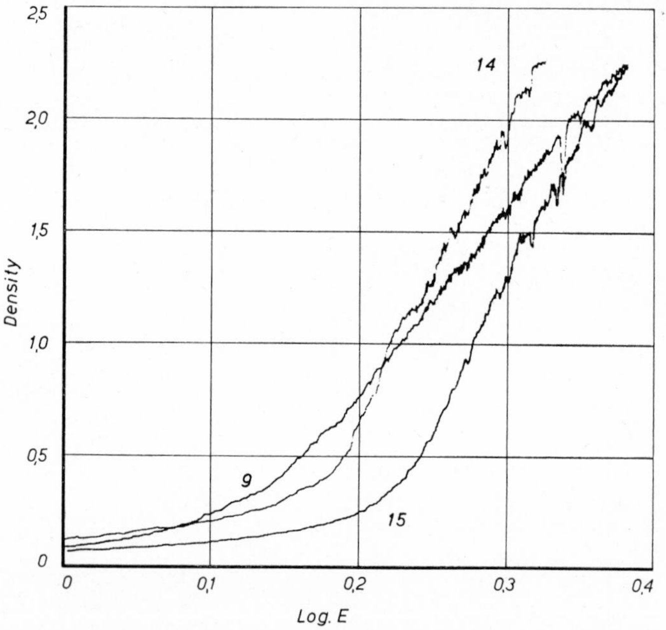

Fig. 4. Normal sensitometric curve of lith films.

2.2. A somewhat different method for testing lith films for screening consists of investigating the density distribution in the halftone dots or lines made on the films.

For a good discrimination it is necessary that the amplitude of the light intensity distribution is low. This can be achieved in several ways, for example by imaging (if necessary unsharp) a line screen on the film to be tested.

This method has been applied to the films 1, 4, 6, 9, 13 and 15. The density distribution of a 50 per cent line is examined by scanning the line with a Joyce and Loebl recording microdensitometer with a slit of 5 × 100 μ (Fig. 5, Table 2).

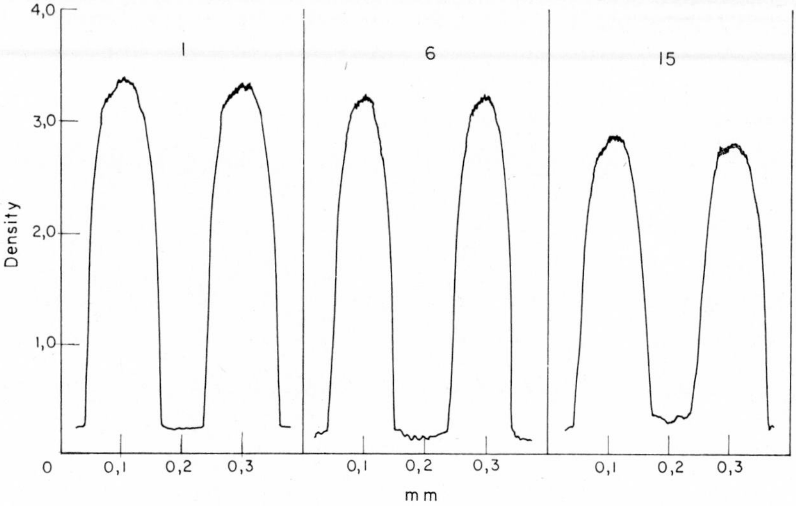

Fig. 5a. Microdensitometer curves of 50% lines.

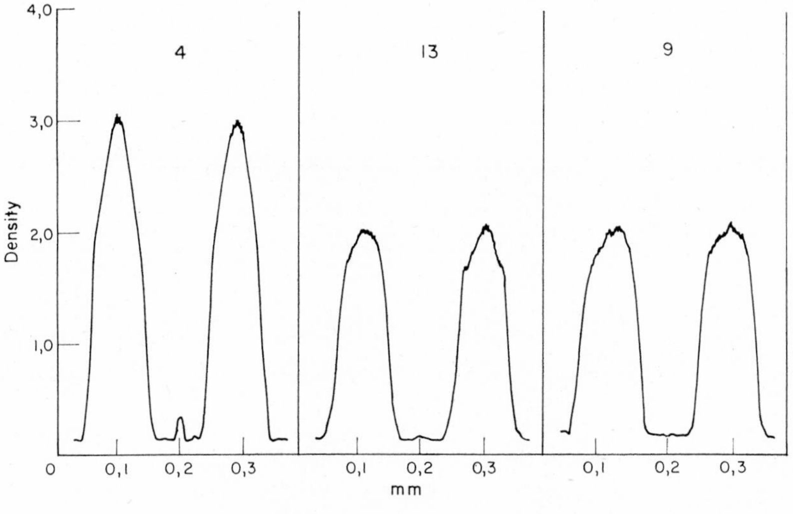

Fig. 5b. Microdensitometer curves of 50% lines.

TABLE 2

	Reproduced density range mean of series 2/3	Maximum density with micro-densitometer	Decreasing line width referred to that at 1 sec printing time		
			2 sec	4 sec	8 sec
Film no. 1	1.43	3.1	8%	14%	25%
6	1.26	3.0	7%	16%	27%
15	1.31	2.5	7%	17%	30%
4	1.33	2.8	8%	16%	31%
13	1.10	1.8	10%	21%	39%
9	1.06	1.8	11%	19%	45%

A rough impression of the quality of the 50 per cent lines can be achieved by making contact prints with different exposure times (Fig. 6, Table 2). A light intensity distribution with a small amplitude can also be produced

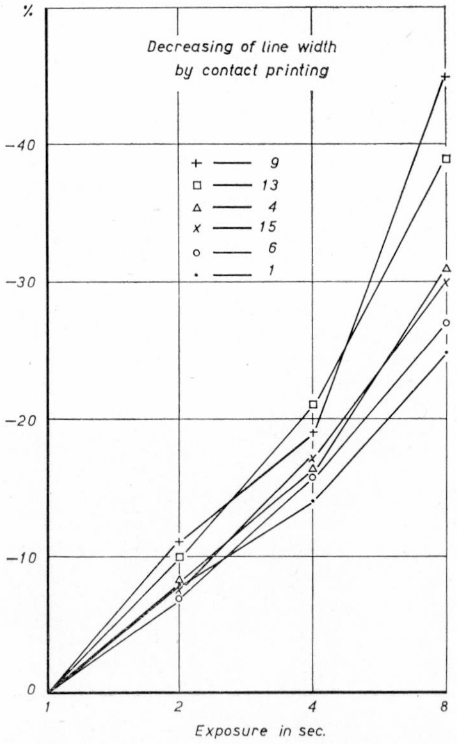

Fig. 6. Decreasing of line width by contact printing.

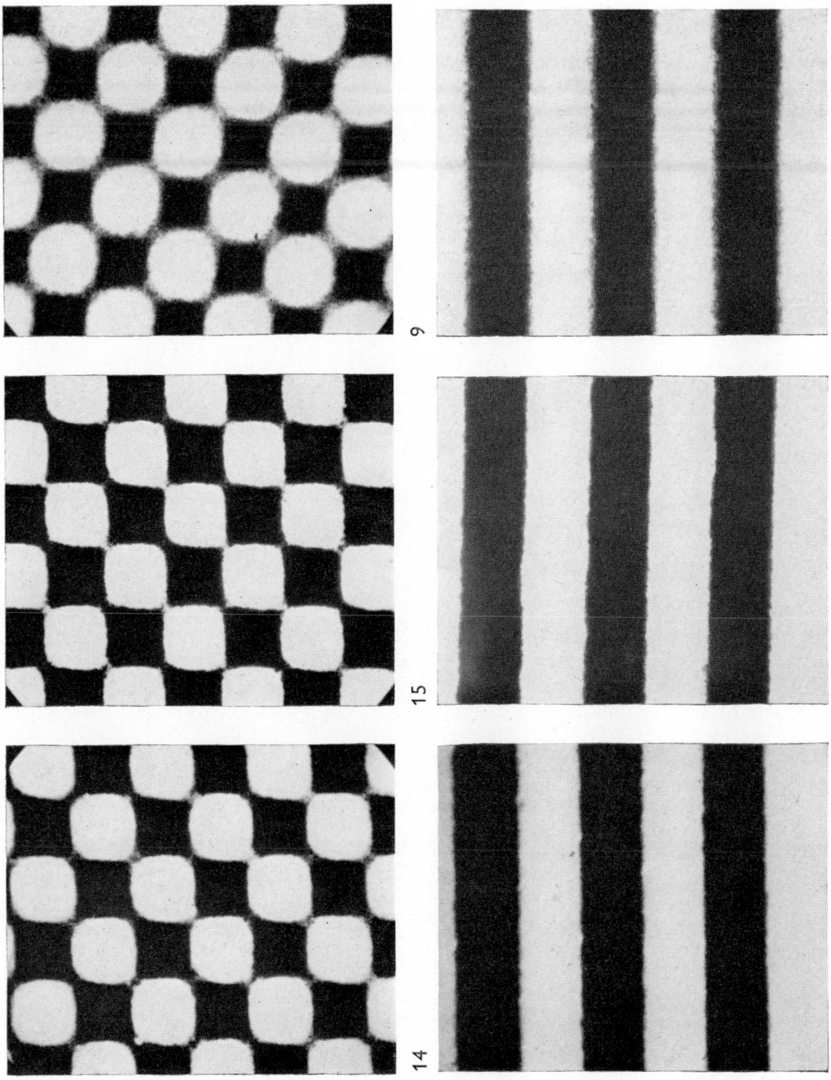

Fig. 7

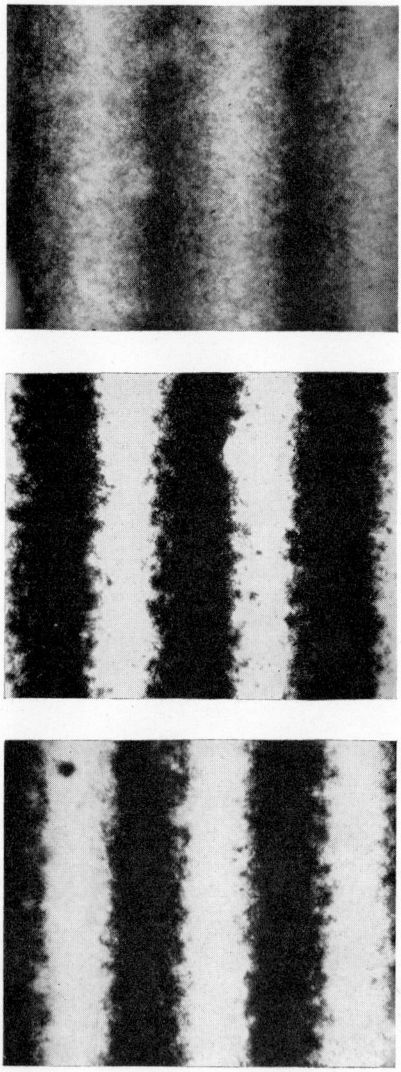

14 15 9

Fig. 8

with a suitable contact screen. In that case the density distribution in the screen is not specified by tone rendering requirements and can be sine shaped or linearly increasing and decreasing. With such a contact screen, density range about 0.4, a 50 per cent line screen is made on the films 14, 15 and 9 (see Fig. 9). When from this 50 per cent line screen contact prints are made with different exposure times the line width alterations which occur can be measured (Table 3).

TABLE 3

Decreasing line width referred to that at 1 sec printing time

	2 sec	4 sec
Film no. 14	8%	10%
15	5%	12%
9	18%	37%

3. SUMMARY

It appears that great differences in reproduced density range can occur when halftone exposures are made with the same contact screen but with different lith films.

These differences cannot always be predicted from the normal sensitometric curves.

As the tone rendering is dependent on the magnitude of the auxiliary exposures and these again are influenced by the reproduced density range, a method similar to the practical use is preferable. The measurement of the reproduced density range with a normal contact screen is simple and appears useful, but also direct measurement of the density gradient from lines made with a small amplitude light intensity distribution is possible.

ACKNOWLEDGEMENT

I want to thank the firm of Negretti–Zambra, who made possible the sensitometric and microdensitometer measurements.

REFERENCES

1. J. E. LUVALLE etc., *J. Phot. Sci.* **6,** 176–184 (1958).
2. W. ROMER etc., *J. Phot. Sci.* **6,** 144 (1958).
3. W. SCHUMAN, *Phot. Sci. and Eng.* **6,** 298 (1962).

DISCUSSION

YULE: (1) Is the "reproduced density range" the same as what we have referred to as "basic density range"?

(2) We have not found a good correlation between dot quality and reproduced density range (RDR). This is probably because RDR depends more on background effect than on infectious development whereas the reverse is true of dot quality. Background effect refers to the local lowering of film speed due to the exhaustion of developer in the neighborhood of developed areas. For example, the RDR decreases with increasing development time, while dot quality goes through a maximum. Also, in one case where we had an excessive RDR we modified the developer to reduce the RDR by about 0.2. The dot quality was, if anything, improved.

Kodalith Fine-Line developer will also give a high RDR with a low dot quality.

SWEERMAN: (1) Yes, I mean by RDR the density range from the original that is reproduced without any supplementary exposure.

(2) Perhaps the explanation is that you measured the RDR of the negative. Apparently the RDR seems large, but although the RDR appears larger in the negative, a positive print will show that the effective RDR is much lower because of the lower dot quality.

ADAMS: (1) What happens if films are developed in recommended developers, rather than in Kodalith?

(2) Has the determination of reproduced density range using both negative and contact positive been correlated with the determination of density range from negatives only?

SWEERMAN: (1) The results are less reproducible because the experiments have to be spread out over a greater time. The average of several experiments must be taken.

(2) I have no exact data for this, but we noticed several times that halftone negatives seeming to have the same RDR, showed a large difference in RDR in the halftone positives; thus there was an obvious difference in dot or line sharpness.

MAKING CONTACT SCREENS WITH IMPROVED TONE RENDERING

by FERENC BUZÁS

The Experimental Plant and Laboratory for the Printing Industry, Budapest

(Paper presented by K. LOVASZ)

Abstract—For making contact screens there are several methods in which the dot structure of the contact screen is determined by calculation or graphically. As a consequence of the complex light distribution behind the glass screen such methods are quite complicated. Tone distortions arising from the image transmission and printing process cannot be taken into account with most of these methods.

Our experiments have shown that the density of the corresponding zones in a tone diaphragm put at an adequate distance before the glass screen has a critical effect on the location of the equal density spots in the contact screen. In our work the density of each of the zones in the dot-forming diaphragm for the contact screen with ideal tone rendering was determined first by calculation. After this, an experimental screen was made, then a printing forme and prints by the usual process. The values measured on the prints were compared with the density in the copy and the tone errors on the prints were introduced into the zones of the dot-forming diaphragm by means of a nomogram. According to the data obtained on the nomogram the dot-forming diaphragm was corrected and then a corrected contact screen well approaching the ideal tone rendering can be produced which takes account of the distortions arising from forme preparation and printing process.

INTRODUCTION

RECENTLY the importance of reproducing halftone pictures has increased. Beside the pictures in black and white, colour illustrations are coming into prominence more and more. The speedy development of reproduction processes has turned attention to the improvement of colour and tone rendering to a greater extent.

Today much attention is being given to eliminating errors occurring in the transfer of halftone pictures into printing elements. The contact screen is especially remarkable in this respect. The possibilities offered by the contact screen can be utilized in improving tone rendering. By means of screens with the proper tone rendering costly skilled work hours can be saved.

The present work explains the production of the contact screen developed in our Institute.

The tone rendering of the contact screen depends on the production process for making it. It is possible to produce a screen with a tone rendering which takes into account and compensates for the effect of printing process on tone rendering. This practically means that tone rendering of the contact screen is to be "distorted" in such a way that tones on the print will correspond to the copy. Of course, it is only possible when the copy does not contain any tones which are not to be rendered by available printing inks. Screens developed in our Institute give a tone rendering and dot shape that is able to fulfil this requirement.

I. SOME PROBLEMS IN USING CONTACT SCREENS

The contact screen is a light absorbing medium which periodically alters the intensity of the light passing through in each direction in the plane of the film material. Figure 1 shows that the lowest and the highest density regions

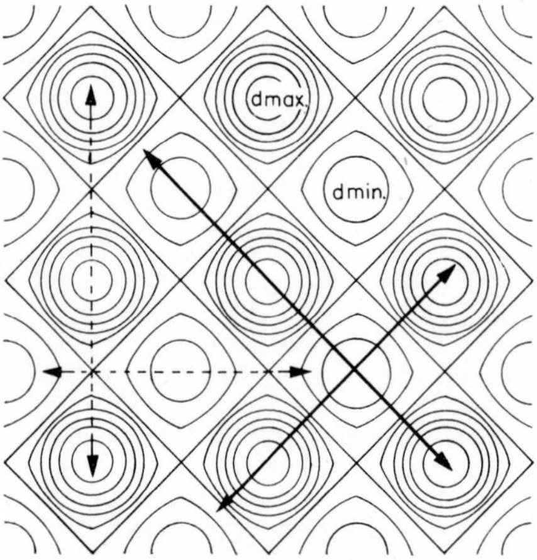

Fig. 1. Main direction and secondary direction of the contact screen.
——— Main direction
– – – – – Secondary direction

of contact screens are located in the main direction and in the direction perpendicular to it.

The secondary direction is at an angle of 45 degrees to the main direction and is characterized by not having at the same time both highest and lowest density values.

When connecting equal density areas with a continuous line (Fig. 2) dot shapes produced with different light intensity and areas enclosed by them can be obtained. The change of dot area caused by light intensity changes is characteristic for the tone rendering of contact screens. When the area enclosed by the line connecting the equal density spots changes with the contact screens produced in different ways the tone rendering of the contact screens will also change. This means that the tone rendering of the contact screens can be modified when the area enclosed by equal density spots changes during the production of the contact screen.

Fig. 2. Equal density spots of the contact screen.

Though tone rendering of the contact screen has received its final shape in production, yet it can be altered by selection of the film material for screen making, through the main exposure and developing process.

With increasing exposure the screen dot increases. The amount of it is controlled by the equal density spots of the contact screen. A dot edge arises where the contact screen still transmits sufficient light energy to achieve proper density. Knowing density and area of the equal density spots, light distribution and dot area behind the screen can be calculated.

II. PRODUCING CONTACT SCREENS

By means of our method the light distribution behind the halftone glass screen can be altered—within acceptable limits—so that an appropriate density arises at definite points on the film behind the glass screen.

1. The dot-forming diaphragm

Equal density spots are determined by the light distribution behind the glass screen and by the characteristics of the light sensitive material.

Light distribution can be most simply modified according to the needs by altering the size and shape of the diaphragm. The same cannot be achieved by changing extension and screen distance. In the case of a given glass screen there is no way for changing the size of the screen openings.

From what has been said, the size and the shape of the diaphragms used in forming tone zones of the contact screen as well as the amount of the light intensity changes of the diaphragm were combined in a so-called "dot-forming diaphragm". The dot-forming diaphragm is a photographic film which consists of zones of different shape and density (Fig. 3). The tone rendering of the contact screen can be controlled by the size and shape of the zones of equal density.

Fig. 3. The dot-forming diaphragm.

In making a dot-forming diaphragm, the photographic material is exposed through each mask corresponding to the shape of a zone for a time necessary to get the required density.

The dot-forming diaphragm is set into the objective in each case so that its sides are parallel to the lines of the glass screen.

The use of a dot-forming diaphragm has the great advantage that tone rendering of the contact screen does not change during serial production. Variations in film material, exposure, or development only affect the tone range of the contact screen.

2. Forming dot shape

When making photographs through a glass screen by means of diaphragms with different shapes, the screen dot shape will approach—as is well-known—very well the shape of the diaphragm when the correct screen distance is used. The deviation is not so great as to be not easily corrected by altering the shape of the zone in the dot-forming diaphragm.

Making use of the dot-forming diaphragm shown in Fig. 4, we made contact screens for halftone gravure.

In Fig. 5 it can be seen that the sides were distorted in order to get square printing dots. This distortion also took into account errors arising in the etching process. The tone zones of the dot-forming diaphragm of a contact screen for halftone gravure can be formed in two different ways. When the edge of the dot-forming diaphragm is clear and the center of it is dense, then a contact screen will be obtained which is suitable for making screen positive

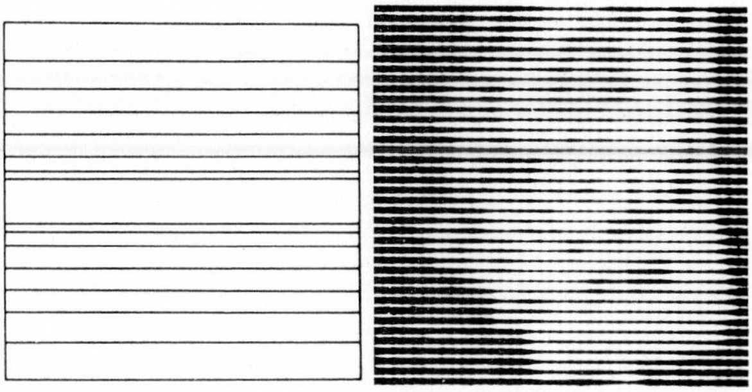

Fig. 4. Dot-forming diaphragm for line contact screen and an enlargement from the print.

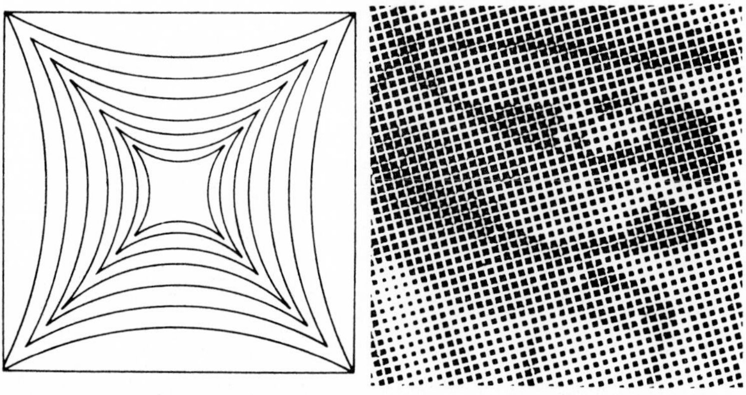

Fig. 5. Dot-forming diaphragm for gravure contact screen and an enlargement from the print.

from a halftone negative. When the center of the dot-forming diaphragm is clear and the edge is dense, we get a contact screen by means of which screen negatives can be made from a halftone positive.

3. Controlling tone rendering of contact screens

The tone rendering of contact screens can be controlled by the distribution of the density range in the dot-forming diaphragm according to the area enclosed by the tone zones. The density of the zones can thus be determined by the area which is enclosed by the zone boundary and by the tone range expected.

The zones of the dot-forming diaphragm reduce the intensity of the light according to their densities. The light energy passing through the individual zones is therefore sufficient for achieving the threshold value at the different exposure times. The difference in threshold values of the individual zones determines the rate of increase of the dot area in the contact screen.

If it is necessary to get a greater difference between some tone densities of the screen positive, it can be done by reducing the density differences in the corresponding zones of the dot-forming diaphragm. Conversely density differences can be increased.

The calculation used for determining density values of the zones in the dot-forming diaphragm will be discussed in part III.

4. Screen distance

The screen distance is chosen so that projected edges of the dot-forming diaphragm come side by side behind the glass screen. The effect of changing

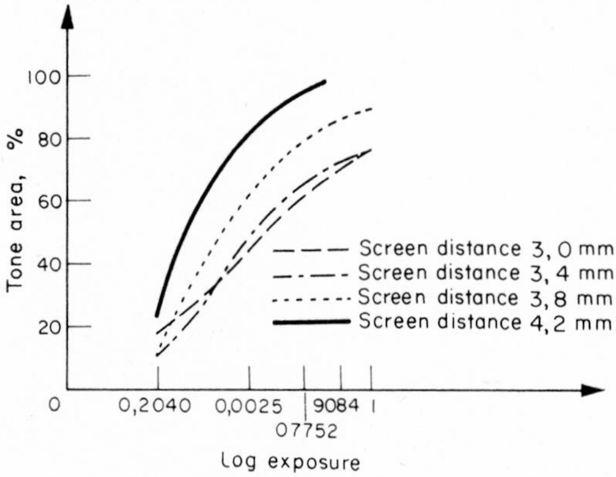

Fig. 6. Variation in the characteristics of a contact screen as a function of screen distance.

the screen distance was investigated considering the tone rendering of the contact screen. According to these tests in the case of any deviation from the halftone ratio, the tone range of the contact screen will change. The tone rendering curve will vary according to the screen distance.

During the trials changes arising in the tone distribution of the contact screen were determined in the following way. A sheet of lith film was put into the contact screen making machine. The film was given a series of exposures to a dot-forming diaphragm. For developing it, a high contrast paraformaldehyde developer was used. In the film sheet the areas corresponding to the various exposures were obtained; these were in direct proportion to the tone areas in the contact screen. This test was repeated while changing the screen distance. Photomicrographs were made from the films and the areas were determined on paper enlargements. The diagram obtained by plotting measured values (Fig. 6) shows that smaller screen distances negligibly affect the tone rendering characteristics. With increasing screen distance, the tone range decreases, and inversely, with decreasing screen distance it increases. Experiments made on other dot-forming diaphragms gave similar results.

5. Photomaterial

The required light distribution behind the glass screen is fixed by the photographic film. The characteristics and technical quality of the film critically determine the tone rendering in the contact screen.

The contact screens are made with different tone range rendering power by means of a dot-forming diaphragm which has a definite tone range. The tone range can be modified through the exposure and the developing time. In the case of an exaggerated increase of the developing time the contact screen will be spotty. To avoid this, the dot-forming contact screens were made with different tone range rendering. In this way contact screens with different tone range rendering could be made without excessive development time.

The sharpness of the screen dots is influenced by the fineness of grain of the contact screen. Hence the finest grain is desirable.

6. Apparatus

A special apparatus shown in Fig. 7 was constructed for making contact screens. As light source a flash lamp was attached to the objective of the apparatus, for which the exposure has been determined. The film sheet is

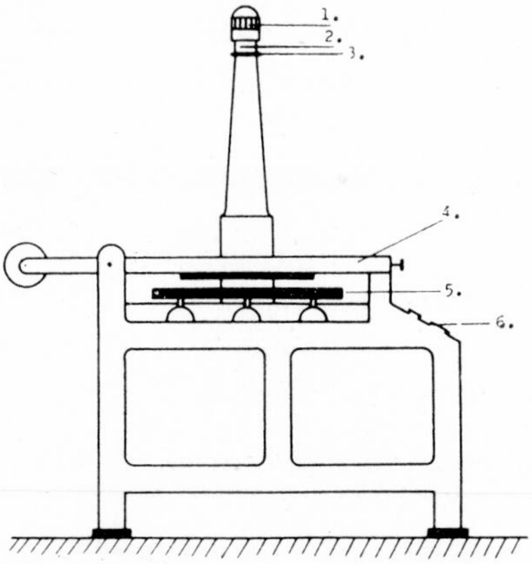

Fig. 7. Contact screen making apparatus.

1. Flash lamp
2. Dot-forming diaphragm
3. Objective
4. Screen holder
5. Suction plate
6. Control desk

fixed on a suction plate. The distance between the glass screen and the suction plate can be altered and readjusted with an accuracy of one hundredth of a millimeter. When putting in the film sheet, the frame supporting the glass screen can be removed.

III. CALCULATION OF CHANGES IN TONE RENDERING FOR CONTACT SCREEN

The tone rendering of our contact screen was determined from consideration of the following operations.

1. Making a halftone photograph or a colour separation from the copy.
2. Making a screen positive by contact printing.
3. Making a screen positive print.

Changes arising in the individual processes are as follows:

The highlights as well as the shadows of the copy are flat. This flatness in the main can be corrected automatically by adjusting the tone zones in the contact screen. Thus no hand retouching was made on the negative or on the screen positive. For making the screen transparency a lith type film and a paraformaldehyde developer was used taking care of the conditions of agitation.

For printing down on metal, dichromated polyvinyl alcohol and the anodized aluminium plate developed by our Institute (Anofsal-plate) were used. Distortions arising during plate making and printing (which remain constant under a controlled method) are demonstrated by means of our method nomogramically and hence corrected.

1. Relationship between the copy and the print

The aim of reproducing a picture is to reproduce the tones of the copy. This condition cannot be perfectly attained because of the limitations of the printing processes. In the copy there are often tones and colours which cannot be reproduced even with the most perfect technology available. These factors were eliminated in our further investigations. It is assumed that only the given tones are to be reproduced, in which case the relation between the copy and the print can be represented by a straight line which goes at an angle of 45 degrees to the horizontal axis.

2. Relationship between the dot area of the screen positive and the print density

The dot area of the screen positive undergoes a change during the plate making and printing. The area and density of the ink film on the paper as well as the whiteness of the paper give together the tone density of the print. The dot area of the screen transparency and the tone density of the print produced by it can be expressed by the well-known Tritton–Wilson's equation for an ideal case:

$$D_{\text{print}} = \log \left[1 \Big/ \left(1 - t \left[1 - \frac{1}{\text{antilog}\, d} \right] \right) \right]$$

where t = the dot area; d = the optical density of the ink.

This equation refers to ideal conditions when assuming that the screen dots on the film will be transferred to the plate and the paper without any change (Fig. 8). It is not possible in practice.

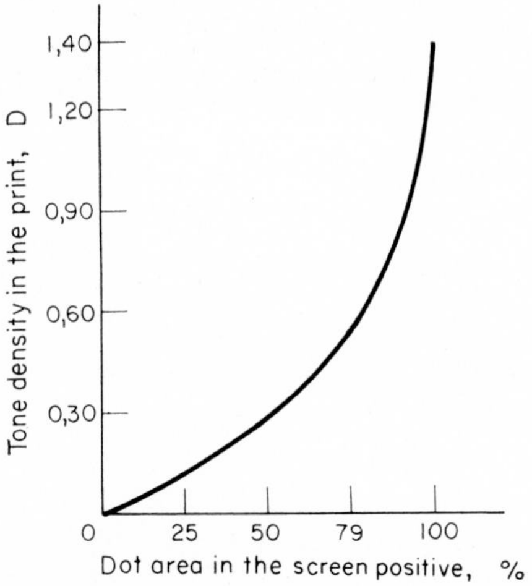

Fig. 8. Relationship between the dot area in the screen positive and the tone density in the print (in the case of ideal conditions).

3. Relationship between the dot area in the screen transparency and the density of the dot-forming diaphragm

Through the production technology for contact screens developed in our Institute the tone zones in the contact screen can be changed by means of the design of the dot-forming diaphragm. A dot-forming diaphragm can be interpreted in general as the negative of a unit area of the contact screen.

When leaving out of consideration the modifying circumstances and assuming an ideal condition, the relationship between the zone density in the dot-forming diaphragm and the area of the screen dot can be expressed by the inverse function of the Tritton–Wilson's equation:

$$D_{\text{zone}} = 1 - \log \left[1 \Big/ \left(1 - t \left[1 - \frac{1}{\text{antilog}\, d} \right] \right) \right]$$

where t = the dot area
d = the dot density.

To obtain contact screens with different density ranges, dot-forming diaphragms with different density ranges are necessary. Density values of each zone can be obtained by multiplying the equation above with the highest density in the dot-forming diaphragm. The equation thus with $d = 1.0$, becomes:

$$D_{\text{zone}} = f\left(1 - \log \frac{1}{1 - 0.9\,t}\right)$$

where t = the dot area

f = the highest density in the dot-forming diaphragm.

The relationship between the screen dot area and the density value in the dot-forming diaphragm is shown in Fig. 9 according to this equation.

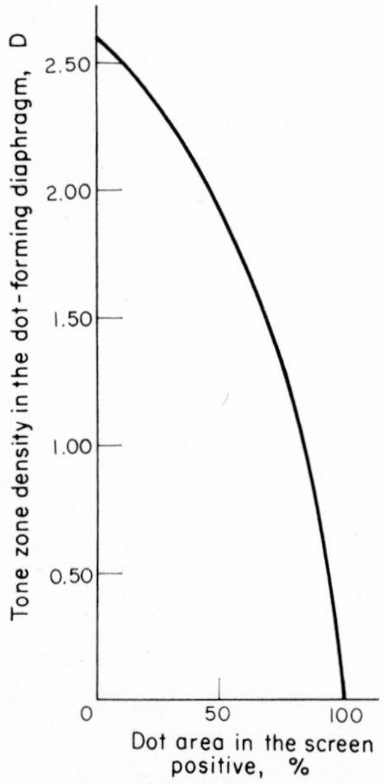

Fig. 9. Relationship between the dot area in the screen positive and the density in the dot-forming diaphragm (in the case of ideal conditions).

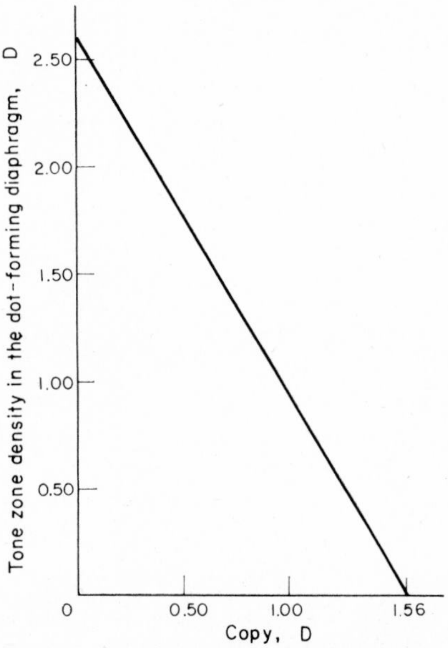

Fig. 10. Relationship between the densities in the copy and in the dot-forming diaphragm (in the case of ideal conditions).

4. Relationship between the densities in the copy and those in the dot-forming diaphragm

The relationship between the zones of the dot-forming diaphragm and the densities in the copy is the same as between the copy and the negative. The shadows in the copy are thus proportional to the highlights in the negative and the clearest spots in the dot-forming diaphragm, respectively. And the same inversely. Thus the relationship between the copy and the zones in the dot-forming diaphragm can be characterized in an ideal case by a straight line (Fig. 10) the equation of which is

$$D_{zone} = \gamma(D_{max} - D)$$

where D_{max} = maximum density in the copy

D = given density in the copy

and $\gamma = D_{max}$ dot-forming/D_{max} copy.

The factors listed here are strictly connected with each other, they can thus be combined into a common nomogram, shown in Fig. 11—

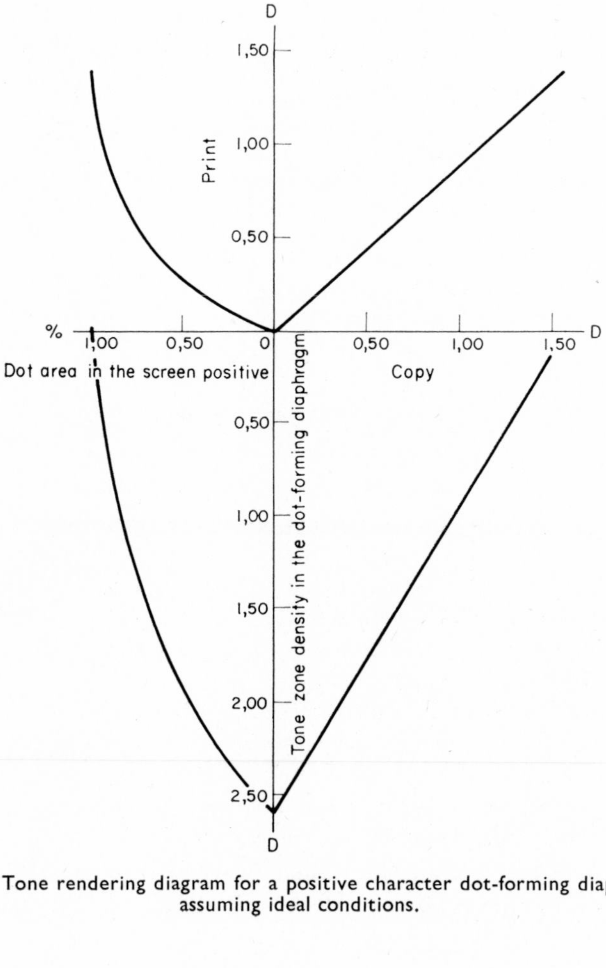

Fig. 11. Tone rendering diagram for a positive character dot-forming diaphragm assuming ideal conditions.

5. Experimental work

A dot-forming diaphragm closely approaching the density values required by the above calculation was made and with it a contact screen was produced. The screen transparency was printed down and proofs were made on art paper in a press.

Some dot areas in the screen positive selected in advance were determined planimetrically on the screen positive, on the plate, and on the print by means of paper prints made from photomicrographs. The density values in the copy and in the print as well as those in the copy and in the negative were measured

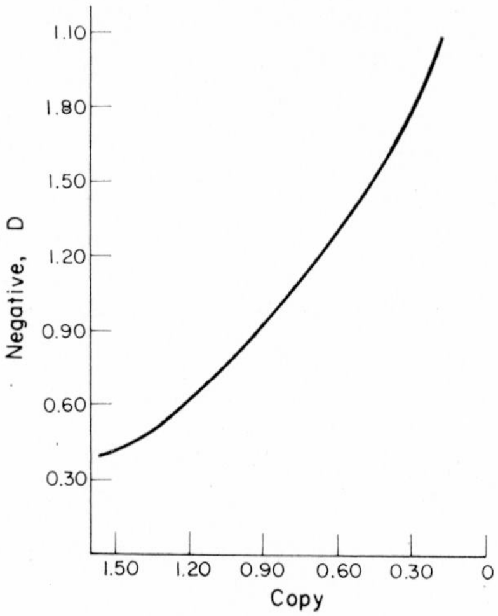

Fig. 12. Density values (actual) in the negative.

on a Kodak Process Densitometer. The relationship between the density values in the copy and in the negative are shown in the Fig. 12.

After having determined each of the relationships, a diagram was drawn giving four steps in the process (Fig. 13). On the basis of the relationships between the copy and the screen positive as well as the densities in the copy and in the negative, the density values in the dot-forming diaphragm were determined from the diagram.

The density values in the dot-forming diaphragm determined by plotting —as in Fig. 13—approach very well the actual ones. According to experiment the tone rendering can be altered within certain limits by selecting correct zone densities in the dot-forming diaphragm. The diagram proved to be useful for tracing deficiencies in tone rendering back to zone densities in the dot-forming diaphragm. When using the screen making process discussed above with the diagram, contact screens with the desired tone rendering can be achieved. With a screen produced in this way, distortions arising from a given forme preparation and printing process can be taken into account and mostly corrected.

When investigating print density as a function of the dot area in the screen positive, it is greater than the value calculated theoretically. As in this

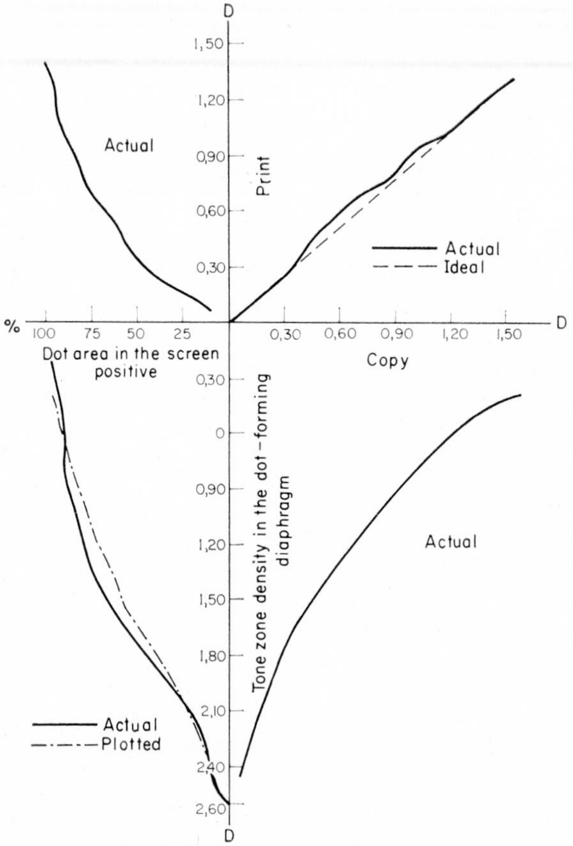

Fig. 13. Tone rendering diagram for a positive character experimental dot-forming diaphragm.

diagram distortion effects due to printing surface preparation, printing, paper, and ink, are presented together, further investigations were made to find the separate contribution of these factors. Photomicrographs were made from the same areas of the screen positive, the printing plate, and the print. Measurements on the areas showed that there is no increase in area on the plate or on the print as compared with the area of the screen dot. It is shown in Fig. 14 that smaller dot areas were obtained both on the plate and on the print than the dot area in the screen positive. The dot size in the screen positive is achieved by the dots on the plate and on the print only in the shadows. The same phenomenon was also observed with other papers.

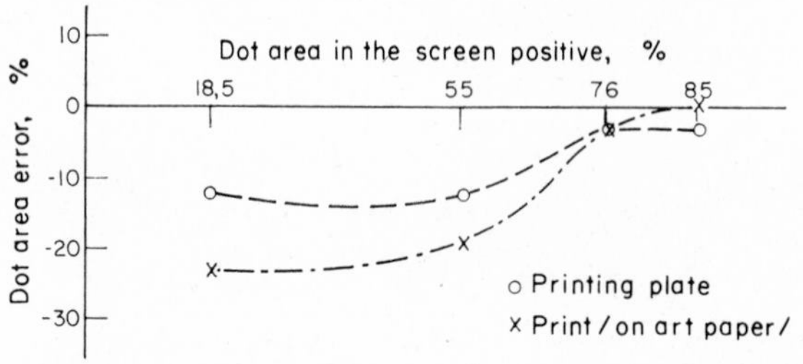

Fig. 14. Variation of the dot area on the printing plate and on the print.

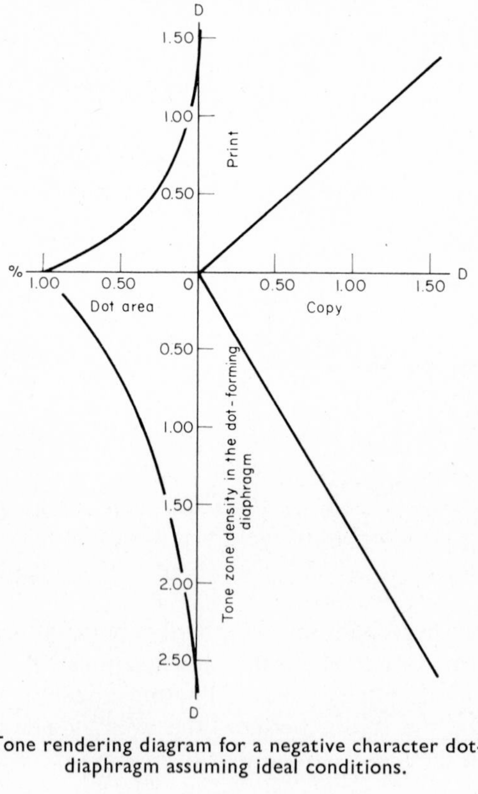

Fig. 15. Tone rendering diagram for a negative character dot-forming diaphragm assuming ideal conditions.

The good tone rendering of the contact screen is shown by the constant proportionality between the density values in the print and in the copy. For the tone rendering obtained, the maximum deviation from the straight line is $D = 0.08$ in the middle tones and still less, $D = 0.03$–0.05 in the shadows. This deviation can be further corrected by adjusting the corresponding zone density in the dot-forming diaphragm.

The result achieved is, however, acceptable in practice since printing surface preparation, printing ink, and paper can give greater variations.

With our method negative working contact screens can be developed. The zone densities in the dot-forming diaphragm must be changed. As a starting-point the diagram assuming ideal conditions shown in Fig. 15 can be assumed.

SUMMARY OF EXPERIMENTAL RESULTS

1. By means of the dot-forming diaphragm used for making contact screens the tone rendering of the contact screen can be varied within certain limits. On the basis of this, contact screens allowing for modifications arising from the different printing processes (offset, letterpress, halftone gravure) can be produced.
2. By appropriate use of zone shapes in the dot-forming diaphragm, contact screens giving different dot shapes can be made.
3. The diaphragm is suitable for reprojecting tone values given by the contact screen on to the density values in the dot-forming diaphragm as well as for determining modifications.

REFERENCES

1. F. J. Tritton and E. T. Wilson, *Phot. J.* **79**, 396, 1939.
2. V. G. W. Harrison, Mitchener and L. E. Lawson, *J. Phot. Sci.* **3**, 97, 1955.
3. A. J. W. Sweerman, Toonweergave en rasters. *I.G.T. Nieuws* 1 **13**, 1, 1960.
4. A. J. W. Sweerman, I.G.T.—Patra contactraster voor offset. *I.G.T. Nieuws*, 7 **13**, 97, 1960.
5. R. E. Maurer, The relation of the contact screen to picture quality, *TAGA Proceedings*, 121, 1959.
6. J. A. C. Yule, The theory of the halftone process. *J. Franklin Inst.* **231**, 28–38, 1941; **235**, 483–498; 1943; **236**, 473–487, 1943.

DISCUSSION

Woods: Is there any fundamental reason for choosing the dot shape used for the diaphragm?

Lovasz: A theoretical basis for the shape is difficult to obtain and, therefore, it is determined experimentally.

Woods: Have you met any objection by the printers to the unconventional dot shape shown in Fig. 5 of your paper?

Lovasz: There have been no objections.

YULE: We have found the zone approach very valuable, but the effect of each zone on the whole curve needs to be taken into account. Although this is more complicated, it saves time in the end. (Maurer, Howe and Yule, *TAGA Proceedings* 17 (1961).)

(1) How is the characteristic curve of the contact screen film allowed for?

(2) The making of a positive screen is described, but negative screens are more difficult to make. Have negative screens been made by this method?

(3) In making experimental gravure screens with dot formation similar to Fig. 5, we originally tried a screen which gave somewhat pincushion-shaped shadow dots, to compensate for the effect of etching on dot shape but we found that customers preferred square shadow dots.

LOVASZ: (1) Its effect is automatically incorporated in the lower lefthand graph of Fig. 13.

(2) Yes, but the results were not as satisfactory.

(3) These were experimental screens and as yet no trade tests have been made.

MEASURING HALFTONE DOTS BY HALFTONE DENSITIES

by E. Rupp
Institut für Grafische Technik, Leipzig

A HALFTONE dot on film is surrounded by a halo in which the optical density varies as illustrated in Fig. 1. In printing down, this variation in transparency leads to a dot of smaller diameter on the printing plate. It is possible by means of microdensitometers to measure the variation in transmission but for practical purposes it is sufficient to know the diameter of the film dot which

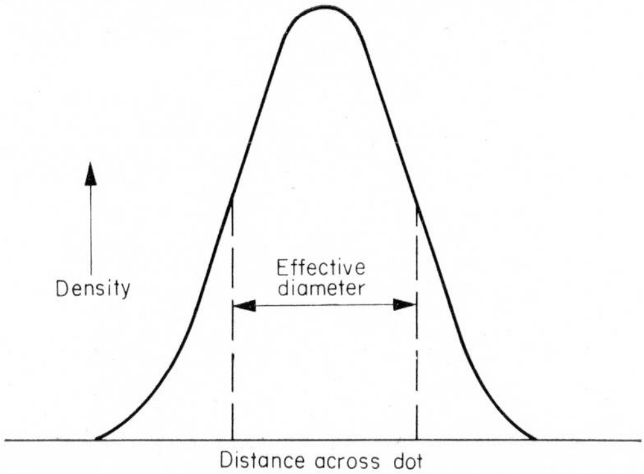

Fig. 1. Variation of density across a halftone dot.

is effective on the printing plate. In a halftone image the effective diameter of the dots ranging from highlight to shadow area determine the density range of the printing plate.

A method of estimating effective diameters has been developed by Ing. B. Gasch.

In Fig. 1 the region bounded by the broken line, the dot core, represents the effective diameter. In order to measure this, we make use of the fact that light incident at an angle to the film is diffusely transmitted and its intensity is a maximum in the regions of medium density. This is because in the low density regions, near the edge of the halo, the smaller number of silver grains do not produce much light scattering. Higher densities, on the other hand, absorb the light, while at intermediate densities the higher number of silver grains cause more scattering. Thus viewing a halftone dot on film using dark field illumination by rays incident at an angle to the film one observes a bright circle of light in the areas of medium density around the dark core of the dot. The variation in intensity of the transmitted light with density is shown in

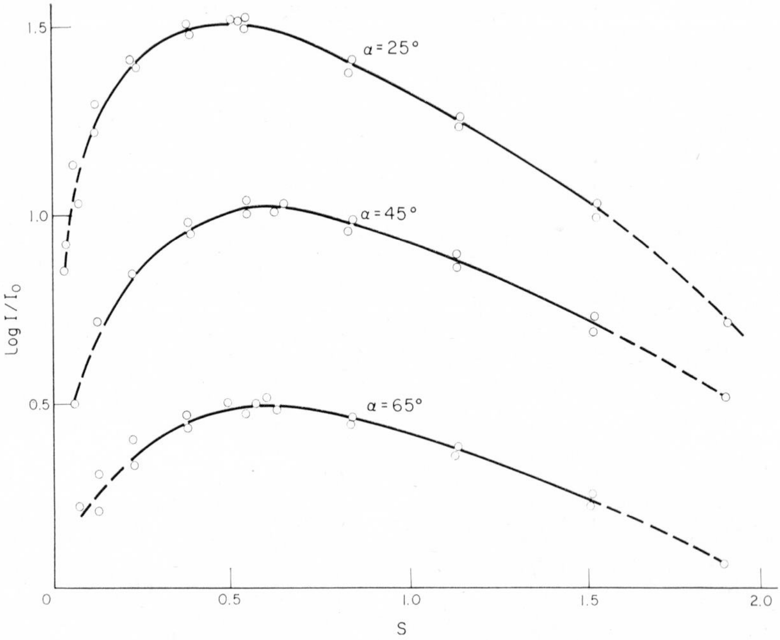

Fig. 2. Diffuse intensity *I*, as a function of density *S*.

Fig. 2 for different angles of incidence (α). This shows that with increasing density S, the transmission (I/I_0) increases to a maximum, and the height of the maximum depends on the angle of incidence. An angle of 25° is more favourable than a larger one. The height of the maximum is also very dependent on the emulsion.

A soft or normal emulsion shows a rather wide maximum, while one of high contrast a sharper maximum. Visually the appearance would be rings of more or less uniform illumination—wide rings in the case of the soft emulsion and narrow rings for the contrasting emulsion (see Figs. 7 and 9). For a high contrast emulsion, the inner ring limits the core of the dot at a density of 0.9–1.0 and this is the effective limiting diameter of a halftone dot when printed down under normal conditions with an arc lamp.

In our studies we have compared film negatives with halftone copies on zinc in five printing works.

Figures 3 and 4 show the equipment used, in which a light-tight box is illuminated with four incandescent lamps. For dark field illumination a microscope lamp projects light at an angle of about 25° into a clear glass

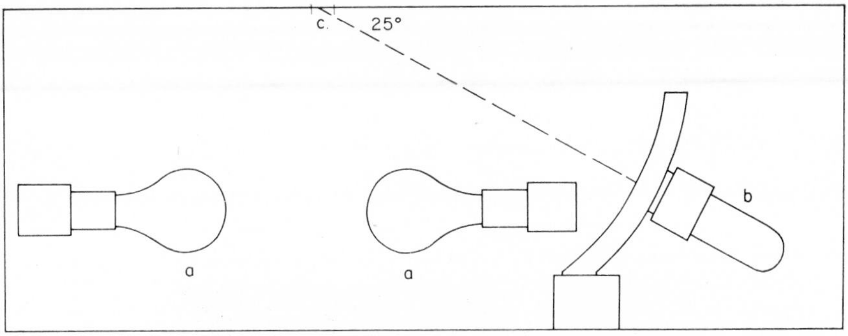

Fig. 3. Illumination box: (*a*) lamps for general illumination; (*b*) light projector lamp; (*c*) clear glass target.

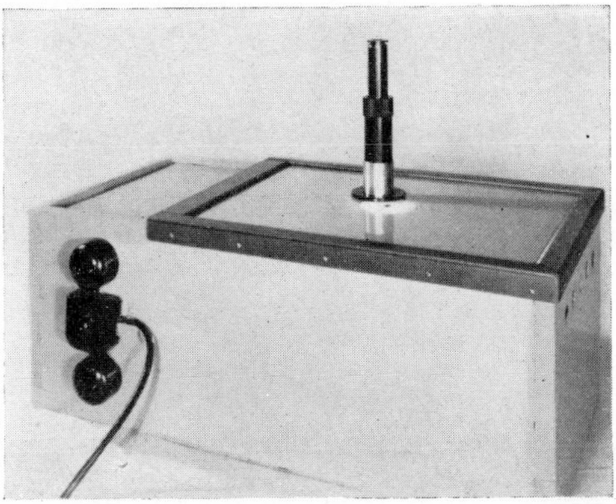

Fig. 4. View of the measuring equipment with microscope.

target 10 mm in diameter fixed in the wall of the box. The area of film to be examined is placed on the external surface of the illuminated glass and is viewed with a microscope (Fig. 4), the eyepiece of which carries a measuring graticule (Fig. 5).

Figures 6 and 7 are photomicrographs obtained with normal (bright field) and dark field illumination of a highlight dot respectively. The distance between two lines on the superimposed graticule grid is 12 μ, while Figs. 8 and 9 similarly show a shadow dot.

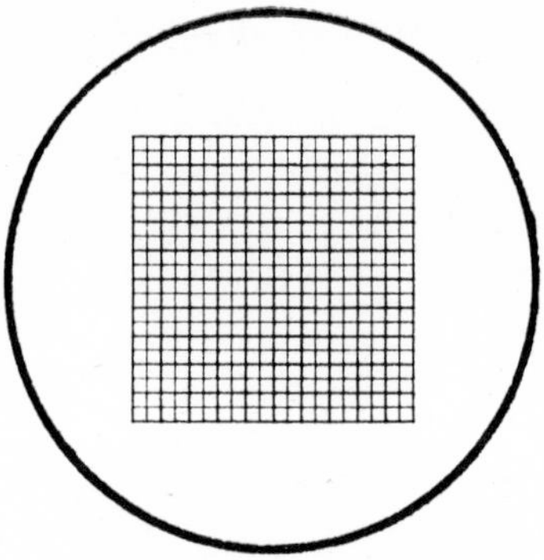

Fig. 5. Eyepiece graticule.

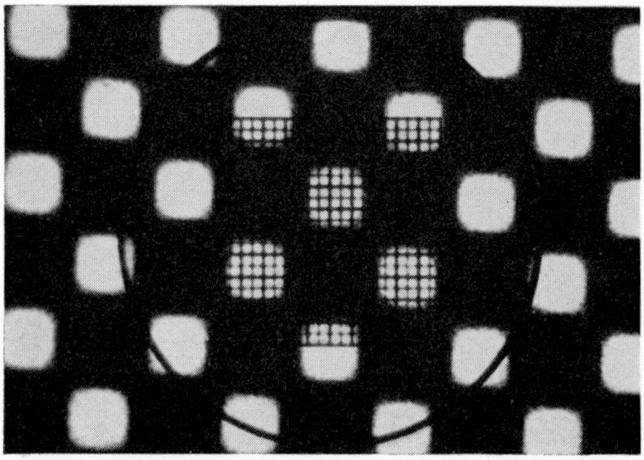

Fig. 6. Photomicrograph of highlight dots with bright field illumination.

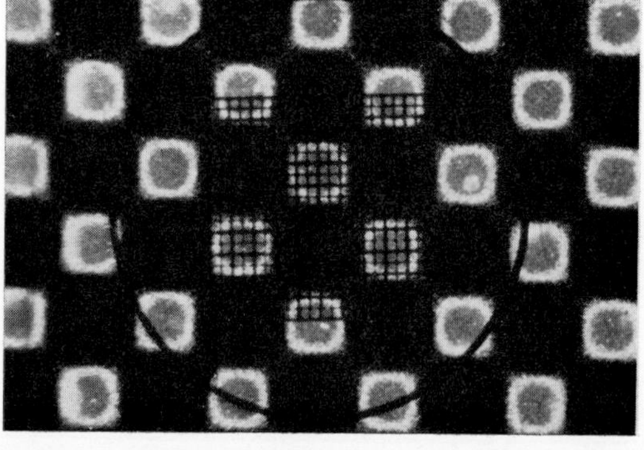

Fig. 7. Photomicrograph of highlight dots with dark field illumination.

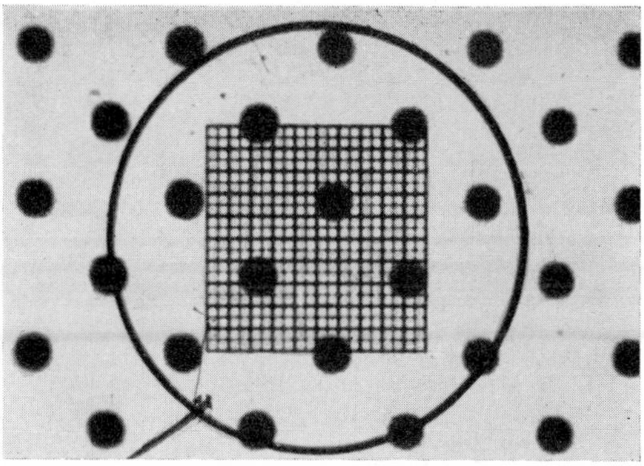

Fig. 8. Photomicrograph of shadow dots with bright field illumination.

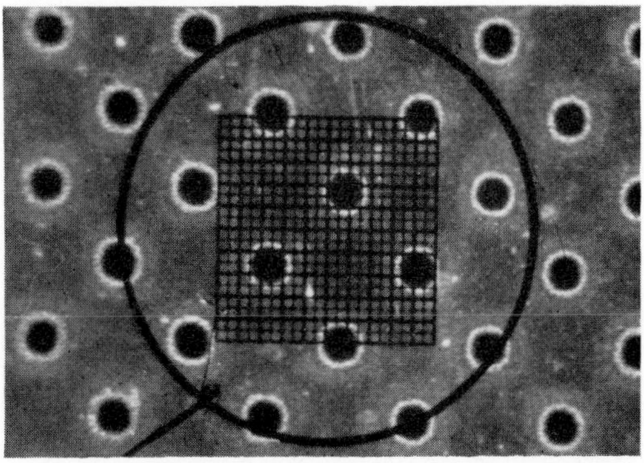

Fig. 9. Photomicrograph of shadow dots with dark field illumination.

DISCUSSION

YULE: "Semi-darkfield illumination" provides a still easier, and perhaps more accurate, method of utilizing scattered light for estimating dot area (YULE, *J. Franklin Inst.* **236** (5), 484, 1943). If a small amount of direct illumination is added to the darkfield illumination, the clear dot opening can be made to match the fringe in brightness. $100(1 - I/I_0)$, then corresponds closely to effective dot area, I_0 being the intensity with an unexposed film. A densitometer with a special illumination system, zeroed on clear film, can be used. The density is converted to percentage transmittance which is subtracted from 100; or preferably a percentage transmittance meter can be used. This method also has the advantage of giving dot area instead of dot diameter. Neither this nor Dr. Rupp's method gives accurate results for dots near 100 per cent, for which it is necessary to make a contact print.

HARRISON: How many dots do you measure?

YULE: About a 4 mm aperture is used.

HARRISON: Then you arrive at an average of a number of dots?

YULE: Yes.

SOME ADDITIVE COLOR PRINCIPLES AND THE CONTROL OF NEUTRAL GRAYS IN PROCESS REPRODUCTION

by FRANK M. PREUCIL

Lithographic Technical Foundation, Chicago

Abstract—In three- and four-color halftone process reproduction, there are areas of both additive and subtractive colors. The differences in additive color and subtractive color were studied with both theoretical calculations and printed dot mixtures. Light tints were found to have a color constancy even though there was considerable variation of the printed dot strength. Dot areas were more important to control than ink strength. Yellow dots were found to require a greater area than magenta dots for neutral grays when bluish magentas were used.

INTRODUCTION

Two industry-wide color surveys have been made by the Lithographic Technical Foundation to determine the current status of the art and to find those areas in which new research and education might help the most. After the first survey, our major emphasis was on changing to better hues of process inks in balanced sets to improve and simplify color correction masking performance. Another area was the study of factors controlling trapping and development of simple ways of visually judging and measuring it.

The new survey has revealed that much better process inks are now being used by more companies, and that wet trapping is no longer a serious problem in most plants. Both surveys, however, have shown very little hue control of secondary color solids, coupled with a very wide range of printed ink strengths. Equally serious to accurate color reproduction is a plant-to-plant, press-to-press, or even unit-to-unit variation of 10, 20, and even 30 per cent in the printed area of standard size halftone dots. Some of these seeming abnormalities are probably attempts at compensation. Solids are run weakly when tints are printing too full, and solids are run too strong if tints are weak. Judging by the lack of standardization, the entire area of color control seems to be incompletely understood. New studies at L.T.F. are being based on the need for better understanding and control of color. This paper is a partial study in the area of the color difference of additive tint mixtures and subtractive solid overprint colors, and a more specific understanding of the control of gray balance.

PROCEDURES

The hue and grayness differences between the subtractive and the additive colors producible by different process inks printed at different solid densities, and always equal dot size mixtures, were studied in two ways. The first study was theoretical from calculated predictions using selected red, green, and blue filter densities. The second was from printed sheets.

The calculated subtractive colors of the pairs of inks making red, green, and blue were obtained by adding the red, green, and blue filter densities of the two separate inks and then calculating their hue and grayness for color circle plotting.[1] The calculated additive color of the same pairs of primary ink colors in equal area and adjacent to one another were obtained by (1) converting the red, green, and blue filter density values to per cent reflectance, (2) adding them, (3) dividing by two, (4) reconverting back to densities, and (5) calculating their hue and grayness. The three color mixtures were calculated in the same manner. Three variables were introduced in the primary colors to compare their relative influence on their subtractive and additive colors. These were hue, grayness, and printed strength.

The correlation of printed additive and subtractive colors and similar calculated colors were obtained with the help of a special gray balance test chart. This chart was a printing of a crossed scale of 5 per cent differences of yellow and magenta ink with uniform squares of cyan at solid, 75, 50, and 30 per cent dot areas. Three per cent differences of yellow and magenta were used on a 15 per cent cyan tint.

Each different color tint strength was separately extended beyond the mixed dots so that the actual printed effective dot area could be evaluated. This was necessary to eliminate the further variables of dot spread which occurred differently with some colors at different printed strengths. The printed equal dot areas were selected from density readings made through complementary colored filters of first, the master cyan dot and then the various yellow and magenta dots. The solid printed ink strength was also read on the densitometer and the corrected effective dot size percentage taken from a conversion chart.

Neutral three-color areas were selected by equal red, green, and blue filter readings, sometimes interpolated between two squares. After determining the actual corrected effective dot areas of their neutral point, they were charted and compared.

DISCUSSION

Figures 1, 2, and 3 show the calculated hue and grayness changes of corresponding subtractive and additive mixtures when the variable of printed ink strength is independently changed for each color of ink separately. In

Additive vs. Subtractive Color

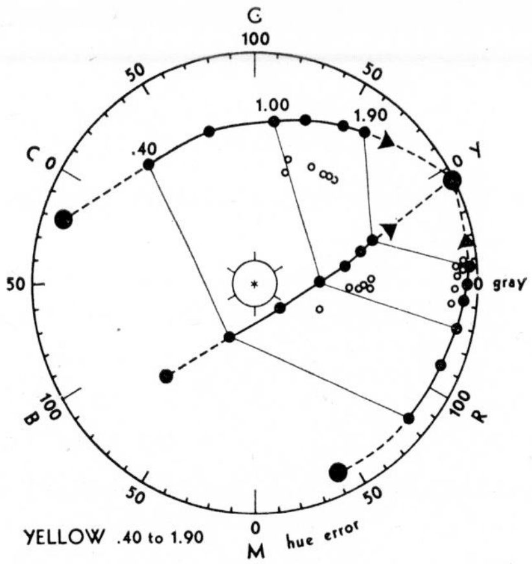

Fig. 1. Effect of increasing yellow strength.

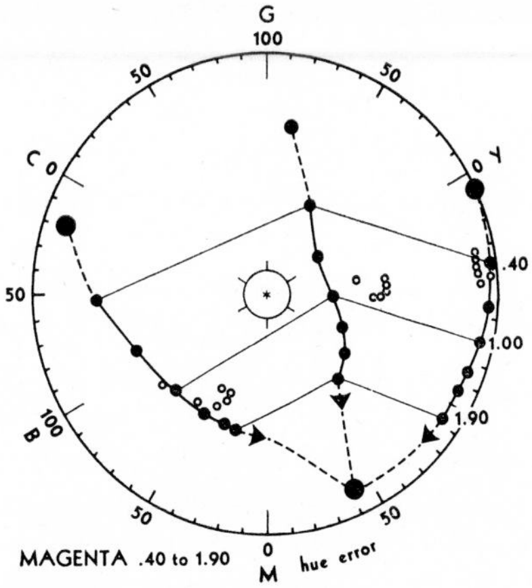

Fig. 2. Effect of increasing magenta strength.

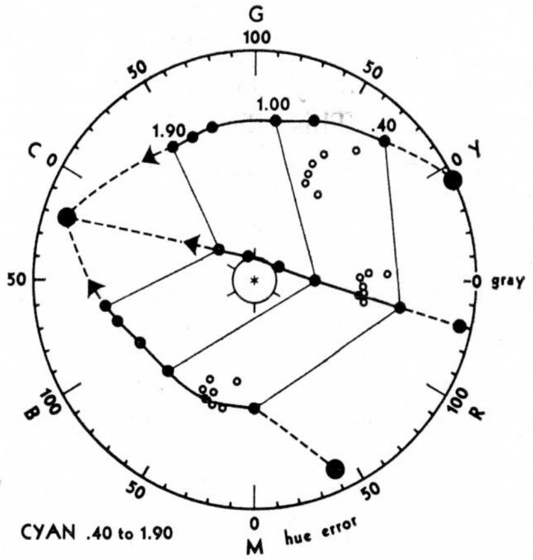

Fig. 3. Effect of increasing cyan strength.

each case, two of the primary colors are constant at a strength of 1.00 density while the third is varied in the calculations by steps of 0.3 from 0.40 to 1.90.

In the Color Circle of Fig. 1, the cyan and magenta as represented by large dots, are the constant along with their blue overlap as a smaller dot. From these three dots are lines connecting them to the other large dots which represent the yellow that is the variable in density strength. Along the three lines are smaller solid dots representing the subtractive in-between colors produced by the 0.30 increases of yellow density strength.

The green, blue and red points related by mutual creation of 0.40, 1.00, and 1.90 yellow density strength are connected by the thin lines. The subtractive green mixtures at the top of the circle are seen to change 130 per cent in hue difference with similar large hue changes in the reds and three-color solid overprint. The corresponding calculated additive mixtures are positioned as open circles and are found to group much closer together than the subtractive overprints.

Figure 2 shows the similar large subtractive color changes and small additive color changes when the magenta strength is the variable.

Figure 3 charts the calculated color changes when the cyan strength is the variable. Again, the little open circles, representing the additive color mixtures, are seen to change very much less than the subtractive colors.

Of very great importance, also, is a complete difference in progression of subtractive and additive changes with increased ink density strength. The subtractive overprint colors always move in hue toward the primary color which is increasing in strength.

With the additive color mixture, however, when cyan or magenta inks are increased in strength, the color chart changes as a little horsehoe. First, the additive hue moves toward the primary color which is increasing in strength. Then the hue remains fairly constant while grayness increases. Then, with still further printed strength density, the additive color hue reverses and goes away from the stronger color. This effect is related to the purity of the ink, being least with this yellow and greatest with this cyan. With reasonably good process inks, there is a surprisingly large range of solid ink strength with which additive hues remain remarkably constant. In Fig. 3, the additive green hue changes only a few per cent when the cyan ink strength ranges from 0.70 to 1.60. The hue of the subtractive green, however, has changed by 70 per cent on the color circle. If the cyan ink is changed to a progressively grayer, less pure reflectance surface, this green hue constancy would be less and the hue would reverse at lower cyan printed strengths. This points out (1) the relative lack of dependence of the hue of lighter secondary colors on practical printed ink strength range, and (2) their almost complete dependence on relative dot areas when fairly pure color primary inks are used.

It also points out that if very pure primary colors could be printed, their strength density could be desirably high but as grayness in the printed primary colors appears, there is some optimum strength beyond which color tints are additively less effective.

Edelman of France defined a "Vivacity" factor for color inks which allowed the calculation of such optimum strength from spectrophotometric data.[2] A simple way of visualizing such a relationship between process inks of different grayness is found in the Color Efficiency Chart of Fig. 4.

This is derived from the red, green, and blue filter percentage reflectances of calculated primary colors by subtracting the lowest percentage from the highest. The chart compares ink colors of zero to 60 per cent grayness varied from a density of zero through 2.70. Starting at the lower left we have the full equal red, green, and blue reflectance of the paper with no excess of any color

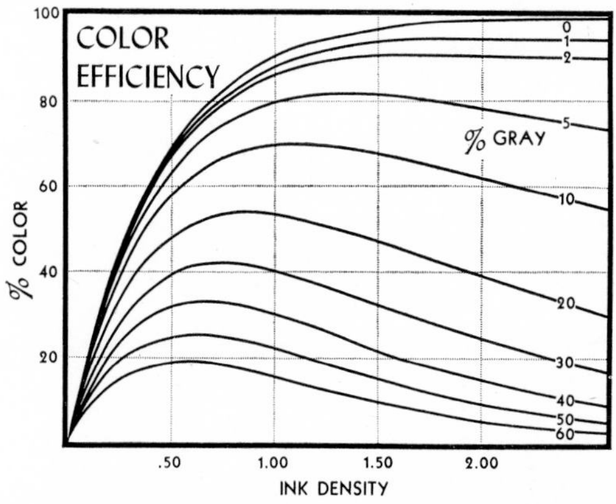

Fig. 4. Color reflectance efficiency of grayed inks.

visible. Moving to the right, the printed ink densities increase, subtracting one of the light primaries proportionately more than the other two primaries of light. The percentage of the major color reflectance available is charted vertically. At a glance, the chart tells an important story for additive color. The top three curves show that relatively pure inks, such as yellows, may theoretically be printed to very high densities without loss of saturation, and their additive color mixtures remain almost constant through a very wide range. The 5 and 10 per cent grayed lines show that additive mixtures, which include the purest magentas and cyans, would also have a wide range of color constancy within the practical range of printed ink strength (say, 0.80 to 1.50). The lower curves show that there is less and less tolerance of the optimum printed density range. Also, the grayer the color of the ink, the lower the density of printed strength that may be run for optimum additive color.

These calculated prediction studies of subtractive and additive color differences showed that the solid overprint hues responded directly to the printed strength of the inks. The additive color mixtures, however, changed correspondingly very little with the same printed ink density changes. The control of additive hues in practice, of course, must be done principally with changes of the area of the dots. However, two other primary ink factors are important in establishing additive color mixtures. These are properties of the color reflectance of the separate inks which must add up to make the resultant color. These are studied with the color circle coordinator of hue and grayness in Fig. 5.

Figure 5 shows as open circles, the color changes of three-color additive mixtures when the hue of the cyan changes by 80 per cent and its grayness by 33 per cent at the 20 per cent hue position. The near grays respond in the same direction to almost the same degree as the cyan solid.

Three-color Additive Tints

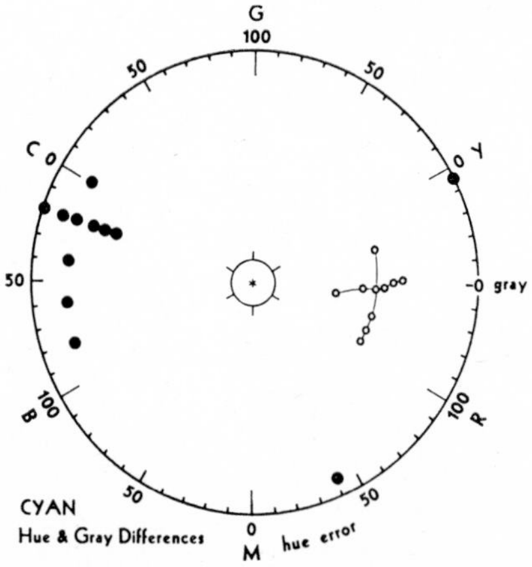

Fig. 5. Influence of cyan hue and grayness differences on three-color grays.

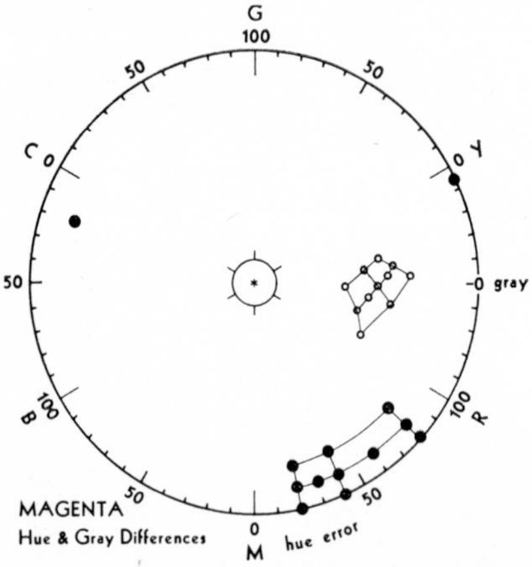

Fig. 6. Influence of magenta hue and grayness differences on three-color grays.

Figure 6 shows the similar matching changes in the additive mixtures created by differences in magenta hue and grayness.

The additive and subtractive color variations we have discussed so far were all derived from calculations. Actual printing of solids and tints with the same type of variables agreed with these same principles.

Figure 7 shows the subtractive colors and corresponding additive three-color mixtures which resulted when several cyan and magenta inks were printed with a standard yellow at a wide range of printed strength densities. The two-color subtractive greens vary in hue by 100 per cent, the three-color solid shifts 160 per cent in hue. The corresponding three-color 15 per cent equal dot size additive colors are the small open circles whose position area is emphasized with an outline. Just as in the pure theoretical calculated comparison, the equal area additive mixtures change very little with large changes of their subtractive solids.

The so-called 15 per cent equal dot sizes we charted on the color circle and the subsequent dot ratios for gray balance we determined next, were not the measured positive dot sizes. The press run created some unequal dot gain between the separate colors and some varied during the run with printed

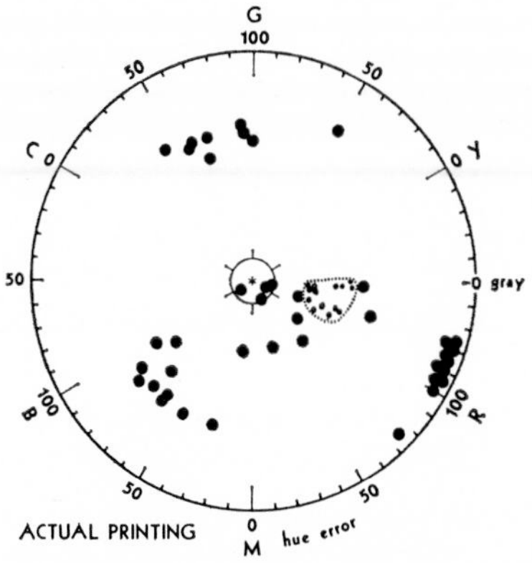

Fig. 7. Constancy of three-color near grays.

strength differences. Corrected equal dot areas and equivalent printed dot sizes were determined by first determining what the constant cyan 15, 30, 50, or 75 per cent tint actually printed and then selecting yellow and magenta tints of these matching values. The conversion chart shown in Fig. 8 was

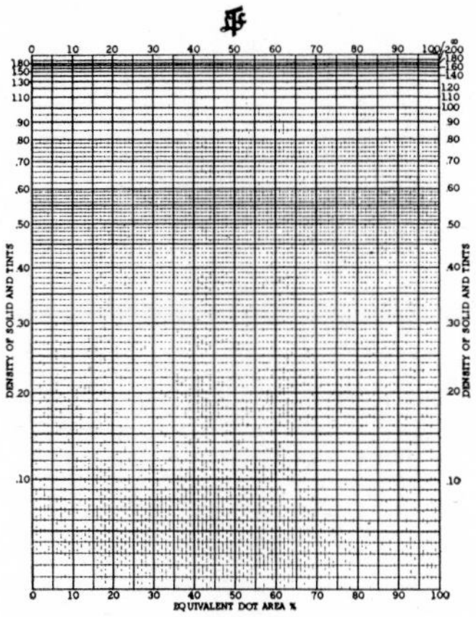

Fig. 8.

used.[3] This takes densitometer reflection densities of a tint and its solid and converts them to effective dot area. This is, of course, not the true printed dot area because of the paper's internal light scatter. However, as they are all on the same paper, the comparison ratios should be proportional.

In Figs. 9 and 10 are curves showing the effective printed dot size of yellow and magenta which gave neutral gray with cyan dots as the linear references. These curves were created from measurements of five neutral areas from the printed gray balance test charts. The 40 per cent cyan point was selected to

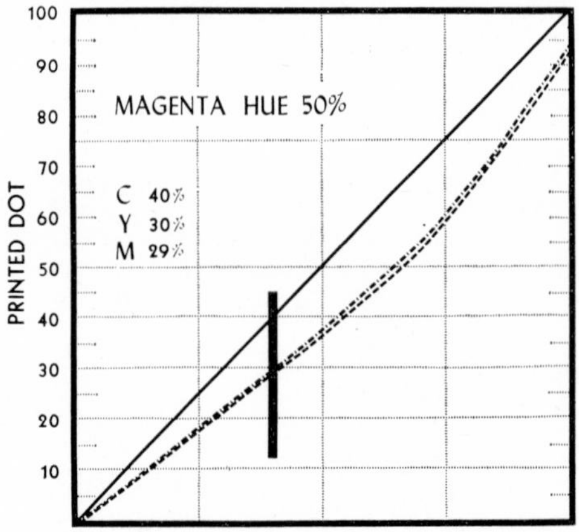

Fig. 9.

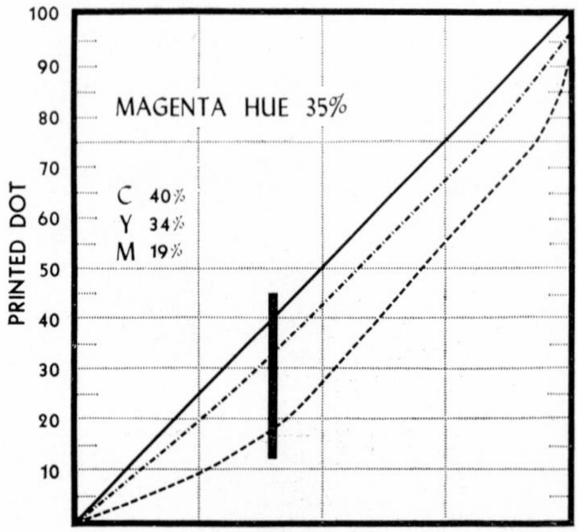

Fig. 10.

compare the yellow and magenta dot requirement with two different sets of inks. In Fig. 9, a magenta with a hue error of close to 50 per cent was printed at 29 per cent dot area for gray balance with a cyan dot of 40 per cent while, in Fig. 10, a bluer magenta was printed at only a 19 per cent dot. The significant relationship of dot areas in these two examples is the yellow-magenta dot ratio. Most printed instructions for gray scale screening of three or four-color positives have specified equal dot sizes for yellow and magenta.

We found here that, while that was true for the rubine type magenta, the rhodamine type required a larger yellow dot than the magenta to balance the increased blue reflectance. Magenta inks which printed redder than the 50 per cent hue example would require the reverse of this condition, that is, larger magenta dots than the yellow.

The relative unequal areas of cyan, yellow, and magenta dots to additively make neutral gray are directly related to the position of three-color equal area mixtures on the color circle. Since this is always to the right of the neutral center, the cyan dot must be larger than the others. The further to the right of center this point is, the proportionately larger the cyan dot area must be.

Gray Balance

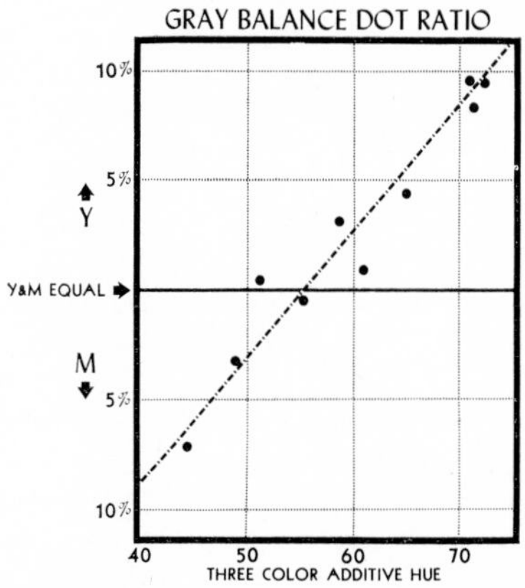

Fig. 11. Relation of yellow and magenta dot size to hue of additive three-color point.

This would be, in some way, numerically related to the circle coordinate gray percentage of the three-color equal area mixtures and also the grayness of the cyan.

The relative size of the yellow and magenta dots for neutral gray are affected by the nearness of the three-color equal point towards the yellow or magenta solid ink position. This is in the direction of hue differences and is so charted in Fig. 11. The ten points plotted were from several different sets of process inks so not only the magenta varied but also the cyan. This scatters the points somewhat from a true line relationship but the close relation of the three-color additive due to the balance of yellow and magenta dot sizes is shown.

At this point, the project is incomplete and further work will endeavor to create some simple chart system of specifying yellow, magenta, and cyan dot proportions from simple measurements of the solid inks on the paper on which the inks are to be printed.

SUMMARY

These studies indicate that while the strong colors in a process reproduction may be widely adjusted in hue by varying the printed ink strength, the lighter tints will remain fairly constant unless their dot areas change. The critical dot size balance for neutral grays may change with every process ink color difference, or paper surface difference, which affects the color of the process ink. Bluer magentas require larger yellow dots than magenta dots. Reddish magentas require smaller yellow dots than magenta and the grayer the cyan ink, the larger the cyan dot area must be.

REFERENCES

1. Frank M. Preucil, The evaluation of process inks. *LTF Research Progress* No. 38.
2. E. Edelman, Contribution a l'application Industrelle de la Colorimetric. Notion de Facteur de U. *Proc. 31st. Conf. Ind. Chem. Liege*, **II,** 407–419 (1958).
3. Paul W. Dorst, Halftone densities. *J. Optical Soc. Amer.* **33,** No. 8, 436 (1934).

AN ANALYSIS OF THE POSSIBILITY OF CONTROLLING THE SEPARATE OPERATIONAL STAGES IN MULTICOLOR REPRODUCTION

by A. WULFF and H. O. JØRGENSEN
Graphic College of Denmark, Copenhagen

MEASUREMENTS OF PRINTING INKS

AT the 12th TAGA meeting in 1960 F. Preucil published a new subtractive color-triangle and a hexagon diagram.

These new diagrams make it possible to treat the color properties of printing inks in an easier way than previously. Individual printing establishments can by means of reflection densitometer measurements and simple calculations thereby judge and control several of the ink properties which are important in the separation processes, and which in this report are named according to L.T.F.

Three filter measurements (reflection densitometer) through a red, a green and a blue filter for each color are used for plotting in these two diagrams. For plotting in the color-triangle the coordinates are found according to the formulae:

$$c = \frac{R}{R + G + B} \cdot 100 \text{ and } y = \frac{B}{R + G + B} \cdot 100$$

where R = density with red filter

G = density with green filter

B = density with blue filter

The coordinates are plotted in the triangle, tracing the c-value from red = 0 towards cyan = 100 and tracing the y-value from blue = 0 towards yellow = 100. The intersection point of these two coordinates represents the measured color.

The distances from the three sides of the triangle to a color in the triangle reveal the contents of ideal yellow, magenta and cyan in the color, expressed in percentages.

The hue error and the grayness of a color is determined by means of an overlay film which the Graphic College of Denmark has made.

The great value of the new triangle diagram is, among other things, that it shows in a very clear way the balance of a set of printing inks with regard to simple masking systems.

The selection of a set of printing inks has often to be made out of consideration for the character of the printed matter, and time and again it cannot be made out of consideration for the masking alone. This will, for instance, often be the case with packaging printing.

However, for the great majority of color reproduction it would be desirable if the printing inks, besides other requirements, were also chosen in the interests of using simple masking systems. Whether a set of printing inks is in balance with respect to a simple masking can be ascertained from the position of the colors in the color triangle, because the criterion for a simple masking of unwanted colors will be that it is possible to draw a line from one vertex of the triangle through the unwanted colors. Such a line will at the same time indicate from which negative the mask is to be made and also the percentage masking.

The position of the printing inks in the color triangle and thus the estimate of masking balance and masking percentages will depend upon filters used in the measurements on the densitometer. It must be a condition that the three printing inks are separated on the films with densities which in percentages correspond to the readings.

Experiments have been made in order to elucidate whether this condition can be fulfilled with an accuracy suitable for practical work. All density measurements were made with a Densichron 2, photometer.

For the experiment we made separation negatives of different color patches on Gevaert P24p film with Kodak 25 red and 58 green filters, and on Gevaert P34p with 47B blue filter. This is a combination which is very common in Denmark. The exposures have been made with a camera and an arc light. The different color patches were photographed together with a gray scale, and from the individual separation the three actinic densities were calculated for each single color. From these three actinic densities we have calculated the color triangle coordinates c and y.

Each individual color can now be plotted in the color triangle according to actinic density and be compared with the position of the same color calculated from densitometer measurement through the same three filters (47B–58–25). Furthermore, the colors can be plotted in the L.T.F. hexagon diagram.

The values for plotting in the hexagon diagram are obtained from the same three filter measurements which may be used by plotting in the triangle, as the grayness of the color represented by the smallest of the three density measurements are subtracted from the other two. These two new density values are used by noting their position in the hexagon diagram.

The color triangle shows differences in hue and grayness (Fig. 1). In the hexagon diagram differences in hue and color-strength will be revealed (Fig. 2).

By studying the position of the colors in both the color triangle and in the hexagon diagram it will be possible to estimate the differences between measured and photographed values in hue, grayness and color-strength.

The experiment shows that the determination of hue and grayness by measuring with the same three filters as those with which the separations have been made are in good agreement, and in spite of the fact that it must be supposed that the phototube of the densitometer and the films used have different spectral sensitivity, just as the measurements have been made with incandescent light and the separations with carbon arc light. This is a result which corresponds to the experience of L.T.F.

Furthermore the experiment shows that in the case of magentas and cyans, the color strength shows good agreement between photographed and measured values, whereas differences of up to 6–7 per cent have been found in the case of some yellow colors.

Color strength, however, has no significance for the judgment of the masking balance of a set of process inks.

The differences appearing between measured and calculated values can be related to various factors:

1. The uncertainty in the calculation of actinic density on account of gloss and the determination of the actinic density of the unprinted paper corresponding to zeroing the individual filters on the densitometer. The experiment showed that for all papers used, practically the same zeroing on the densitometer could be used with the three filters whereas the same papers when photographed resulted in rather big density differences on the negatives. When calculating the actinic densities of the colors it was therefore necessary to allow for this fact. Small inaccuracies in the calculations of these zero values could easily influence the calculated grayness value and thus the position in the triangle.
2. Differences in color sensitivity of phototube and film.
3. Difference in light source (measurements versus photography).

The apparently bigger differences for yellow colors in the color triangle are, in percentages, not bigger than for cyan and magenta colors, inasmuch as there is no proportionality between distances and different positions in the triangle diagram.

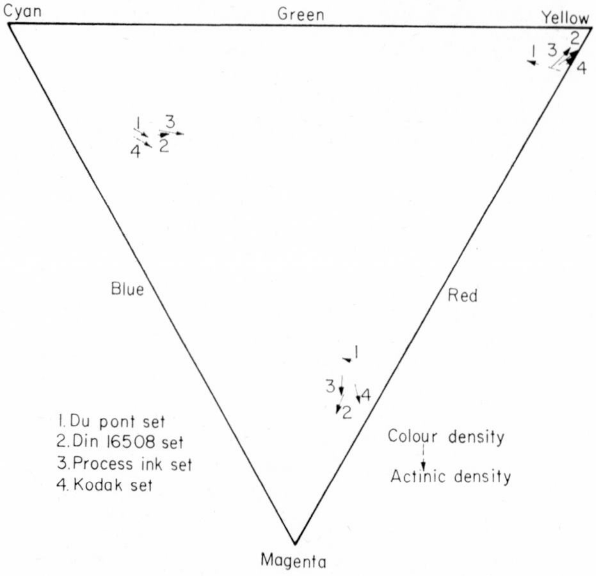

Fig. 1. Shift in hue and grayness between values from color density measurement and values from actinic density calculations.

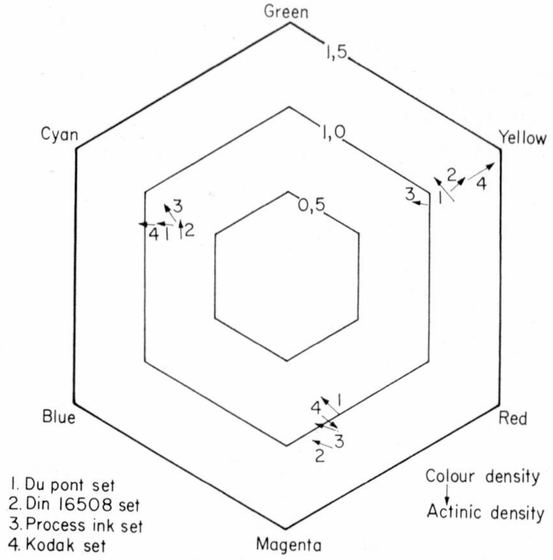

Fig. 2. Shift in hue and color strength between values from color density measurement and values from actinic density calculations.

MASKING

The actual hue error and grayness of the printing inks expressed in percentages are important in order to establish which errors and their magnitude in the individual separation negatives or positives; again, these errors will decide how much color correction is needed.

One of the most serious errors in a separation negative will be that the unwanted colors do not have the same density as the white paper. Yellow, will for instance, be printed in cyan and magenta areas. Consequently, the main purpose of all photographic masking will be either to add to negatives the missing density in unwanted colors or, as for instance is the case by masking of color transparencies, to add to white and to other colors in the original such a color and gray that the unwanted colors and white separate with the same density in the negatives.

In order to be able to make this correction of unwanted colors photographically by means of a single mask for each negative, the position of the printing inks in the color triangle must fulfill certain conditions. For the masking of yellow negative or positive by means of a green-filter positive or negative the condition is:

$$\frac{y \text{ cyan}}{m \text{ cyan}} = \frac{y \text{ magenta}}{m \text{ magenta}}$$

and in the case of the magenta negative:

$$\frac{m \text{ cyan}}{c \text{ cyan}} = \frac{m \text{ yellow}}{c \text{ yellow}}$$

where m, c, and y are the coordinates of the colors in the triangle.

These conditions, in the color triangle, will mean that a straight line can be drawn from the cyan angle of the triangle through cyan and magenta colors in order to mask yellow separation, and for magenta separation a line from the yellow angle of the triangle through yellow and cyan colors.

If cyan separation is required to be masked it should also be possible to draw a straight line from yellow, possibly magenta angle of the triangle through yellow and magenta. By common one-step masking systems the quantity

$$\frac{y \text{ cyan}}{m \text{ cyan}} \,.\, 100 \quad \text{or} \quad \frac{y \text{ magenta}}{m \text{ magenta}} \,.\, 100$$

must be considered as the masking percentage by which the blue-filter separation has to be masked from the green-filter separation.

A displacement of one of the colors from the straight line through the angle of the triangle will mean that this color will require an altered masking percentage, which again will require different masking percentages for the two unwanted colors, and this can only be obtained by some masking film curve which is not straight. This could be possible, but here we would come into conflict with the "unwanted" overlap color, which, as is well known, always requires a masking percentage somewhere between the masking percentages required by the two colors of which it is made up. If we consider yellow separation with a mask from the magenta, both the blue-filter and the green-filter readings will be bigger for the blue color than for the magenta color. This will mean that the masking film curve has to be S-shaped which is difficult to obtain.

By a two-step masking of unwanted colors in a separation, the masking percentage and thus the γ-value of the masking film will for the yellow and magenta separations be calculated respectively from

$$\gamma = \frac{y}{m - y} \text{ and } \gamma = \frac{m}{c - m}$$

In order that the masking shall be satisfactory, the requirements for the balancing of the printing inks will be of even greater importance because the previously mentioned S-shaped masking curve will become still more pronounced as the γ-value for the masking film by double masking can be found from the γ_1-value for the masking film by single masking from the formula

$$\gamma = \frac{\gamma_1}{1 - \gamma_1}$$

The limit for how high masking percentage will be chosen in practice for single masking will generally be 45–50 per cent corresponding to a contrast reduction of the same percentage. Owing to the fact that no contrast reduction is made by double masking it may be possible to mask printing inks which require a comparatively high percentage correction, but according to

$$\gamma = \frac{\gamma_1}{1 - \gamma_1}$$

very contrasty masking films will soon be needed. It is also possible by means of the triangle diagram to get an impression of the masking properties of wanted colors in a separation. Here again we will study the color control patches in a yellow separation. We must assume that the density of a yellow color in a yellow negative is correct, whereas the lesser densities in the negative of red, green, and three-colors, are in error (over-corrected). This is due to the hue error and grayness of the magenta contents of the red color, the cyan contents of the green color, and the magenta and cyan contents of the three-color. On account of the additivity behaviour it need not be the same magenta and cyan with which we have to calculate here as those with which the printing is made.

In order to find the hue error and grayness (i.e. the coordinates) of the magenta and cyan colors which together with yellow give green and red, we could subtract the densitometer measurement of yellow from the measurements of green, red, and three-color.

These new "cyan", "magenta", and "blue" colors can be plotted in the triangle, and they have to fulfill the same masking conditions as those mentioned previously for unwanted colors.

Under fully ideal additivity conditions these new "magenta" and "cyan" colors will be indistinguishable from magenta and cyan inks respectively,

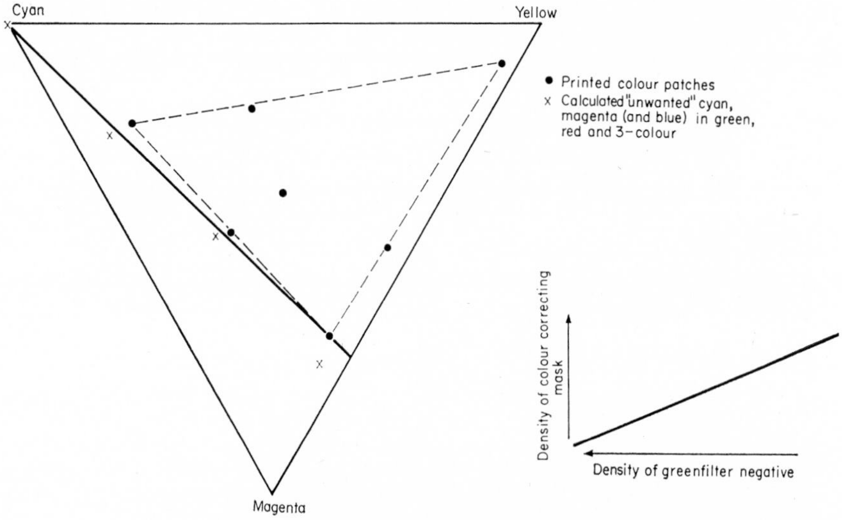

Fig. 3. Single masking of wanted and unwanted colors in the yellow printer.

and three-color will be indistinguishable from blue over-printing ink. If these original printing inks can be corrected ideally with some percentage masking, then wanted colors can also be fully corrected with the same mask. Figure 3 shows an example taken from practice. X in Fig. 3 indicates the position of "cyan", "magenta", and "blue" colors calculated from green, red, and three-color. In order that it should be possible to correct wanted as well as unwanted colors with one mask, it should also be possible to draw a straight line from the cyan vertex (which here at the same time indicates the yellow color, which is not to be corrected) through all six points, but this is impossible in the example shown. By double masking, the demand need not be that both wanted and unwanted colors fall on the same masking line. In this case the percentage masking line for unwanted colors could be considered as representing the masking curve over neutral density in the mask, and the percentage masking line for wanted colors as the masking curve under the

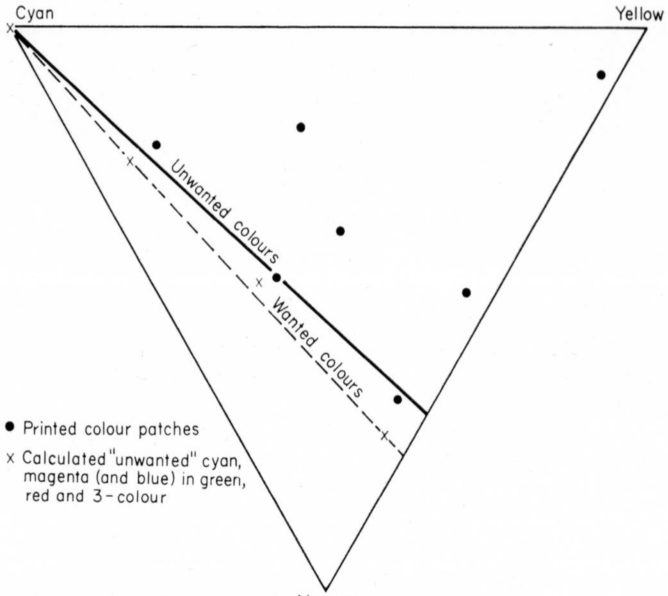

Fig. 4. Two-stage masking of wanted and unwanted colors in the yellow printer.

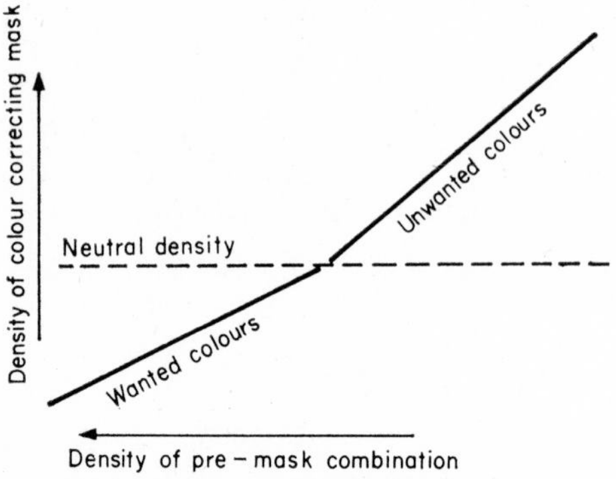

Fig. 5. Color correction curve for the yellow printer in two-stage masking.

neutral density. The line, ideal cyan to ideal red separates the colors which will be corrected over and under neutral density in the mask. The two curve inclinations (Fig. 5) for wanted and unwanted colors respectively in a mask by two-step masking could be calculated from the formula:

$$\gamma = \frac{\gamma_1}{1 - \gamma_1}$$

where $$\gamma_1 = \frac{\text{masking percentage for one-step masking}}{100}$$

This method gives us the possibility of analyzing the practicability of color correction with due regard not only to the printing ink errors, but also the additivity failure (and trapping).

All these masking considerations which have been explained here, will apply to solids, i.e. without halftone dots. However, printing inks will show proportionality behaviour in tints which to some extent will change both grayness as well as hue. A printing ink, for instance, in solid and the same color in 50 per cent tint will by measurement not be placed at the same position in the triangle.

This proportionality behaviour will entail that already found masking percentages will not apply when the inks are printed with halftone dots. Tints of the printing inks will demand increasing masking percentages. The choice of masking percentage will therefore always be a compromise.

COLOR BALANCE

It is important to realize that whether masking has been done or not, will have no influence upon what balanced halftone curves one should try to obtain in order to meet the demand of color balance. This means that the halftones must be harmonized in such a way that a neutral gray scale in the original will produce a neutral in the print. This demand for color balance will determine the mutual relationship of the individual halftone curves.

Over the years several systems have been given for calculating what the halftone curves of yellow, magenta and cyan should be in order to meet the above requirements. To this end a number of concepts are used such as proportionality behaviour, additivity curves, END, etc. These systems for the calculation of the color balance have it in common that they require great knowledge of the problems, and only with difficulty can they be brought into effect in a shop, where it is necessary to pay attention to own paper stocks, printing inks and printing methods.

We will here go through still another system which in practice may prove to be more easily understood. The prerequisite for the method is that from the outset the grayness of the individual process colors can be disregarded. The system is based upon the application of the hexagon diagram from L.T.F. In the example mentioned here the printing sequence will be yellow, magenta, cyan.

Halftone positives with percentage dot areas of 90, 50, 25 are transferred to a printing plate and are printed in such a way that we get a yellow, a magenta and a cyan scale; a red scale where the magenta scale has been printed on yellow, and a three-color scale where cyan has been printed on red. All patches are then measured on a Densichron reflection densitometer with the Kodak filters 47, 58, 25, because other investigations have shown that a range which has equal densities with these three filters is gray to the human eye.

The grayness of the individual colors, represented by the smallest densitometer reading for each individual color, has to be subtracted for plotting in the hexagon diagram. The two remaining densities which each color patch gets in this way will represent the hue and color strength of the colors. The individual screen percentage patches for yellow, magenta and red are plotted in the hexagon diagram with their respective values. If the individual points for each color in the diagram are connected, three curves appear which in a way represent the proportionality behaviour of the colors (see Fig. 6). With

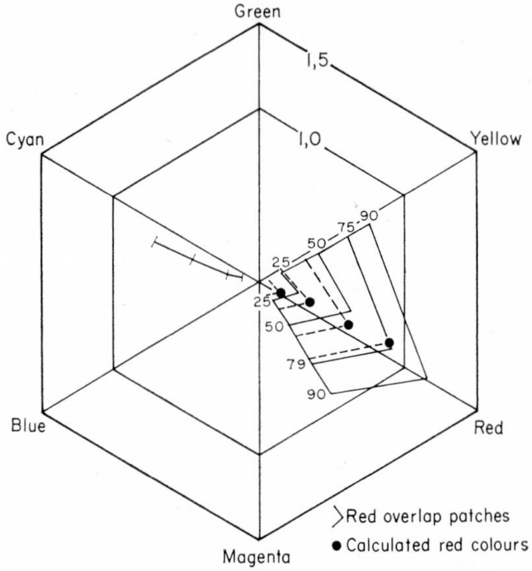

Fig. 6. Determining balanced halftone separations for process color.

this printing sequence it is unnecessary to measure and plot the values for cyan because these are not used. The line which connects the various percentage values for red shows how the hue and color strength of red varies for various equal dot values of yellow and magenta. In order to get numerical values as to how cyan is actually printing on red we could subtract the 90 per cent red measurements from the 90 per cent three-color measurements. The smallest figure which represents the grayness is subtracted from the "cyan" figures in the same way as previously. This results in two values which indicate hue and color strength for the cyan color which we actually have to calculate with when over-printing on yellow + magenta. In order to form a neutral with this "cyan", a red is required which is complementary in hue and color strength. The new "cyan" coordinates are therefore traces from neutral in order to find this red complementary color (Table 1). The coordinates for

TABLE 1. MEASUREMENTS AND CALCULATIONS NEEDED FOR DETERMINING BALANCED HALFTONE SEPARATIONS

Color	Filter	90% dot area			75% dot area			50% dot area			25% dot area		
		Densities × 100	Minus least		Densities × 100	Minus least		Densities × 100	Minus least		Densities × 100	Minus least	
Yellow	R	0		0	0		0	0		0	0		0
	G	5		5	4		4	3		3	2		2
	B	77		77	61		61	40		40	17		17
Magenta	R	10		0	8		0	5		0	2		0
	G	100		90	73		65	41		36	19		17
	B	60		50	45		37	26		21	12		10
Red	R	12		0	10		0	8		0	5		0
	G	127		115	93		83	57		49	25		20
	B	130		118	101		91	72		64	33		28
3-color	R	116			81			47			22		
	G	151			109			67			28		
	B	144			111			76			35		
3-color minus red	R	116– 12	104	90	81– 10	71	61	47– 8	39	35	22– 5	17	15
	G	151–127	24	10	109– 93	16	6	67–57	10	6	28–25	3	1
	B	144–130	14	0	111–101	10	0	76–72	4	0	35–33	2	0
Complementary to 3-color minus red	R	90– 90	0		61– 61	0		35–35	0		15–15	0	
	G	90– 10	80		61– 6	55		35– 6	29		15– 1	14	
	B	90– 0	90		61– 0	61		35– 0	35		15– 0	15	
% Dot area for neutral gray	C	90%			75%			50%			25%		
	Y	75%			43%			27%			15%		
	M	72%			57%			35%			19%		
END		116 − 2 = 114			81 − 2 = 79			47 − 2 = 45			22 − 2 = 20		

this red color are inserted in the hexagon diagram (Fig. 6). Knowing how magenta prints on yellow, it is now a question of finding out what dot values yellow and magenta should have in order to give this calculated red color. For this purpose a line is drawn from 90 per cent yellow to 90 per cent red and from 90 per cent red to 90 per cent magenta, and similarly for the 75, 50 and 25 per cent values. By drawing lines from the calculated red color parallel with the lines mentioned previously, intersection points with the "proportionality" curves of yellow and magenta will appear. It will not be possible to interpolate what per cent dot area should be attributed to yellow and magenta in order to give the red color which over-printed with 90 per cent cyan will give neutral. It is here assumed that 90 per cent cyan does not print otherwise on these smaller dot areas for yellow and magenta than it does on 90 per cent yellow and magenta. It would be possible to make this experiment more exactly if the dot areas from the outset had been made with some sort of balance, because then the interpolations could have been made also more exactly. We have now succeeded in finding three connected dot area percentages for yellow, magenta and cyan which over-printed in the sequence stated give neutral. Now it remains to find what END value this neutral has.

Looking at the measurements for three-color, Table 1 ($R = 1.16$, $G = 1.51$, and $B = 1.44$) it is evident that $R = 1.16$ is the largest measurement a neutral can have with the red filter. If, as in this instance, the dot percentage of red is reduced from 90 per cent yellow and magenta to about 75 per cent yellow and magenta, the blue filter reading and the green filter reading will be reduced appreciably while the red filter reading is reduced only by $0.12–0.10 = 0.02$ from magenta. No correction will come from yellow as the red filter reading here is zero. A neutral formed with 90 per cent cyan will therefore get a red filter density very close to $1.16–0.02 = 1.14$, and consequently an END of 1.14.

With the same procedure we now calculate the dot percentages for yellow and magenta which form neutrals with 75, 50, 25 per cent cyan, and what densities these neutrals will get.

It is now possible to draw the curves for yellow, magenta and cyan with dot area as a function of equivalent neutral density (END), Fig. 7.

In these three curves the following factors have been taken into consideration when offset is involved.

1. Printing down.
2. Development of the plate.
3. Printing, conditions, including sequence.
4. Paper.
5. Printing inks.
6. Ink strength.

In the case of letterpress, the etching of the plates is also accounted for. For gravure we could in a similar way have calculated the curves for the three continuous-tone positives.

It is possible by alteration of the above factors to alter the balance curves in such a way that they become somewhat closer than those found in this

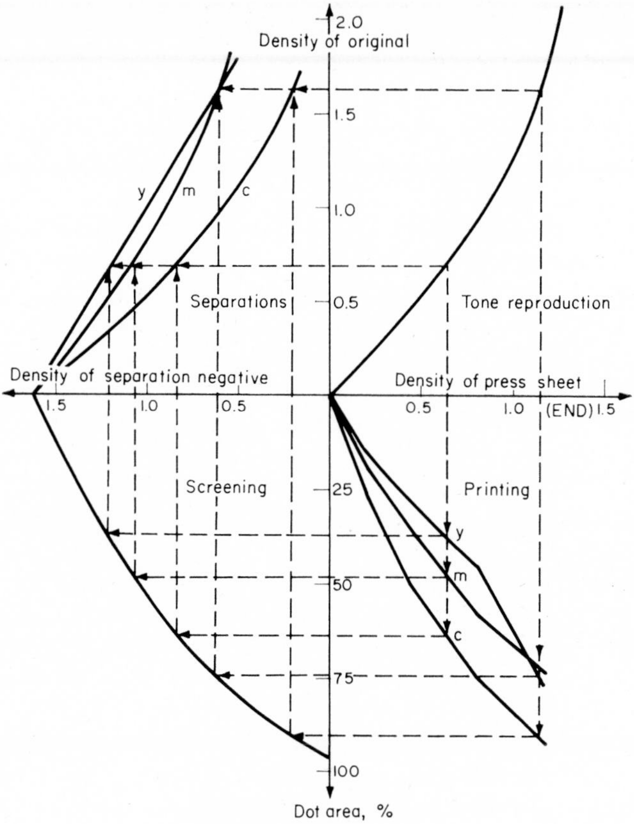

Fig. 7. Reproduction cycle.

example. Generally, it is possible to obtain almost the same curve for yellow and magenta, e.g. by harmonizing the ink strength and hue of yellow and magenta.

It is desirable to establish the color balance already in the separation negatives. This is preferable to establishing the balance at the screening stage because the screen curve which shows the relationship between halftone density and % dot area is comparatively firm. The curves of the magenta coloured contact screen, however, may be altered by means of filters (cf. the CC filters for the Kodak magenta contact screen). By experiment we can find the possible screening curves which could be used. By means of a photomechanical reproduction cycle diagram, Fig. 7, we can find the film curves for the separation negatives.

Let us now examine the possibilities of (by means of as few and simple experiments as possible and through measurements and diagrams) taking into consideration so many of the known variables through the whole reproduction process that one or more firm production programs really can be laid down, and which at the same time may be controlled.

The first thing to do is to get control of the whole cycle of ideas connected with printing inks, printing conditions, and paper; these factors will have a decisive influence upon the whole photographic part of the process, i.e. masking and colour balance. Provided it does not conflict with other more important requirements, the color values of the printing inks have to be chosen on the basis of the possibility of masking their errors by a simple and standardized method. With certain reservations it will be possible to predetermine and control this by means of reflection density measurements on solid yellow, magenta, and cyan which do not deviate too much in ink strength from those to be used for the printing. The reservations which are made here will be due to differences in measuring conditions compared with photographic conditions (filter, light source, color sensitivity of phototube versus film). The color values of the printing inks have to be considered in relation to the characteristics of the paper to be printed. According to the investigations of L.T.F. these paper characteristics may be unified in the PSE per cent (Paper surface efficiency factor). This PSE factor, which can be determined by measuring the absorption and gloss of the papers, will influence the color values of the inks in such a way that at least two main groups of papers have to be considered, roughly classified as coated and uncoated paper. Each of these groups of paper will demand varying masking percentages and different color balances.

The printing conditions, the paper and the color strength of the process inks have an influence upon what color balance has to be chosen. If possible, the mutual ink strength and hue of yellow and magenta must be chosen in such a way that we could work with the same color balance for these two colors.

For the masking of wanted colors these demands must also be made on the printing, i.e. trapping of over-printing has to be controlled. This control can be made with a densitometer and the triangle diagram. In order to get all these demands and requirements well in hand it will be practical to make a set of halftones with the per cent dot area 90, 75, 50, and 25, and to make printing experiments as mentioned under color balance upon the paper and with the process inks and ink strength which are to be examined. By measuring and plotting in the triangle diagram, the color values of the printing inks on the paper in question and the trapping may be estimated (of importance for the masking). Insertion in the hexagon diagram will give information on the halftone balance relationship.

The masking is more or less determined by the choice of the printing inks and the paper; it then remains to choose a suitable number (as few as possible) of masking systems, taking into account the character of the originals (reflection and transparency). However, it must be remembered that all masking with the methods in practical use have to be a compromise on account of proportionality and additivity behaviour.

The separations have always to be considered together with screening, because the separation curves will depend upon what screening characteristics it will be possible to obtain when the requirements of color balance are fulfilled at the same time.

The choice will then lie between making separation negatives which as to balance are alike and then to create the desired colour balance by the screening, or to achieve the desired color balance in the separation step and adhere to the standard conditions during the screening.

Usually the screening will be the most difficult operation in the over-all process. But if the desired color balance is made already in the separation negatives the screening becomes relatively simple (cf. the new Kodak half-tone positive computer).

The UCR masking has not been discussed here as this form of masking will depend very much upon the wishes of the individual shop, and upon the printing presses used.

The printing down has already been considered, as the printing experiments from which the color balance has been calculated include this process. The balance has been calculated from screen positive to the finished print (END). The efforts in the printing down have therefore to be concentrated on adhering to the standard conditions, e.g. by using L.T.F's sensitivity guide and star target. Finally, the printing may to a certain extent be controlled by means of reflection densitometer measurements of the print. The most important thing here will probably be to measure the ink strength through a complementary color filter and control the dot size by means of the L.T.F. star target. The purpose of this paper has been to point out that it is possible through rational production planning not to go beyond using two different masking percentages and two different color balances, corresponding to two groups of paper; for each of these possibilities fixed developing and basic exposure times could be found for the different steps in the reproduction work. The thing which is most badly needed in order to utilize a standardized procedure is controlled film processing.

CONTROLLED FILM PROCESSING

We know enough about the photographic process to say that commercially acceptable reliability from the process is within our grasp. We do have the know-how, but some additional equipment is needed. The most important process variables are broadly divided into exposure variables, processing variables, and film variables.

Exposure variables:

Ultraviolet radiation
Flare
Reciprocity failure
Voltage fluctuation

Processing variables:

Processing temperature
Processing agitation
Drying

Film variables:

Emulsion numbers
Storage time

Ultra-violet radiation. Most photographic films are very sensitive to u.v. Identical exposures may therefore give highly varying results, the original either being (a) u.v. reflecting, (b) u.v. absorbing or u.v. fluorescing (cf. the photography of white paper, which on the densitometer gives very similar readings but which have very different optical densities on the film). The difference between (a) and (b) may to a great extent be remedied by means of a u.v. absorbing filter over the light source. To put a filter in the lens does not solve the problem with a u.v. fluorescing material.

Flare. Each time the process camera is used flare appears, and this is the cause of much trouble. Flare may be reduced in the following ways. No stray light around the copyboard should be allowed. The areas around the copyboard glass should be covered with black paper, the room should be painted a dark color, and a clean lens should be used. However, the biggest problem is flare from the copy itself, which results in the original not giving the densities on the film as calculated from the densitometer measurements of the original. The problem can only be solved by measuring at the back of the camera so that the measurement would include the flare component.

Reciprocity failure. The fact that the density which a film gets, does not only depend upon the amount of light which the film receives, but also depends upon how long it takes to admit this amount of light, may be the reason for erroneous calculations when the exposure time is calculated on the basis of densitometer measurements of the original. Wherever possible it should be ensured that the calculated exposure time comes as close as it can to the standard time, possibly by means of changes in aperture or by using neutral density filters.

Voltage fluctuation. As a rule the modern types of camera have phototubes, which electronically adjust the amount of light in such a way that possible fluctuation in the luminous intensity of the lamps does not become important. On other types of equipment, such as enlargers and printing-frames, the exposure time is generally used as a measure of the amount of light. Such apparatus has then to be equipped with a constant voltage transformer because variations in mains voltage of ±10 V—which is often experienced—could give up to 40 per cent variation in the exposure time.

Processing temperature. The permissible processing temperature variation will of course depend upon the demands of precision. With PDI where they use the 'Time-Life' scanner, they have fixed the tolerances at ±0.1°F for developer and fixative bath, and ±0.5°F for wash water. The same tolerances are recommended by Du-Pont. Both sources claim that this is comparatively easy to maintain.

Processing agitation. Even if fresh developer is used and the temperature control is strict, it is well known that the method of agitation is of great importance, especially for the development of lith films.

Mechanical tray-rocking systems and nitrogen-burst systems have proved capable of reducing the uncertainty to about 1/3 of that which is general for manual tray-rocking agitation.

The consequence of this fact must be that mechanical developing should be introduced if possible. This, of course, does not necessitate very expensive fully automated processing equipment. We still lack a good and low-priced developing plant.

Film variables. The film itself is variable. As it ages, the speed normally diminishes. An investigation by Du-Pont has shown that if a box of film near its expiration date is used alongside a fresh box of film, the variation could reach about 10 per cent referring to per cent dot area. It is the practice in many shops to recognize this variation and to calibrate the films as they are received, and as they use them. Under such conditions, in terms of practical performance, the variation might be expected to be reduced to about 2 per cent.

REFERENCES

1. F. R. Clapper, Balanced halftone separations for process color. *TAGA Proceedings* 177 (1959).
2. Paul J. Hartsuch, Balanced offset process inks. *TAGA Proceedings* 29 (1958).
3. Irving Pobboravsky, Theoretical determination of color error. *TAGA Proceedings* 127 (1960).

4. FRANK M. PREUCIL, Highlights of the LTF survey of process color inks. *TAGA Proceedings* 143 (1957).
5. FRANK M. PREUCIL, The influence of paper on color reproduction. *Advances in Printing Science, Technology* Vol. I, 9, Pergamon Press (1961).
6. FRANK M. PREUCIL, Color diagrams. *TAGA Proceedings* 151 (1960).
7. FRANK M. PREUCIL, The influence of paper surface on the color of printed inks. *TAPPI* **45**, No. 10, 823 (1962).
8. K. H. SCHIRMER and KARL GROSS, The evaluation of different sets of process inks. *TAGA Proceedings* 133 (1939).
9. J. A. C. YULE and F. R. CLAPPER, Additivity of ink densities in multicolor halftone printing. *TAGA Proceedings* 153 (1956).
10. J. A. C. YULE and F. R. CLAPPER, Basic considerations in reflection copy color reproduction. *TAGA Proceedings* 163. Proceedings of the 12th Annual Conference Research and Engineering Council of the Graphic Arts Industry (1958).

DISCUSSION

YULE: (1) This paper contains a lot of interesting new material. I agree that it is very important to develop a single method of determining neutral balance, and I hope this one will prove to be satisfactory.

(2) We have found a density difference as high as 0.12 between two of the three filter measurements for an exactly neutral (visually) three-colour overprint. However, there is no need to use colour separation filters for this purpose, since colour separation properties are not involved in the selection of a neutral. Could tristimulus densities not be used instead?

(3) We have always assumed that the masking percentages derived from these density measurements and diagrams are optimum. Has it been established that these percentages do give the best reproductions?

WULFF: (2) Using tristimulus densities it might be possible to calculate the neutral gray balance a little more exactly. We have not tried to find the most exact method, but an easy one which can be carried out in the shops with existing equipment. The uncertainties in the whole reproduction process today are so great that to determine a more exact gray balance serves no useful purpose.

(3) As stated in the paper all simple masking systems had to be a compromise. The percentage masking derived from unwanted colours could only give the best results if we had ideal proportionality, additivity and trapping conditions. If you take the wanted colours into account it may be possible to find an even better compromise.

ADAMS: Are your instrumental measurements sufficiently accurate to allow a prediction of a neutral gray?

At PATRA we have found visual comparison with a Munsell scale quicker and more accurate than colorimetric measurements when selecting neutral grays.

WULFF: This method does not necessarily give an exactly neutral gray unless the densitometer sensitivities are related to the colour sensitivities of the eye. However, experience indicates that with process inks and the broad-band filters used, Kodak No. 25, No. 58, and No. 47, equality of density is a satisfactory indication of neutrality for the present purpose.

VARIATIONS OF DENSITIES IN MULTICOLOUR OFFSET PRINTING

by Aa. Frøslev-Nielsen and Chr. W. Christensen
The Graphic College of Denmark, Copenhagen

INTRODUCTION

There is a general need to reduce the variations in quality which are often too great in offset printing. The efforts which are constantly made in order to reduce the variations are principally based upon both technological improvements as well as standardization and control. Owing to the fact that the fields of standardization and control often meet greater obstacles than technological improvements, the latter alternative is often chosen. The discretionary character of the general technical developments in relation to the problems of printing establishments means that progress is slow, and consequently it would be advisable to examine the possibilities of using more extensive standardization and control of the offset process than hitherto.

There is no doubt that the reluctance to accept standardization and control met in practice largely stems from the fact that throughout the offset process there are so many variables that their control appears to be an insuperable task. However, it is also a foregone conclusion that the deviations of these variables will be of a widely different magnitude and therefore will differ in their contribution to variations in the resulting print.

It is, therefore, of interest to determine the number and to analyze the deviations of the most important variable factors in the entire offset process. In such an analysis the process has to be considered from the original to the finished print. The problems begin when judging the originals for their uniformity and suitability for reproduction.

The more recent developments in process photography have made this field the most controllable one within the entire process. Moreover, the use of presensitized one-purpose plates has resulted in much more certainty in platemaking than has been possible to obtain to date.

Many problems are connected with proof printing, but above all serious problems are encountered during the run of the job itself. These arise from the fact that the printed result, in spite of much advanced technology, still largely depends upon the pressman. Such matters depend on his individual judgment of the printing job in hand, his ambitions to produce good quality, and his ability to maintain the balance between water and ink.

Finally there are a number of technical phenomena relating to papers and inks, which can be difficult to forecast, and which influence both the print quality and the stability during the printing.

AIMS OF THE INVESTIGATION

The aim of the studies to be described has been to find the magnitude of some of the causes of variations in ink supply occurring when printing offset, as influenced by the pressman and the machine, and to obtain a measure of inking variations throughout the stack, across the individual sheets and finally from colour to colour.

CONDITIONS OF INVESTIGATIONS

Over a period of each of the years 1960, 1961 and 1962 a new team of 24 pressmen printed the same job on three different one-colour offset presses in such a way that each printing press was operated by 8 pressmen, each of whom without supervision, printed the job in question. A total of 72 pressmen were involved in the experiments.

Each pressman made a run of 600 sheets after adjustment and the press had settled down.

Four colours were printed and the same type of printing ink and the same quality of paper were used each time; all pressmen used the same proof print as reference (Fig. 1). On the front edge of the print, four colour bars, one for each colour were printed and were used to adjust the machine and the ink supply, by subjective judgment.

The actual total run involved in the experiments was therefore:

$$3 \times 24 \times 4 \times 600 = 172{,}800 \text{ sheets}$$

when each run of colour is counted as an individual run of the job.

The colour sequence was: yellow, followed by black, magenta and cyan.

METHODS OF MEASUREMENT

In the first year, 1960, only two sheets were taken out of each pressman's run, but 5 measurements of colour were made across the sheet.

In the two other years, 1961 and 1962, 20 sheets were taken out of each run, and each colour was measured at the very same point.

As it was assumed that the variations in optical densities could be taken as a measure of the variation in ink supply, the measurements of the colours were made only with complementary filters. A densitometer (Kodak), was used for the measurements.

Thus the number of measurements was:

$$1960{:}\ 24 \times 4 \times 2 \times 5 = 960$$
$$1061{:}\ 24 \times 4 \times 20 \times 1 = 1920$$
$$1962{:}\ 24 \times 4 \times 20 \times 1 = 1920$$
$$\underline{\underline{4800}}$$

ANALYSIS OF THE MEASUREMENTS

The density measurements were analyzed statistically with a view to examining the influence of pressmen and machine. Variations are expressed as standard deviations σ, and the variance σ^2.

Thus, for example, if the mean value of a number of measurements is called m, σ may be used to characterize the spread of the individual results by the expression $(m \pm \sigma)$.

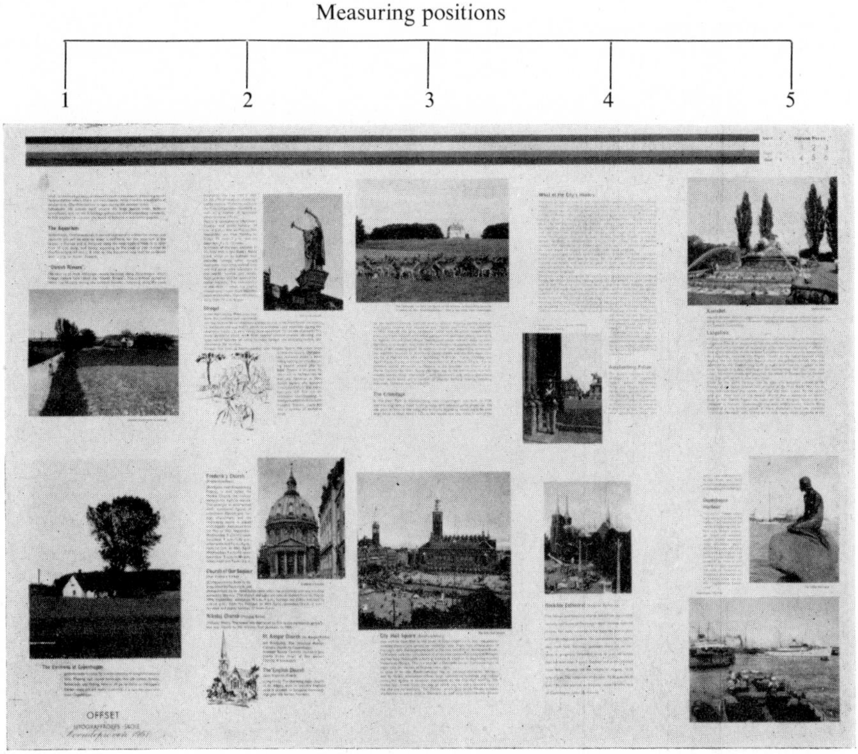

Fig. 1. The lay-out of the print.

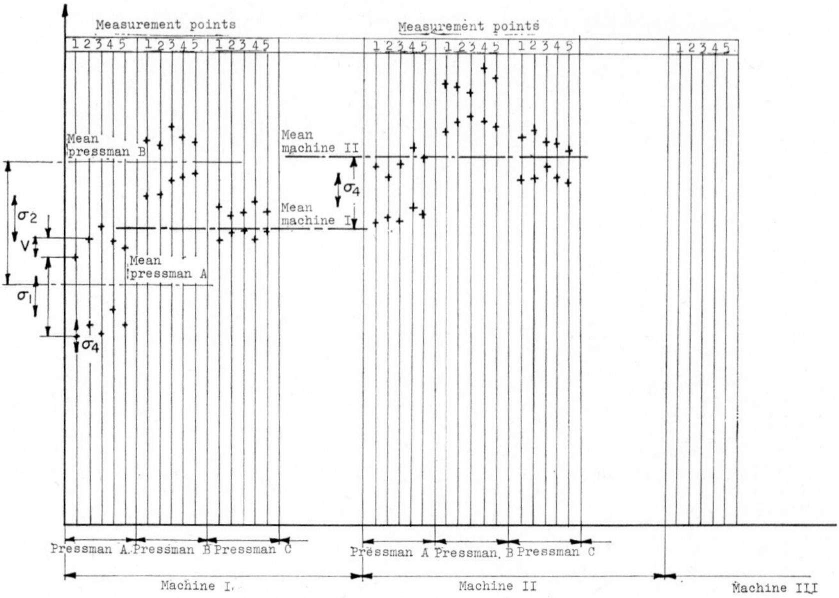

Fig. 2. Diagram showing the different standard deviations in relation to each other for the measurement made in 1960.

SOURCES OF VARIANCE

The following sources of variation may influence the charges in optical density for each machine:

1. Analytical error, σ_0, for the actual densitometer measurements.
2. Variation on the same point from sheet to sheet σ_1 (Fig. 3).

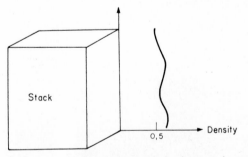

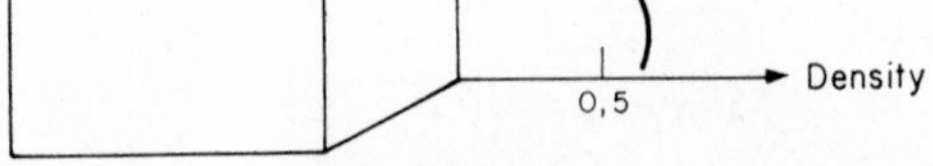

Fig. 3. Variation on the same point from sheet to sheet σ_1.

3. Variation of the mean value for pressmen about the mean value for the machine, σ_2 (Fig. 4).
4. An estimate, V, of the true difference between the densities at various points in a colour bar. This is not a chance variation, and is thus not

strictly a standard deviation, but it may be calculated in the same manner. V depends only on the lay-out of the printed job in question, and may thus be solely attributed to the fact that the offset ink fountain has been adjusted according to the ink requirements of the various parts of the

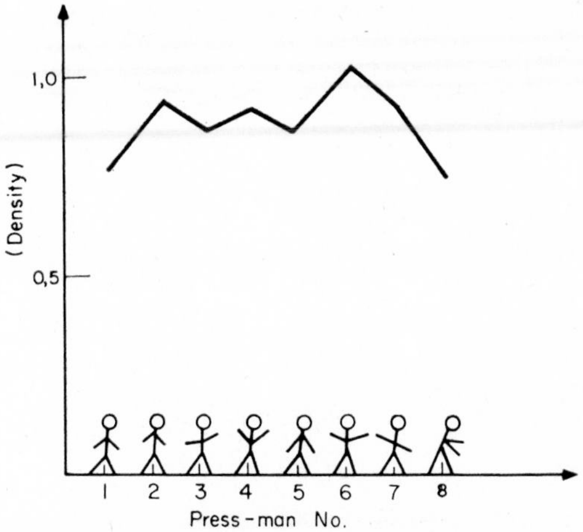

Fig. 4. Variation of the mean value for pressmen about the mean value for the machine, σ_2.

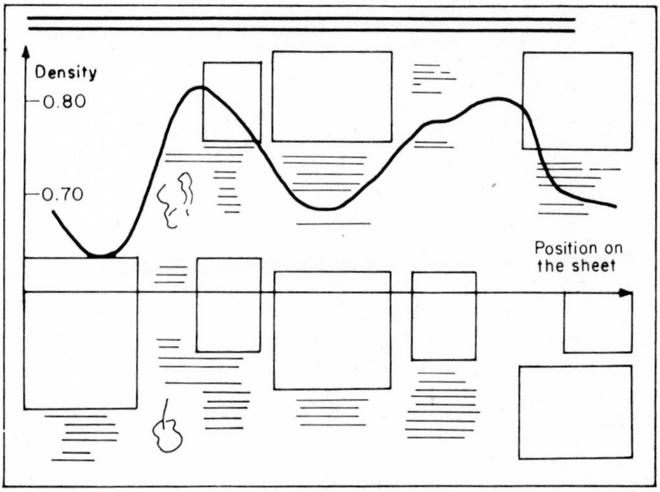

Fig. 5. An estimate, V, of the true difference between the densities at various points in a colour bar. This is not a chance variation, and is thus not strictly a standard deviation, but it may be calculated in the same manner. V depends on the lay-out of the printed job in question, and may thus be solely attributed to the fact that the offset ink fountain has been adjusted according to the ink requirements of the various parts of the forme in such a way that the more solid and the tighter parts during the whole printing process were inked-up with the same ink film.

forme in such a way that the more solid and lighter parts during the whole printing process were inked-up with the same ink film (Fig. 5).

5. Interaction between positions on the ink bar and pressmen, σ_3. This may be due to changed conditions relating to the ink and the ink duct for the individual pressmen, which thus could mean an altered adjustment of the ink supply. The variation may also be due to careless adjustment.

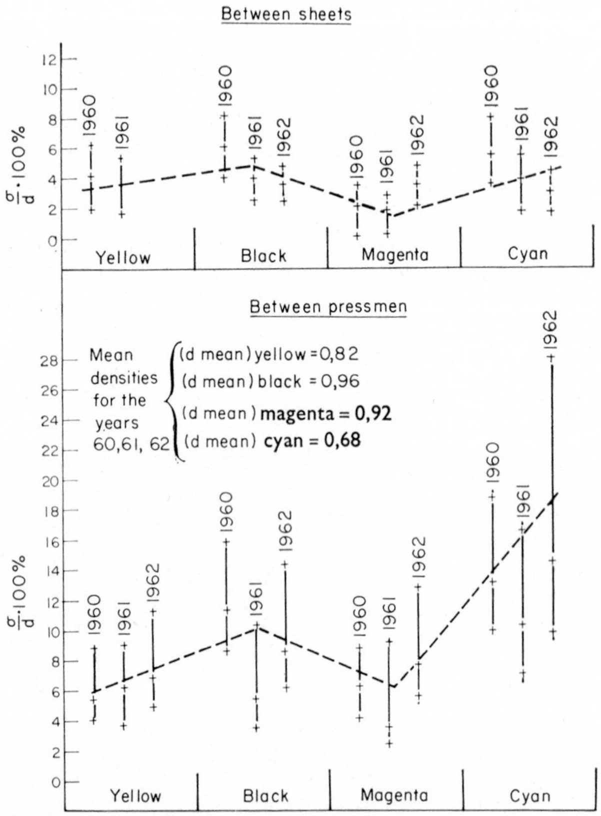

Fig. 6. The percentage standard deviations for the four colours.

The σ_0-value was determined by measuring the densities at 15 positions chosen at random on each of the four colour bars.

The σ_0-values given in Table 1, were calculated from tables of the χ^2-distribution for 15 degrees of freedom and 90 per cent confidence. Furthermore, the upper and the lower limit for σ_0 is stated.

TABLE 1. CALCULATED σ_0-VALUES AND LIMITS

Colours	Lower confidence limit	Standard deviation	Upper confidence limit
Magenta	0.013	0.017	0.024
Yellow	0.016	0.021	0.031
Cyan	0.011	0.015	0.021
Black	0.006	0.008	0.012

MEASUREMENTS OF THE OPTICAL DENSITIES, 1960

Table 2 shows the complete scheme of the analysis of variance for each machine assuming that all variances can be calculated for all pressmen and points.

In consequence it was necessary to examine these assumptions before it was possible to make an actual analysis of variance, and the quantities $(\sigma_0^2 + \sigma_1^2)$ and $(\sigma_0^2 + \sigma_1^2 + p\sigma_3^2)$ were therefore calculated for each measuring position and for each machine. A comparison of the limits for σ_1^2/σ_0^2 with 90 per cent confidence limits for all 5 measuring positions shows that it is permissible to calculate $(\sigma_0^2 + \sigma_1^2)$ for the measuring positions 2, 3, and 4, but not for 1 and 5. It is, however, also known from practice that it is difficult to control the inking during the run at the edges of the printing plate, and therefore it is natural to exclude these two measurement points in the following calculations. In the variance analysis of Table 2 we can therefore establish:

$$p = 2, k = 3, q = 8$$

The pressman mean square $(\sigma_0^2 + \sigma_1^2 + p\sigma_3^2)$ has also been calculated for each of the positions 2, 3, and 4, and similar calculations to those above also show that it is possible to calculate σ_2^2 from the mean value of the densities for the three positions by calculating $(\sigma_0^2 + \sigma_1^2 + pk\sigma_2^2)$.

Consequently, these calculations lead to values for mean squares as shown in Table 3 for the magenta colour. For the sake of clarity, only the results for the magenta colour have been included in this form. As will appear from the following, further efforts have been made to calculate a common mean square for all three machines.

The mean squares for the three machines may for each variation group be considered as independent estimates of the variance in question, and in order to establish whether the individual mean squares for the three machines can be combined, an *F*-test (O. L. Davies, *Design and Analysis of Industrial Experiment*, London 1956), has been made between the individual machines.

These comparisons between machines I and III, I and II, and II and III have in Table 4 been called I–III, I–II and II–III, and a non-significant

TABLE 2. ANALYSIS OF VARIANCE FOR EACH COLOUR AND MACHINE (1960)

Source of variation	Degrees of freedom	Sum of squares	Quantity estimated by the mean square
Between measurement points	$(k-1)$	$\frac{1}{pq}\left[\Sigma(R^2) - \frac{1}{k}T^2\right]$	$\sigma_0^2 + \sigma_1^2 + p\sigma_3^2 + pqV$
Between pressmen	$(q-1)$	$\frac{1}{pk}\left[\Sigma(S^2) - \frac{1}{q}T^2\right]$	$\sigma_0^2 + \sigma_1^2 + p\sigma_3^2 + pk\sigma_2^2$
Interaction between points and pressmen	$(k-1)(q-1)$	$\frac{1}{p}\left[\Sigma(B^2) - \frac{1}{k}\Sigma(S^2) - \frac{1}{q}\left(\Sigma(R^2) - \frac{1}{k}T^2\right)\right]$	$\sigma_0^2 + \sigma_1^2 + p\sigma_3^2$
Between sheets	$qk(p-1)$	$\Sigma y^2 - \frac{1}{p}\Sigma B^2$	$\sigma_0^2 + \sigma_1^2$
Analytical error (measuring app.)	0		σ_0^2
Total	$qkp-1$	$\Sigma y^2 - \frac{1}{pqk}T^2$	

y is the optical density on each point for the colour in question
Σy^2 is the summation of y^2 for all points and pressmen
B is the sum of the densities (Σy) for each colour at the same position of the two selected prints for each pressman
$\Sigma(B^2)$ is the summation of B^2 for all measuring positions for each sheet and for all pressmen
S is ΣB for all measuring positions for each pressman
R is ΣB for all pressmen for each point
T is Σy for all sheets, points and pressmen
V is an estimate of the true difference in density from measurements made on the colour bars
p is the number of sheets taken out
q is the number of pressmen per machine
k is the number of measuring positions

TABLE 3. COMPLETE ANALYSIS OF VARIANCE FOR THE MAGENTA COLOUR

Source of variation	Degrees of freedom	Sum of squares	Mean square	Quantity estimated by the mean square	Machine
Between measurement points	2	0.0071	0.00355	$\sigma_0^2 + \sigma_1^2 + 2\sigma_3^2 + 16V$	
Between pressmen	7	0.1080	0.01543	$\sigma_0^2 + \sigma_1^2 + 2\sigma_3^2 + 6\sigma_2^2$	
Interaction between points and pressmen	14	0.0128	0.00091	$\sigma_0^2 + \sigma_1^2 + 2\sigma_3^2$	I
Between sheets	24		0.00060	$\sigma_0^2 + \sigma_1^2$	
Analytical error	0		0.00028	σ_0^2	
Total	47				
Between measurement points	2	0.0322	0.01610	$\sigma_0^2 + \sigma_1^2 + 2\sigma_3^2 + 16V$	
Between pressmen	7	0.2172	0.03103	$\sigma_0^2 + \sigma_1^2 + 2\sigma_3^2 + 6\sigma_2^2$	
Interaction between points and pressmen	14	0.0534	0.00382	$\sigma_0^2 + \sigma_1^2 + 2\sigma_3^2$	II
Between sheets	24		0.00076	$\sigma_0^2 + \sigma_1^2$	
Analytical error	0		0.00028	σ_0^2	
Total	47				
Between measurement points	2	0.0220	0.01100	$\sigma_0^2 + \sigma_1^2 + 2\sigma_3^2 + 16V$	
Between pressmen	7	0.1030	0.01471	$\sigma_0^2 + \sigma_1^2 + 2\sigma_3^2 + 6\sigma_2^2$	
Interaction between points and pressmen	14	0.0188	0.00134	$\sigma_0^2 + \sigma_1^2 + 2\sigma_3^2$	III
Between sheets	24		0.00187	$\sigma_0^2 + \sigma_1^2$	
Analytical error	0		0.00028	σ_0^2	
Total	47				

TABLE 4. *F*-TEST BETWEEN VARIANCES FROM DIFFERENT MACHINES

	Between sheets			Interaction between points and pressmen			Between pressmen			Between measurement points		
Compared machines	I–III	I–II	II–III	I–III	I–II	II–III	I–III	I–II	II–III	I–III	I–II	II–III
Magenta	−	+	−	+	−	−	+	+	+	+	+	+
Yellow	+	+	+	−	−	+	+	+	+	+	+	+
Cyan	+	−	−	+	+	−	+	+	+	+	+	+
Black	+	+	+	+	+	+	+	+	+	+	+	+

difference of 5 per cent has in the table been indicated by +, a significant difference by —.

As will be seen, there is only a small significant difference between the groups for the three machines. For the groups "Between pressmen" and "Between points" the difference is on the whole without importance for a common calculation for the three machines.

In the case of the other groups the procedure has been that the machine which shows significant difference in relation to the two others, has been rejected from the total calculation. By an *F*-test for the cyan of the group "Interaction" it will be seen that only one minus occurs, viz. on comparison of the machines II and III, and consequently all three machines are included in the calculation of a common mean square.

The mean square between the mean value of the machines cannot immediately be calculated, because the three machines have not been operated by the same pressmen, but a sufficient determination of the mean square between the mean values of the machines may be immediately obtained by (confer Table 2):

$$\sigma_0^2 + \sigma_1^2 + 2\sigma_3^2 + 6\sigma_2^2 + 14\sigma_5^2 + 48\sigma_4^2 = \frac{1}{96}\left[\sum(T^2) - \frac{1}{3}\left(\sum_{\mathrm{I}}^{\mathrm{III}} T\right)^2\right]$$

if an *F*-test between this and the mean square for pressmen shows high significance for σ_4^2, which is the variance between the average densities of the machines.

σ_5^2 is a variance which may be attributed to interaction between machines and points. These *F*-tests have thus been made, the mean squares of the individual measurement points between pressmen having been used, consequently an adequate evaluation of the limits within which *F* is located, is obtained.

TABLE 5. COMPLETE ANALYSIS OF VARIANCE FOR ALL THREE MACHINES, 1960

Source of variation	Degrees of freedom					Mean square				Quantity estimated by the mean square
		Magenta	Yellow	Cyan	Black	Magenta	Yellow	Cyan	Black	
Between machines (m)	$b-1$	2	2	2	2	0.17355	0.11710	—	—	$\sigma_0^2+\sigma_1^2+2\sigma_3^2+6\sigma_2^2+14\sigma_5^2+48\sigma_4^2$
Between points (p)	$k-1$	2	2	2	2	0.02710	0.10297	0.05110	0.00196	$\sigma_0^2+\sigma_1^2+2\sigma_3^2+14\sigma_5^2+48V$
Interaction between m and p	$(b-1)(k-1)$	4	4	4	4	0.00178	0.00054	0.00080	0.00574	$\sigma_0^2+\sigma_1^2+2\sigma_3^2+14\sigma_5^2$
Between pressmen (P)	$b(q-1)$	21	21	21	21	0.02039	0.01624	0.04836	0.07016	$\sigma_0^2+\sigma_1^2+2\sigma_3^2+6\sigma_2^2$
Interaction between P and p	$b(k-1)(q-1)$	28	28	42	42	0.00113	0.00276	0.00171	0.00157	$\sigma_0^2+\sigma_1^2+2\sigma_3^2$
Between sheets ..	$bkq(p-1)$	48	72	48	72	0.00068	0.00155	0.00158	0.00329	$\sigma_0^2+\sigma_1^2$
Analytical error ..	0	0	0	0	0	0.00028	0.00045	0.00022	0.00007	σ_0^2

These investigations showed that the variance between machines σ_4^2 was significant for magenta and yellow, but not for cyan and black on 90 per cent level.

In Table 5 the final result of the analysis of variance is given. Since some of the calculations for the variations "Between pressmen" and "Interaction between points and pressmen" have been based on two machines, others on three machines, an addition of the figures for the degrees of freedom will not result in the characteristic figure $bkqp \div 1 = 143$ for $b = 3$.

The result of a significance test between the individual mean squares is given in Table 6, where a + indicates that the variance in question is significant while a – indicates that the variance is non-significant.

TABLE 6. SIGNIFICANCE TEST BETWEEN VARIANCES

	Between sheets	Interaction between points and pressmen	Between pressmen	Interaction between points and machines	Between measurement points	Between machines
Magenta	+	–	+	–	+	+
Yellow	+	+	+	–	+	+
Cyan	+	–	+	–	+	–
Black	+	–	+	+	–	–

The individual significant variances have been calculated. In this connection it should be mentioned that σ_4^2 has been determined by deducting the mean square for variation between pressmen, which has been calculated for all machines, from the mean square between machines. This can be done, as the mean square between pressmen predominates in order of magnitude compared with the other mean squares and, moreover, the former does not show significant differences between any of the machines.

In Table 7 the individual standard deviations and their limits are given. Here "calc" indicates that the variance and standard deviation in question have been calculated directly from Table 5, while a minus indicates a non-significant magnitude.

As will be seen, the interactions between pressmen and points and between machines and points are without importance. A narrowing down of the limits for the variation between points can therefore be made when calculating the variation between points over the mean value for each machine instead of between the mean value of the points over all three machines. Only to an insignificant degree does the calculated mean square become different from the one which was calculated first, but the limits are narrowed down on account of an alteration of the figure for the degree of freedom from 2 to 6.

The result of this calculation has been included in Table 7 against "variation between means of points about means of machines". The new calculation alters only insignificantly the variation between machines, and consequently is ignored.

TABLE 7. STANDARD DEVIATIONS CALCULATED FOR ALL MACHINES, 1960

Source of variation		Magenta $d = 0.92$	Yellow $d = 0.81$	Cyan $d = 0.66$	Black $d = 0.94$
Analytical error	(σ_0)min.	0.013	0.016	0.011	0.006
	(σ_0)calc.	0.017	0.021	0.015	0.008
	(σ_0)max.	0.024	0.024	0.021	0.012
Between sheets	(σ_1)min.	0.002	0.016	0.024	0.038
	(σ_1)calc.	0.020	0.033	0.037	0.057
	(σ_1)max.	0.032	0.050	0.053	0.077
Interaction between	(σ_3)min.		0.008		
points and pressmen	(σ_3)calc.	—	0.025	—	—
	(σ_3)max.		0.041		
Between pressmen	(σ_2)min.	0.039	0.032	0.064	0.081
	(σ_2)calc.	0.057	0.044	0.088	0.106
	(σ_2)max.	0.081	0.071	0.125	0.149
Interaction between	(σ_5)min.				0.002
machines and	(σ_5)calc.	—	—	—	0.017
points	(σ_5)max.				0.047
Between measurement	$(\sqrt{V})$min.	0.013	0.024	0.017	
points	$(\sqrt{V})$calc.	0.023	0.046	0.032	—
	$(\sqrt{V})$max.	0.104	0.202	0.144	
Between means of	$(\sqrt{V})$min.	0.017	0.027	0.019	
points about means	$(\sqrt{V})$calc.	0.024	0.045	0.032	—
of machines	$(\sqrt{V})$max.	0.049	0.090	0.064	
Between machines	(σ_4)min.	0.020	0.019		
	(σ_4)calc.	0.057	0.049	—	—
	(σ_4)max.	0.264	0.238		

At the top of the columns which show the individual colours, the mean value for all densities over pressmen, points and machines has been inserted and in this way it is possible to compare these directly with the individual standard deviations.

PLANNING OF THE MEASUREMENTS OF THE OPTICAL DENSITIES IN 1961 AND 1962

To ensure that the above numerical values for the variation between sheets, between pressmen and machines are acceptable, similar measurements were made in the two consecutive years, 1961 and 1962. The layout is the same as the one used previously. As it appears from these and from the initial calculations, the variances between sheets and between pressmen showed no significant difference for the three middle positions on the sheet. Furthermore, the true differences in density across a sheet are of minor interest because it varies with the layout and of course with mechanical effects such as the adjustment of the doctor blade in the inking system.

The measurements on the new series of prints were therefore made only in the middle of the sheets, but the number of selected sheets per pressman was increased to 20 copies—evenly selected down through each pile.

The sheets were measured in random order, and the measurements made for each colour, machine and pressman were examined for normal distribution. It appeared that not all pressmen's results show a normal distribution, and this is not immediately explicable.

It might be expected that if a run is made without interruption or alteration in mechanical or inking conditions the density measurements for each run would show normal distribution, but at the same time it must be stressed that 20 measurements are a relatively small number for an estimate of the distribution. On the assumption that a normal distribution exists, and that the densities are not influenced by variations of a non-accidental character, only the runs which show a normal distribution of densities were statistically evaluated. Here it was possible to select 4 pressmen for each colour and each machine which met these requirements, and the table of variance analysis for 1961 and 1962 then appears as shown in Table 8, the analytical error being directly transferred from the previous measurements.

TABLE 8. ANALYSIS OF VARIANCE 1961 AND 1962 FOR EACH MACHINE AND COLOUR

Source of variation	Degrees of freedom	Sum of squares	Mean square
Between pressmen	$q - 1$	$\Sigma(S)^2 - \frac{1}{q}T^2$	$\sigma_0^2 + \sigma_1^2 + p\sigma_2^2$
Between sheets	$q(p - 1)$	$\Sigma y^2 - \frac{1}{p}S^2$	$\sigma_0^2 + \sigma_1^2$
Analytical error	0		σ_0^2

For the sake of clarity only the results of the analysis of variance are given for the magenta colour, in Table 9. As in the case of the first year's measurements the results of the three machines were tested against each other while the individual mean squares for each source of variation were considered as independent estimates of the source of variation in question.

TABLE 9. COMPLETE ANALYSIS OF VARIANCE FOR THE MAGENTA COLOUR

Source of variation	Degrees of freedom	Mean square	Expectation of mean square	Machine	Year
Between pressmen	3	0.11468	$\sigma_0^2 + \sigma_1^2 + 20\sigma_2^2$		
Between sheets	76	0.00059	$\sigma_0^2 + \sigma_1^2$	I	
Analytical error	0	0.00028	σ_0^2		
Between pressmen	3	0.04430	$\sigma_0^2 + \sigma_1^2 + 20\sigma_2^2$		
Between sheets	76	0.00062	$\sigma_0^2 + \sigma_1^2$	II	1961
Analytical error	0	0.00028	σ_0^2		
Between pressmen	3	0.00568	$\sigma_0^2 + \sigma_1^2 + 20\sigma_2^2$		
Between sheets	76	0.00108	$\sigma_0^2 + \sigma_1^2$	III	
Analytical error	0	0.00028	σ_0^2		
Between pressmen	3	0.07372	$\sigma_0^2 + \sigma_1^2 + 20\sigma_2^2$		
Between sheets	76	0.00106	$\sigma_0^2 + \sigma_1^2$	I	
Analytical error	0	0.00028	σ_0^2		
Between pressmen	3	0.16728	$\sigma_0^2 + \sigma_1^2 + 20\sigma_2^2$		
Between sheets	76	0.00146	$\sigma_0^2 + \sigma_1^2$	II	1962
Analytical error	0	0.00028	σ_0^2		
Between pressmen	3	0.03215	$\sigma_0^2 + \sigma_1^2 + 20\sigma_2^2$		
Between sheets	76	0.00124	$\sigma_0^2 + \sigma_1^2$	III	
Analytical error	0	0.00028	σ_0^2		

An estimate of the mean square between machines according to the formula

$$\sigma_0^2 + \sigma_1^2 + 20\sigma_2^2 + 80\sigma_4^2 = \frac{1}{160}\left[\sum_{\mathrm{I}}^{\mathrm{III}}(T^2) - \frac{1}{3}\left(\sum_{\mathrm{I}}^{\mathrm{III}} T\right)^2\right]$$

shows no significant difference from machine to machine for the years 1961 and 1962. When arranging the final table of analyses for these two years this source of variation has consequently not been included. The calculations were made as in 1960, on the basis of the results from Table 10.

TABLE 10. *F*-TEST BETWEEN VARIANCES FROM DIFFERENT MACHINES

Compared machines	Between sheets I–III	Between sheets I–II	Between sheets II–III	Between pressmen I–III	Between pressmen I–II	Between pressmen II–III	Year
Magenta	—	+	—	—	—	+	1961
Yellow	+	+	+	+	+	+	
Cyan	+	+	+	+	+	+	
Black	—	—	+	+	+	+	
Magenta	+	+	+	+	+	+	1962
Yellow	+	—	+	—	+	+	
Cyan	+	+	—	—	—	+	
Black	+	+	+	+	+	+	

In Table 11 the analysis of variance for the years 1961 and 1962 is given.

The results of a test of significance between the individual mean squares are given in Table 12.

The variance between sheets, yellow 1962, is the only value which cannot be calculated. For all other values a calculation of the individual variances and their limits can be made as shown by the measurements for 1960. In Table 13 the standard deviations for the individual colours and their limits are given, and in Table 14 the standard deviations and their limits for the three years are summarized. In this connection it would be of interest to estimate the ratio σ/d, since it is important in the discussion of standard deviations to take the actual density in consideration. In Fig. 6 the percentage ratio between the standard deviations and mean densities for the different colours are plotted, the values σ_{calc}, σ_{max} and σ_{min} having been involved in these calculations as shown. Furthermore, the mean densities for the four colours are shown.

The colour sequence on the abscissa is that used in the printing and so it is evident that in the case of the variation "Between pressmen" the percentage deviation is largest in the case of cyan, the last printed colour. Undoubtedly,

Table 11. Complete Analysis of Variance for all Three Machines, 1961–62

Colour	Source of variation	Degrees of freedom	Mean square	Expectation of mean square	Year
Magenta	Between pressmen	6	0.02499	$\sigma_0^2 + \sigma_1^2 + 20\sigma_2^2$	1961
	Between sheets	152	0.00061	$\sigma_0^2 + \sigma_1^2$	
	Analytical error		0.00028	σ_0^2	
	Between pressmen	9	0.09105	$\sigma_0^2 + \sigma_1^2 + 20\sigma_2^2$	1962
	Between sheets	228	0.00125	$\sigma_0^2 + \sigma_1^2$	
	Analytical error		0.00028	σ_0^2	
Yellow	Between pressmen	9	0.04781	$\sigma_0^2 + \sigma_1^2 + 20\sigma_2^2$	1961
	Between sheets	228	0.00130	$\sigma_0^2 + \sigma_1^2$	
	Analytical error		0.00045	σ_0^2	
	Between pressmen	9	0.07356	$\sigma_0^2 + \sigma_1^2 + 20\sigma_2^2$	1962
	Between sheets	228	0.00086	$\sigma_0^2 + \sigma_1^2$	
	Analytical error		0.00045	σ_0^2	
Cyan	Between pressmen	9	0.08120	$\sigma_0^2 + \sigma_1^2 + 20\sigma_2^2$	1961
	Between sheets	228	0.00087	$\sigma_0^2 + \sigma_1^2$	
	Analytical error		0.00022	σ_0^2	
	Between pressmen	6	0.23423	$\sigma_0^2 + \sigma_1^2 + 20\sigma_2^2$	1962
	Between sheets	228	0.00075	$\sigma_0^2 + \sigma_1^2$	
	Analytical error		0.00022	σ_0^2	
Black	Between pressmen	6	0.05300	$\sigma_0^2 + \sigma_1^2 + 20\sigma_2^2$	1961
	Between sheets	228	0.00148	$\sigma_0^2 + \sigma_1^2$	
	Analytical error		0.00007	σ_0^2	
	Between pressmen	9	0.15038	$\sigma_0^2 + \sigma_1^2 + 20\sigma_2^2$	1962
	Between sheets	228	0.00137	$\sigma_0^2 + \sigma_1^2$	
	Analytical error		0.00007	σ_0^2	

TABLE 12. SIGNIFICANCE TEST BETWEEN VARIANCES

Year	1961				1962			
Colours	Magenta	Yellow	Cyan	Black	Magenta	Yellow	Cyan	Black
Between pressmen	+	+	+	+	+	+	+	+
Between sheets	+	+	+	+	+	−	+	+

TABLE 13. STANDARD DEVIATIONS CALCULATED FOR ALL MACHINES, 1961–62

Source of variation		Magenta $d = 0.96$	Yellow $d = 0.78$	Cyan $d = 0.63$	Black $d = 0.95$	Year
Between sheets	(σ_1)min.	0.003	0.013	0.011	0.025	1961
	(σ_1)calc.	0.018	0.029	0.024	0.038	
	(σ_1)max.	0.028	0.042	0.036	0.050	
Between pressmen	(σ_2)min.	0.023	0.028	0.045	0.033	
	(σ_2)calc.	0.035	0.048	0.065	0.051	
	(σ_2)max.	0.088	0.066	0.105	0.099	
Source of variation		Magenta $d = 0.87$	Yellow $d = 0.88$	Cyan $d = 0.74$	Black $d = 1.00$	Year
Between sheets	(σ_1)min.	0.018		0.012	0.024	1962
	(σ_1)calc.	0.031	–	0.023	0.036	
	(σ_1)max.	0.043		0.033	0.048	
Between pressmen	(σ_2)min.	0.048	0.043	0.073	0.062	
	(σ_2)calc.	0.067	0.060	0.108	0.086	
	(σ_2)max.	0.112	0.100	0.208	0.144	
Analytical error	(σ_0)min.	0.013	0.016	0.011	0.006	
	(σ_0)calc.	0.017	0.021	0.015	0.008	
	(σ_0)max.	0.024	0.031	0.021	0.012	

TABLE 14. STANDARD DEVIATIONS AND SIGNIFICANCE LIMITS OF OPTICAL DENSITIES OF THE DIFFERENT COLOURS
OPTICAL DENSITY × 10^3

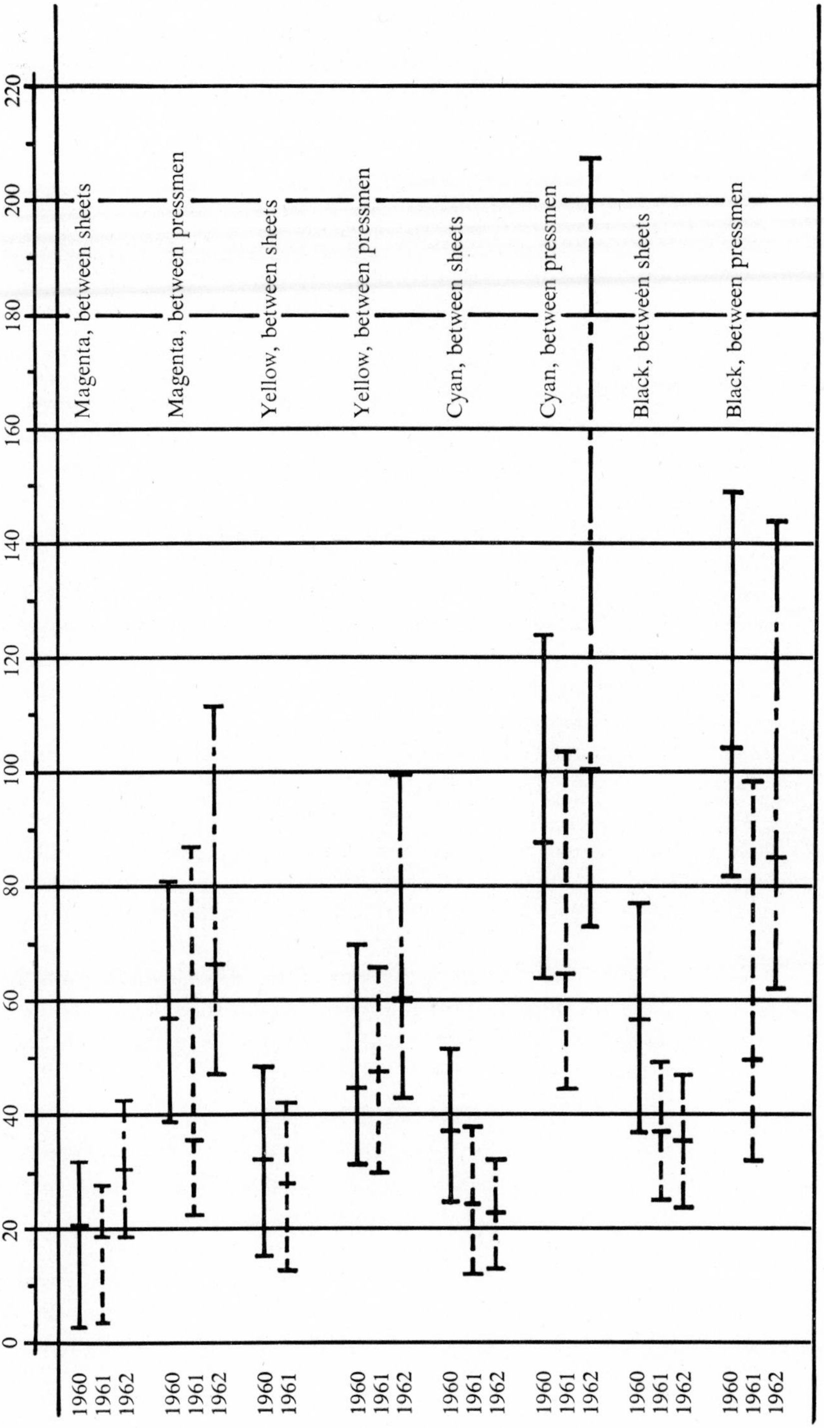

it can be explained by the fact that the solid density of the last printed colour is to some extent dependent on the standard deviations of the previous printed colour, since the printer tries to harmonize the final overlapped colours by the last colour.

SUMMARY

On the basis of measurements of optical densities of offset printed solids the standard deviations for the individual variations between printed sheets in the separate runs across the individual sheets, between pressmen and between machines have been determined for the four colours yellow, magenta, cyan, and black.

The printing was repeated for three consecutive years, and has each year been made with the same proof print as standard on three one-colour sheet offset presses by 8 pressmen per machine, and with a run of 600 sheets per pressman. The total number of printed sheets for all four colours of the job given has thus been 172,800.

The colour sequence in the printing was: yellow, black, magenta, and cyan. In the first year two sheets of each of the 24 pressmen's runs were taken out, and on each of the 4 colours 5 points across the sheets were measured. Thus a total of 240 measurements was made for each colour. In the following two years the variation across the sheets was not examined, but only the variation between machines, pressmen and sheets. For this purpose 20 sheets were taken out of each pressman's run, and the measurements were made at the middle of the colour bars on the sheets. Thus 480 measurements per colour were made in each of the years 1961 and 1962.

The statistical analysis of the results of the measurements has revealed that a general calculation of the mean squares over all three machines is not permissible, but for each source of variation it is possible to find accordance between the mean squares for at least two machines. Therefore, only a common calculation for the machines which show significance in comparison with each other was made. For the tests of the two last years it was shown that the densities through the individual runs do not show a normal distribution for all pressmen, but only for half of them, and the calculations were made only in these cases.

CONCLUSION

A comparison of the results of the individual years shows good agreement. However, the first year revealed a significant difference between machines for two colours, while the following years showed no significant difference, but perhaps future measurements will throw more light on this.

A direct comparison of all three years' results cannot be made, because the mean squares of the first year contain other coefficients than the mean squares of the following years. An F-test between the mean squares of the two last years shows, however, significance for all sources of variation at a 5 per cent level with the exception of "magenta, between sheets". Here again, however, there is only a slight difference.

The most important conclusion from these measurements might be reached by a comparison of the variations between sheets through the run and the variation between pressmen, because on the basis of these values it might be possible to evaluate the importance of automatic control of the ink supply. The variations across the sheets cannot be eliminated, because they are due to the layout of the job and mechanical conditions, and consequently to establish limits for this variation would serve no purpose.

From Table 14 it is evident that the variation between pressmen is a more important factor than the variation between sheets. The big difference in the variation between pressmen could first and foremost depend on the fact that it is quite insufficient to evaluate the ink supply by the means of the human eye.

The negligible values for the interaction between pressmen and points and between machines and points further show, that the reproducibility between pressmen and machines is good concerning the adjustments of the ink supply across the sheet, and so the significant deviations between pressmen are only due to different levels of the mean densities for the individual pressmen.

Only the yellow colour shows a slight interaction with the pressmen, which undoubtedly is due to the fact that the yellow is the first printed colour and difficult to adjust because of its brightness.

It must be pointed out, however, that although no trend in the optical densities has appeared during the printing of these relatively short runs of this job, the fact that a non-accidental change could appear during the printing of long runs cannot be disregarded. It is then possible that a change in densities could appear during the runs which approaches or even exceeds the pressman variation. A study of the alteration in densities between sheets during the printing of long runs will therefore be included in future research work.

This, however, does not alter the fact that the pressman variation is of significant magnitude, and that by simply controlling this variation a substantial degree of uncertainty in the printing can be removed. Owing to the fact that all printings in this investigation have been made without considerable intervention from the pressmen's side during the printing, this uncertainty must first and foremost be due to different starting points in the adjustment of the ink supply for the individual pressmen. Furthermore, the statistical analysis has shown that it is sufficient to make only one measurement at one point of the four colour bars.

Only for the yellow colour may there be some reason for controlling the densities across the sheets according to the slight, but significant, value of the interaction between points and pressmen.

Such a control in measuring the density on the colour bars of an approved proof print and the adjustment of the inking unit accordingly depends upon the fact, however, that the specimen sheet in its layout corresponds exactly to that of the practical printing job, and that it has been made upon the same type of paper and with the same printing ink as used during the actual printing.

A further condition is that the colours of the individual printing inks have been correctly selected beforehand, possibly by the use of a three-filter measurement of a proof print in comparison with a selected original.

If these conditions are acceptable, the following simple procedure for the adjustment of the ink supply in a one-colour sheet offset press can therefore be laid down as follows:

(1) Adjustment of the feed mechanism of the fountain roller in such a way that a measurement made with a densitometer at one point on the individual colour bars, printed at the front edge, shows a value which has been predetermined from a proof print. Allowances must be made for an alteration in density due to the drying of the inks.

(2) Subjective adjustments of the ink duct in such a way that the individual areas receive the correct amount of ink corresponding to uniform film, and in such a way that the adjustment of the blade remains undisturbed at the point where the density according to (1) has been adjusted.

(3) Density-control during printing of the stock to the extent given by frequency of press-stops, number of sheets, quality-demands, etc.

If there is no proof print available, the adjustment of the ink supply for the individual colours can be made by measuring at one point of the colour bars where the rest of the printing sheet in the longitudinal direction is unprinted. The adjustment can then be made by comparing the density value on the print with an empirical density value which has been predetermined for the type of paper and ink in question.

It appears from the above, that this simple procedure does not solve all practical problems relating to ink supply. But the method is practicable and controls—independently of other sources of error—one of the most important uncertainties in production.

REFERENCES

Owen L. Davies, *Design and Analysis of Industrial Experiments*, London, 1956.

H. O. Jørgensen and A. Wulff, *Farvemålinger. Den grafiske Højskoless måskrifter.* nr. 20, København, 1962.

DISCUSSION

Bruno: Our results agree with yours in general except that we would question the validity of using the density of one point to control the printing. We have found considerable wandering in density readings from sheet to sheet indicating that the densities should be arranged over 5–10 sheets. Crosfields have found this true in their Inkatron work and they now average the readings over 10 sheets before making any adjustments.

NIELSEN: It is important to select the two quantities "variation between pressure" and "variation between sheets" in the discussion of control. Our conclusion is that the pressman deviation is larger than the sheet-to-sheet deviation, and since the former is much easier to control due to the fact that a control for this means an adjustment of the level of the densities on the colour bars before the actual printing, it is possible to eliminate the biggest deviation with a simple densitometer measurement. What the Inkatron does is to remove the residual deviation, i.e. the sheet-to-sheet deviation. I agree that it is important to take care of the variations between the sheets on different points across the sheet as you have pointed out, but the sheet-to-sheet deviation is very expensive to control, because it needs automatic control, and I think it is impossible for printing shops with one colour machines or a few multi-colour machines to justify such investment.

CHRISTENSEN: I will just make a comment on Mr. Bruno's question. It must be emphasized that we have made a clear distinction between the variations through the pile, across the sheet, from machine to machine and from pressman to pressman. Many pressmen habitually adjust the ink supply all the time during run. Usually this is not necessary. Having adjusted the ink supply at the beginning of a run it is unnecessary to adjust the duct for a long period. Within this period the relative variation across the sheet will be constant from point to point. Therefore you only need to make control measurements at one point.

MYERS: (1) What kind of paper was used for these printing tests? (2) Was there any attempt to measure the difference in reflectance between the sheets of paper? It might be that if the inks are transparent there might be some significant variation in the density of the printed ink due to the effect of variations in the reflectance of the base paper.

NIELSEN: (1) Normal, uncoated offset paper was used. (2) No, we have not included the variations due to differences in reflectances of the sheets used, because we primarily wanted to investigate the variations, due to the influence of the pressman under practical printing conditions, but I agree that there may be such an influence of variation in the optical properties of the sheets.

BANKS: In selecting data for the pressmen according to whether the results were normally distributed or not, what proportion were selected?

NIELSEN: Four pressmen from each group of eight show a normal distribution.

CARLSSON: (1) Was it possible for you to establish any special difference between the two groups of pressmen, the one with normal distribution and the other with non-normal distribution of the densities. Was there any difference between them in skill, experience or colour aptitude? (2) I suppose that the pressmen had to match their prints against a proof approved by an overseer. Was it the same overseer during all the runs, otherwise you may have another source of variation.

NIELSEN: (1) I think this is an important question, because it concerns the details of the printing operation. Unfortunately we could not follow all the printings, but we will certainly have to study the printing procedure in a more detailed way to find out how and why the pressmen adjust the ink supply. (2) The pressmen had no overseer, but made their own judgments.

WOODS: Since the pressman must make a visual judgment of colour match, could we have details of the conditions under which he was working, particularly lighting, both with regard to quality and quantity?

NIELSEN: The pressmen had to judge the densities in normal daylight. It must also be emphasized that the investigation concerns a comparison between press print and proof print.

YULE: (1) Was the pressman furnished with a set of progressives and asked to match them without making any density measurements? (2) The results given, refer to variations in the press runs. Were any comparisons made between the press runs and the proofs?

NIELSEN: (1) The pressmen as a whole were, for each year, furnished with only one set selected from three sets of progressives printed in the three machines separately. The pressmen were asked to match the selected set without density measurements.

(2) Generally no comparisons were made between the press runs and the proofs, but it can be pointed out that the mean densities for black and yellow in 1962 were very close to the mean densities for the same colours, calculated over all prints in the set of progressives, and the mean densities for cyan and magenta were lower than the mean densities for the progressives.

Taking the standard deviations into consideration, however, the difference between production and proof prints seems to be negligible.

THE USE OF CONVENTIONAL CONTACT SCREENS FOR REPRODUCING HALFTONES DIRECTLY ON ZINC OXIDE–RESIN COATED LITHOGRAPHIC PLATES

by FREDERICK C. MYERS
Reproduction Branch, Graphics Division U.S. Army Engineer Geodesy, Intelligence and Mapping Research and Development Agency
Fort Belvoir, Virginia, U.S.A.

1. BACKGROUND

THE U.S. Army Engineer Geodesy, Intelligence and Mapping Research and Development Agency (USAEGIMRADA) is located at Fort Belvoir, Virginia, U.S.A. It is the principal field agency of the U.S. Army Corps of Engineers for the accomplishment of research and development of equipment, procedures and techniques in the specific field of geodesy, engineer intelligence and mapping for application to troop and to base plant operations. The organization consists of six working divisions. The Graphics Division has the responsibility for conducting applied research, development, design and testing of cartographic, map reproduction and display systems, equipment and techniques including terrain model and other related requirements for the collation, preparation, dissemination and display of topographic information.

The Corps of Engineers has been actively engaged in research and development in the field of xerography and electro-photography for eleven years. The original work was concentrated on developing a suitable technique for reproducing lithographic plates by the use of a selenium coated aluminum plate. Breadboard equipment was developed for processing a toner image on the selenium xerographic plate and then transferring this image to a grained zinc lithographic plate. However, this process had one major limitation in that it was incapable of reproducing halftones, necessary for the photomap phase of topographic mapping. For this reason, it was decided to investigate the zinc oxide-resin binder coating system for possible application in preparing lithographic press plates.

However, as this work progressed, it was noted that the main advantages of the electrophotographic process was not in the preparation of lithographic press plates, but in the development of a complete electrostatic printing system. This work leading up to an electrostatic printing system is covered in a paper titled, "Electrostatic Procedures for Map Reproduction" by John T. Pennington. This paper was presented at the Second International Course for Map Printing and Reproduction in October 1960 at Munich, Germany.

The purpose of this paper is to discuss a specific laboratory approach to the problem of preparing halftone images using the electrophotographic process on metal plates containing a zinc oxide-resin coating. Much of the work reported in this paper was done under sub-contract by Battelle Memorial Institute, Columbus, Ohio. The prime contractor was Xerox Incorporated, Rochester, New York.

Unlike the conventional bichromated colloid or light sensitive diazo process, the electrophotographic process depends on a physical phenomenon, while the former depends on a chemical phenomenon. The heart of the electrophotographic process is a photoconductive coating. In this case the coating consists of zinc oxide suspended in an insulating binder. This coating has the unique property of being an electrical insulator in the absence of light and an electrical conductor in the presence of light. Thus, a plate carrying this coating is first charged or sensitized by passing it under a corona charging device to receive a blanket negative electrostatic charge. The next step is to expose the plate to a light image. The resulting latent electrostatic image is developed by using a magnet containing iron filings and a pigmented thermoplastic toner. This technique, known as magnetic brush development attracts toner to the latent electrostatic image, thus resulting in a visible image. This image is next placed in an oven to fuse or fix the image so that it is permanently bonded to the coating surface. The plate is then treated with a chemical solution to make the non-image areas water receptive. The plate is then ready to print. More details on preparing and processing these plates are given later in this paper.

The plates used in these tests were dye sensitized with rose bengal dye. The spectral sensitivity of these coatings are such that there are two peaks of maximum sensitivity. The first is in the near ultraviolet and the second at approximately 5500A°. There is little sensitivity to light between 4000A° to 5000A°, and essentially no sensitivity to light above 6200A°.

The coating formulation consisted of 1000 parts Green Seal No. 8 zinc oxide manufactured by the New Jersey Zinc Company. The resin binder was 400 g of Silicone SR-82 resin manufactured by the General Electric Company, and 1 part rose bengal dye. All weights are on a dry-weight basis.

2. SCREENING BY CONTACT

The first attempts to prepare halftones directly on zinc oxide-resin coated plates utilized contact exposure techniques. The plate was charged and then exposed under a glass plate, placing a magenta contact screen between the continuous-tone positive and the coated plate. The light source was 100 W incandescent light with a color temperature of 2850°K, 27 in. from the plate. The light intensity at the plate was 20 ft-c. When using a high contrast continuous-tone transparency with a density range of around 1.5–2.0, two

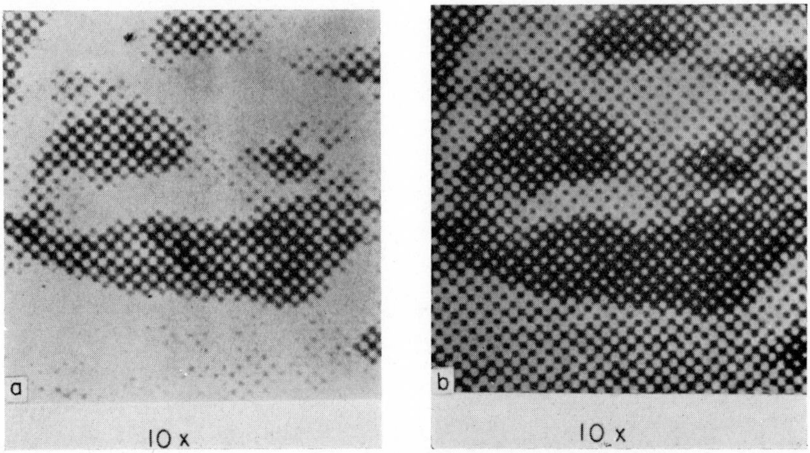

Normal Exposure — Flash Exposure followed by Normal Exposure

Fig. 1. Photomacrographs showing the improvement obtained in halftoning a xerographic image by using the "flash" exposure technique.

types of results were noted. Either the shadow areas developed as solids containing no dot structure, or the highlight areas contained no dots. Attempts to eliminate these defects by varying the exposure time were not successful.

To help alleviate these defects, a two step exposure technique was tried. With this technique, a short exposure or flash exposure of about 3/4 sec was made using only the halftone screen. Following this a second and longer exposure was made with the screen and continuous-tone transparency placed over the plate. The effect of the flash exposure is shown in Fig. 1. A 150 line magenta contact screen was used for these tests. It can be observed from examining the photographic enlargements of identical areas that the flash exposure did result in reproducing dots in the highlight areas.

In a further effort to reduce the time for exposing images on zinc oxide-resin coated plates, a 150 line Eastman Kodak gray contact screen was obtained. Using the gray contact screen, contact exposures were made using the same procedures as with the magenta contact screen. Although early tests suggested some possible advantages of the gray contact screen over the magenta contact screen in terms of the exposure time required, further tests indicated little difference in the required exposure. There did appear to be some difference in dot sharpness between images made with the two screens. This can be best demonstrated by observing Fig. 2, showing photographs

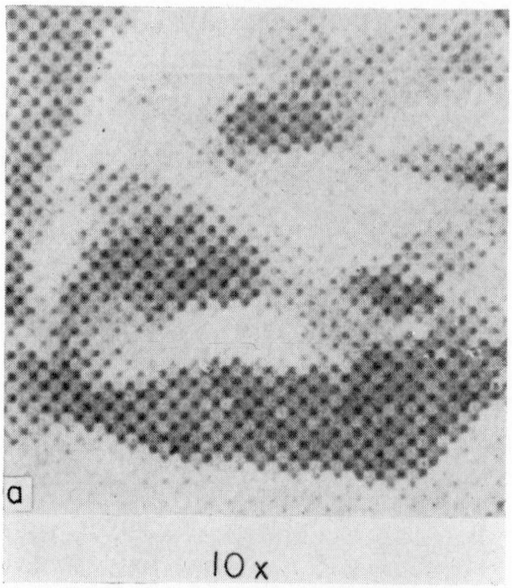

Zinc Oxide Plate; Magenta Screen.

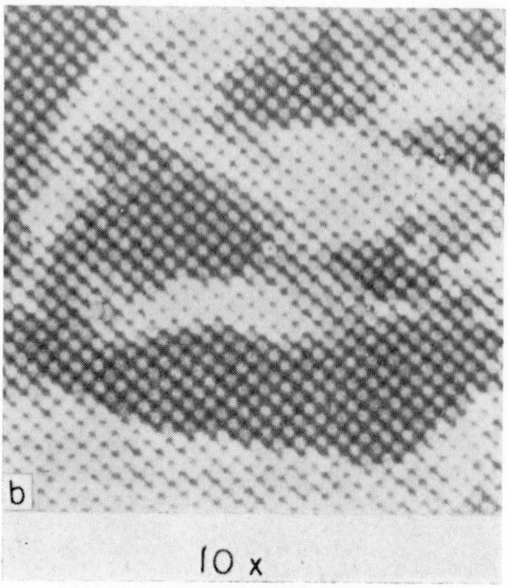

Zinc Oxide Plate; Gray Screen.

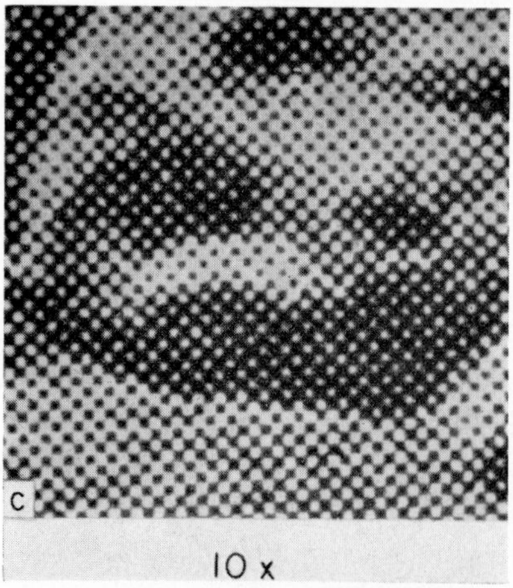

Zinc Oxide–Rose Bengal Plate; Magenta Screen.

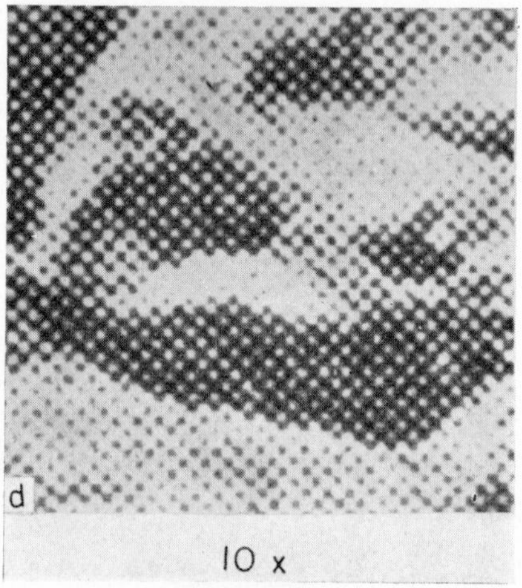

Zinc Oxide–Rose Bengal Plate; Gray Screen.

Fig. 2. Photomacrography comparing the image quality obtained with a magenta contact screen and that obtained with a gray contact screen. The original was a high-contrast continuous-tone positive transparency.

enlarged 10 times comparing the results of tests with the two screens. In these examples, plates a and b were given identical exposures, as were plates c and d. It can be observed that although contrast appears to be a bit higher with the gray screen, the magenta screen resulted in much sharper dots and less background.

3. SCREENING BY PROJECTION

The contact screening technique proved to be rather difficult since great care had to be taken to avoid disturbing the contact screen while removing

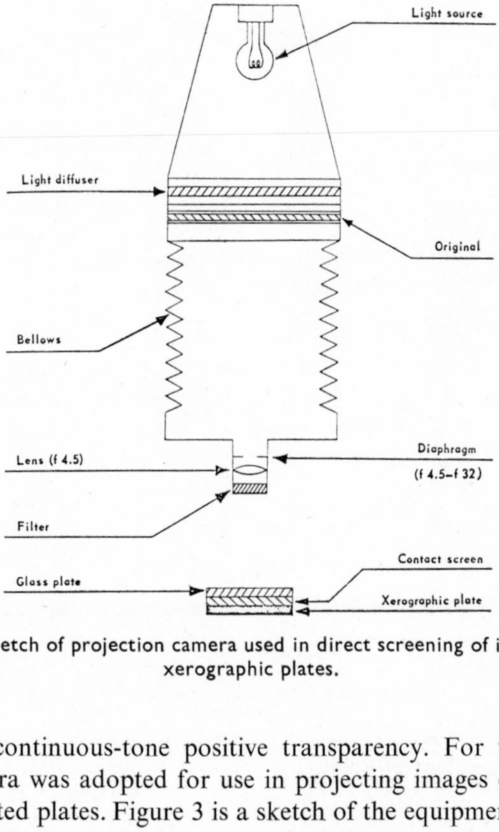

Fig. 3. Sketch of projection camera used in direct screening of images on xerographic plates.

the overlying continuous-tone positive transparency. For this reason, an enlarging camera was adopted for use in projecting images directly on zinc oxide-resin coated plates. Figure 3 is a sketch of the equipment next used for tests. The continuous-tone transparency, held flat between two glass plates, is placed in a projector below a frosted-glass light diffuser. This section through which the original is placed is light tight. The lens diaphragm is set at the desired stop opening. The desired filter is inserted in the lens assembly. The image is then focused onto the plane of the coated plate. The charged plate is placed in position and the desired contact screen is placed over it and covered with a glass plate to insure contact.

In operation, the exposure for subject detail is made first. Then the continuous-tone transparency is removed from the projector and the opening

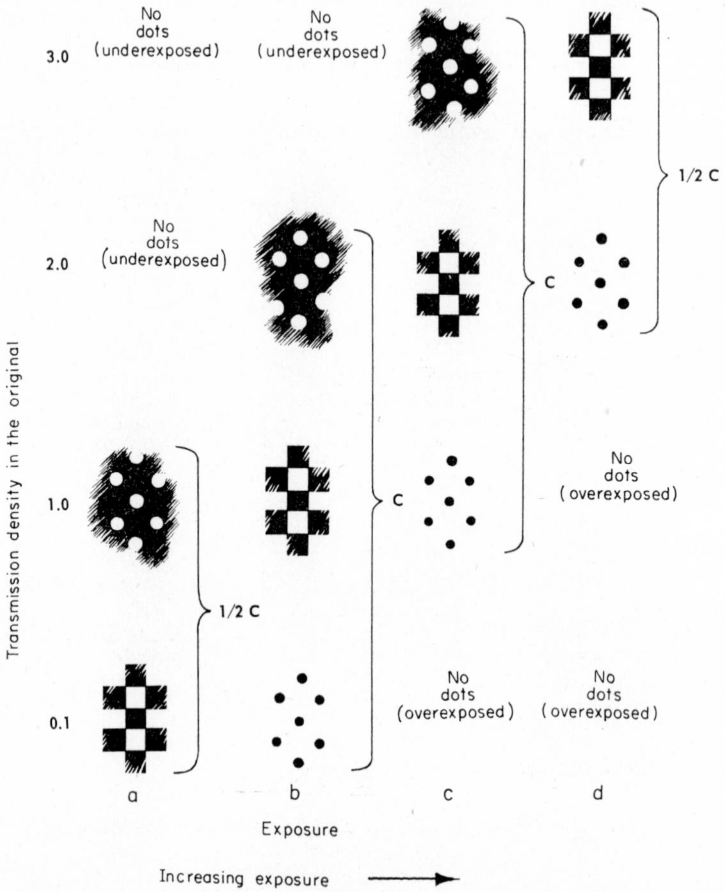

Fig. 4. Nature of screened images obtainable when exposing zinc oxide–silicone–rose bengal plates with white light through a magenta contact screen.

resealed prior to the flash exposure. The flash exposure may be made at same *f*-stop number or a smaller opening than the detail exposure. In effect, the projector may function in a manner similar to that of a process camera, with the advantage that more light is available than is normally found at the image plane of a copy camera. The light intensity may be varied at the image plane between 0.2 and 2.0 ft-c, the exact amount being controlled by a Variac wired into the light source.

Figure 4 shows the general relationship obtained when exposing zinc oxide-resin coated plates with white light through a magenta contact screen. When a photographic step-wedge was substituted for the continuous-tone transparency, the optimum exposure conditions produced halftone images corresponding to a transmission density range of 2.0. The optimum exposure

Fig. 5. Photographs of directly screened 150 line images of high contrast subjects using white light and a magenta contact screen.

would result in the highlight dot approximately corresponding to a density of 0.1 and the shadow dot would correspond to a density of 2.0. This would be approximately equal to exposure b of Fig. 4. Additional exposure would result in the condition shown in exposure c of Fig. 4 where the highlight dot corresponded to a density of 1.0 and the shadow dot would correspond to a density of 3.0.

Figure 5 shows photographs of plates containing images screened using a 150 line magenta contact screen and shows the effects of length of exposure. Figures 5a and 5b are approximately equivalent to exposure a of Figure 4, and 5c and 5d are approximately equivalent to exposure b of Figure 4. The density range of the step-wedge was 0.1 to 3.0 and the density range of the aerial transparency was 0.1 to 2.1. In addition, in Figures 5a and 5b, the areas corresponding to the highlight areas of the original contained approximately 50 per cent. This suggested that these areas were underexposed dots. Figures 5c and 5d would represent the optimum exposure.

It is obvious from the preceding tests, that the use only of a magenta contact screen and white light utilizing a basic exposure and a flash exposure

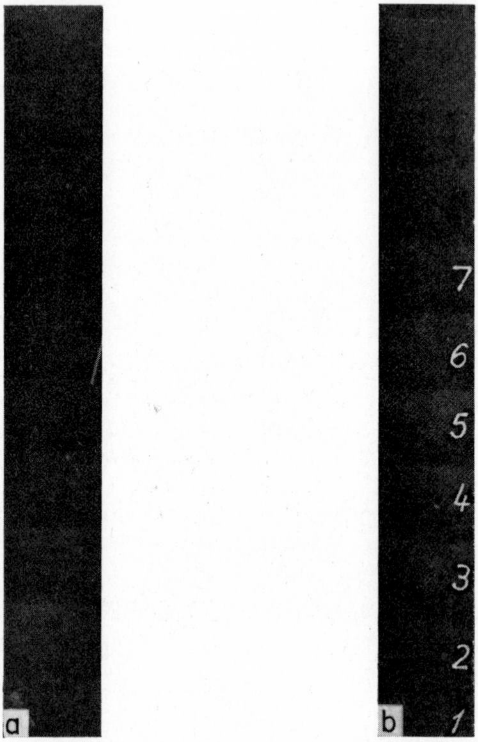

Standard exposure without filter. Standard exposure × 16 with filter.

Fig. 6. Illustration of the increase in contrast of screened images on zinc oxide–rose bengal plates by use of a No. 31 Wratten red filter.

did not produce sufficient contrast for the normal range of continuous-tone transparencies. For this reason, it was decided to use filters to vary the contrast of the resulting print.

One of the first filters evaluated for increasing contrast was the Eastman Kodak Company No. 31 red filter. This filter has a fairly high transmittance between 3200A° and 4800A° and beyond 6000A°. Figure 6 shows photographs of directly screened 150 line images and clearly shows the effect of the No. 31 red filter. It can be seen that the red filter increased contrast appreciably. The ten step gray scale reproduced in Figure 5a has halftone dots ranging from approximately 25 per cent to approximately 80 per cent, while Fig. 5b, reproduced using the red filter resulted in halftone dots ranging from 25 per cent to a complete solid.

In an attempt to decrease contrast, it was decided to use an Eastman Kodak Company Wratten K2 filter (No. 8). This filter is characterized by a high transmittance beyond 4800A°. The effect of a yellow filter in decreasing contrast was less dramatic than the use of the red filter to increase contrast. However, preliminary experiments did show some minor decrease in contrast.

4. REDUCTION TO PRACTICE

Following the above work which was performed by Battelle Memorial Institute, an in-house effort was established to reduce this information to practice. By use of the reproduction camera and a 133 line magenta contact

Fig. 7. Approximately 4000th impression from a zinc oxide resin coated plate halftoned directly in the camera using a 133 line, magenta-contact screen.

screen, a more satisfactory halftoning technique was devised. A further evaluation of the Battelle procedures disclosed that a modification of the milling, treating and printing procedures was required. The coating milling time was reduced and the treating solution modified to one half the strength used by Battelle. A sodium ferrocyanide-acetic acid-glycerine fountain solution was substituted for a proprietary fountain solution. In addition, variations in the procedure for halftoning directly in the camera were evaluated, until the best exposure combinations for the basic and flash exposure were obtained. Finally procedures were developed for processing 10 by 15 in. coated plates in the camera. Runs of up to 5000 copies were run on a duplicator resulting in printed images of fair quality. A photographic reproduction of a sample print, showing approximately the 4000th impression is shown as Fig. 7. This photograph demonstrates the feasibility of this process.

Since this work may have possible application as a technique for reproducing halftone images directly in the camera, the complete processing procedure as well as the equipment used, is given.

5. DESCRIPTION OF THE EQUIPMENT

The equipment used in processing the zinc oxide resin coated plates is described in the following paragraphs.

a. *Milling equipment.* The ball mill used for mixing and grinding an intimate mixture of zinc oxide dispersed in silicone resin consisted of a size 00,

Fig. 8. Coating device.

Roaflox Barundum-fortified mill jar of 0.30 gal capacity. The jar was rotated at 104 r.p.m. The grinding media used was $\frac{1}{2}$-in.-diameter porcelain balls.

b. *Coating equipment.* The coating device (Fig. 8) uses a simple flow-coating technique for applying a zinc oxide-silicone coating on an aluminum plate. The device consists of a piece of cardboard 13 in. wide and 18 in. high to which is attached a metal plate held firmly at the top with a 2-in.-wide metal clip. The cardboard-support coating rack was placed in an aluminum tray 14 in. long, 3 in. wide, and 3 in. high with the top of the cardboard supported against a wall. The tray catches the excess coating applied to the plate. The desired angle for coating the plate was obtained by moving the bottom of the cardboard and tray away from the wall and measuring the desired angle with a 6-in. semicircle protractor.

Fig. 9. Drying and fusing oven.

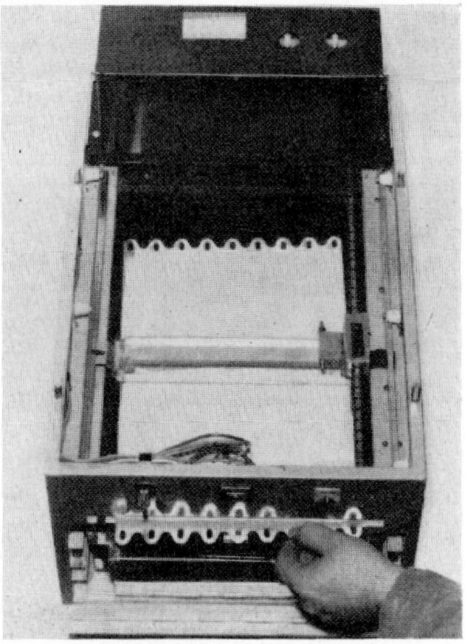

Fig. 10. Charging device.

c. *Drying and fusing oven.* The drying and fusing oven (Fig. 9) is used for drying the zinc oxide used in the coating formulation, drying the coated plate, and also for fusing the developed image on the coated plate. The temperature in the oven is thermostatically controlled over the range of 150°F to 550°F. A mercury-type thermometer is inserted through the top of the oven for measuring the inside temperature.

d. *Charging device.* The charging device for placing a negative charge on the duplicator-size binder plate (Fig. 10) is a Model D processor unit manufactured by Xerox Incorporated. It was modified to provide either a positive or negative potential on the xerographic plate by the operation of a switch located on the rear of the unit. The unit operates on 115 V, 60-cycle current. The storage shelf normally placed over the charging unit was removed as shown in Fig. 10.

The high-voltage power supply which supplies direct current to both the corona wires and ground grid is a complete unit attached to the back of the charging unit. The corona wires are a series of three wires located approximately $\frac{3}{4}$-in. above the plate and perpendicular to the direction of travel of the plate. Approximately $\frac{3}{16}$-in. beneath the corona wires is a series of wires that constitute the ground grid. The potential on the corona wires was preset at −8500 V and the potential on the ground grid was preset at −900 V, both in respect to ground. The charging wires, a complete-assembly containing both the corona wires and ground grid, are driven at the fixed rate of 18 f.p.m. by a reversing lead screw. The movement of the wires is stopped after each double pass, and the movement is started again by pressing a microswitch at the front of the instrument.

e. *Reproduction camera.* The reproduction camera (Fig. 11) is used for processing halftones directly on the coated plates. It is a standard, mobile,

Fig. 11. Reproduction camera for direct screening of images.

24- by 30-in. processing camera. The back of the camera, with a duplicator-size binder plate attached to the vacuum back, is shown in Fig. 11. A 133-line, magenta contact screen manufactured by Eastman Kodak was used to prepare the halftones.

f. *Developing device.* The magnetic brush (Fig. 12) is used for developing the latent electrostatic image on the coated plates. It consists of a permanent iron magnet, 6 in. long by 1 in. wide by $\frac{1}{2}$-in. thick, which attracts a mixture of iron filings and xerographic toner. The device is used as a brush to apply the toner.

g. *Treating tray.* The treating tray (Fig. 13) contains the chemical solution for converting the non-image areas of the plate from water-repellent to water-receptive areas. The tray is 11 in. wide by 16 in. long by 5 in. deep and is porcelain coated.

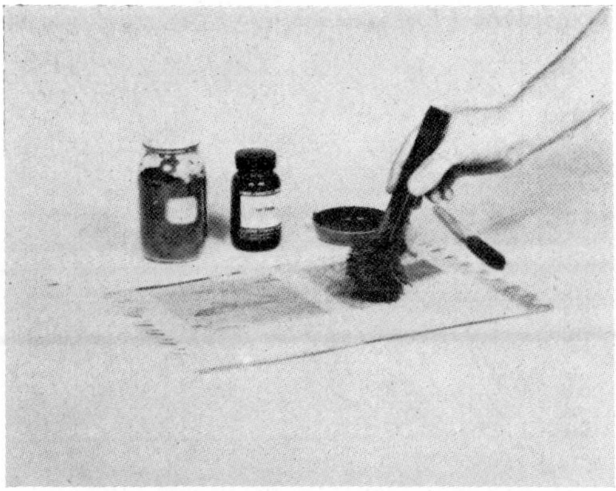

Fig. 12. Magnetic brush developing device.

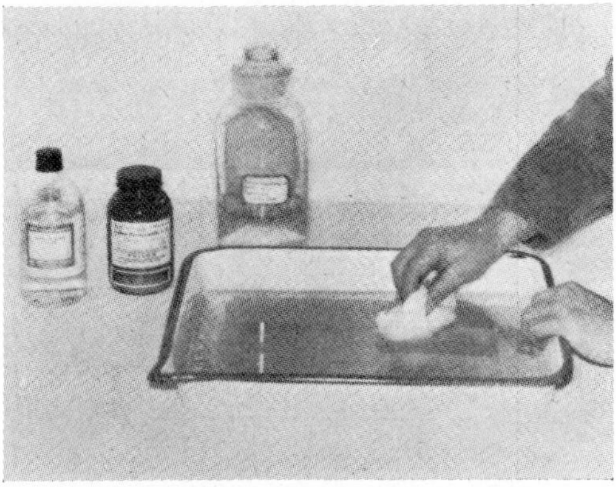

Fig. 13. Chemical treating of binder plates.

h. *Supplies.* The supplies used in this evaluation are described in the following paragraphs:

(1) Coating supplies

(*a*) Zinc oxide, Florence Brand, Green Seal No. 8, New Jersey Zinc Company.
(*b*) Silicone Resin, No. SR-82, 60 per cent solids, General Electric Company.
(*c*) Rose Bengal Dye.
(*d*) Toluene, Certified, ACS.
(*e*) Methyl Alcohol, ACS.

(2) Treating supplies

(*a*) Sodium ferrocyanide, C.P. grade.
(*b*) Acetic Acid, Glacial, Reagent grade.
(*c*) Cotton, absorbent, grade B.

(3) Developing supplies

(*a*) Iron metal powder, electrolytic, Catalog No. I-60 Fisher, through 200 mesh, retained on 325 mesh.
(*b*) Experimental xerographic toner BXT-34, Battelle Memorial Institute.

(4) Other supplies

(*a*) Aluminium plates, 10 × 15$\frac{1}{4}$ × 0.006 in. thick, ungrained, for 1250 Multilith, National Plate Grainers, Washington, D.C.
(*b*) Ink, lithographic offset, black.
(*c*) Glycerine.

6. PROCESSING PROCEDURES

The processing procedures, as modified at USAERDL and used for preparing binder plates, are described in the following subparagraphs.

a. Coating procedure

The procedure for preparing the photoconductive coating and for coating the plates by use of a flow-coating technique was as follows:

(1) *Drying zinc oxide*. The zinc oxide was dried by placing it in an oven for 2 hr at 250°F to remove excess moisture. It was then removed and weighed immediately.

(2) *Coating formulation*. The following ingredients were weighed and added to a 0.3-gal, porcelain-jar ball mill: zinc oxide, 300 g; silicone resin, 200 g; toluene, 125 g; porcelain balls, 600 g.

(3) *Milling*. The jar was sealed and the formulation was milled at 104 r.p.m. for 3 hr and 40 min. Ten cubic centimeters of a 2.4 per cent solution of rose bengal in absolute methanol was added and the mixture was milled for 5 min. At this point, 125 g of toluene was added and the mixture was again milled for 5 min making a total milling time of 3 hr and 50 min. The mill was discharged by the coating being filtered through a 60-mesh screen and the coating being funneled into a 1-quart aspirator bottle. The coating was then stored in the dark until used.

(4) *Coating and drying*. One 10- by 15$\frac{1}{4}$ by 0.006-in.-thick aluminum plate was placed on the coating rack and fastened securely at the top with a metal clip. The rack was tilted until the angle of the plate was 70 degrees from the horizontal as measured with a protractor. The bottom of the rack was placed inside a catch tray. The plate was coated by the aspirator bottle being raised slowly, which allowed the coating to flow by gravity through a plastic tube attached to the bottom of the bottle.

The tube was gradually moved across the top of the plate until the entire plate was coated (see Fig. 8). The excess coating was allowed to run off the plate for approximately 20 sec. Then the plate was placed on a flat surface in the dark. This procedure resulted in a coating thickness of 0.0007 in. The coating procedure was repeated until the required number of plates was produced. By returning the excess coating from the catch tray to the aspirator bottle, one batch of coating was sufficient to coat approximately 40 plates. The plates were dried by placing them in the oven (Fig. 9) for 30 min at 200°F. After the coated plates were removed from the oven, they were stored at a relative humidity of 50 per cent or less for 24 hr. The plates were then ready for processing xerographic images.

b. **Platemaking procedure**

The platemaking procedure was as follows:

(1) *Charging.* The coated plates were removed from the storeroom and placed in a box in the darkroom. All lights but the red safelights in the darkroom were turned off. The plates were charged in the charging unit by inserting the plates coated side up under the charging wires and making three double passes of the charging wires over the surface of each of the plates (see Fig. 10). The potential on the corona wires was −8500 V and the potential on the ground grid was −900 V. This produced a potential of −1200 V on the plate in respect to ground potential as measured with a Keithley Model 210 Electrometer.

(2) *Exposing.* The procedure for preparing halftones directly by projection exposure was to place the plates on the vacuum back of the reproduction camera immediately after charging (see Fig. 11). A 133-line, magenta contact screen was placed over the plate. With a continuous-tone print as the subject, the plates were given a basic exposure of 35 units with a Luxometer light-integrating unit. The lens opening was $f/11$ and two 35 A carbon-arc lamps provided illumination. One unit exposure is an arbitrary unit which is approximately equivalent to one second with a light intensity of 1800 ft-c on the copyboard. Immediately following the basic exposure, the plates were given a flash exposure of 25 units at $f/11$ by use of white paper over the copy and a No. 30 rose-colored gelatin filter over the camera lens. Immediately after the flash exposure, the plates were removed from the camera and placed on a table.

(3) *Developing.* While still under red safelight conditions, the plates were removed from the camera and developed with the magnetic brush with one part BXT-34* xerographic toner and 30 parts of −200 + 325 mesh iron filings (see Fig. 12). Development consisted of making two passes in a direction parallel to the length of the plate and two passes parallel to the width of the plate. Care was taken to see that the metal part of the magnetic brush did not come into contact with the plate.

* BXT-34 toner is a proprietary toner of Xerox Incorporated.

(4) *Fusing*. After development of the plates, the lights were turned on and the plates were examined visually for complete development. The plates were then placed in an oven (Fig. 9) for 90 sec at 375°F to fuse the toner permanently to the plates. After the fusing process, the plates were stored in a box.

(5) *Treating*. After the plates were processed with toner images, the plates were chemically treated (Fig. 13). The purpose of this step was to convert the coating in the non-image areas to a water-receptive surface in preparation for printing. The treating solution consisted of sodium ferrocyanide and acetic acid prepared by dissolving 30 g of sodium ferrocyanide in 180 cm^3 of warm water and 12 cm^3 of glacial acid in 48 cm^3 water. Twenty cubic centimeters of the sodium ferrocyanide solution, 6.0 cm^3 of acetic acid solution and 1152 cm^3 of water were put into a photographic tray and mixed. The plates were immersed for 30 sec in the tray containing the treating solution. At the same time, the surface of the plate was rubbed lightly with cotton to remove air bubbles. After 30 sec, the plate was removed from the solution, immediately placed in a processing sink and flushed with water, and rubbed lightly with fresh cotton. Following this, the plate was fan dried and stored in a box.

(6) *Printing*. Printing tests were conducted by mounting the plates in the model 1250 Multilith. Just before the plates were printed, they were moistened with fountain solution. Contents of the fountain solution were: sodium ferrocyanide (0.5 per cent by weight), glacial acetic acid (0.2 per cent by volume), and glycerine (1.0 per cent by volume). The damper rollers were dropped first, followed by the ink rollers. The remaining procedure was identical with that used for printing conventional plates.

7. AREAS FOR FURTHER WORK

Although the feasibility of this process was demonstrated, reproductions from these plates were only of fair image quality. Halftone dots were not sharp and well defined, but appeared to be fuzzy along the edges. It is believed that this is due primarily to the fact that these coatings had a rather low contrast. In fact, measurements made on these coatings indicated a gamma of around 2.5. It is expected that a gamma of at least 7.0 would be required before sharp and well defined halftone images can be obtained by direct halftoning techniques.

A second area requiring additional work is in the development of improved toners for use with this process. One shortcoming of the toner used in these tests was the fact that this material appeared to be compatible with the silicone resin used in the coating formulation. In addition, it was somewhat soluble in gum arabic and normal press solvents such as varsol. Due to these limitations, the plate could not be gummed or "wet washed" to clean up the non-printing areas, without adversely affecting the image areas. The compatibility of the toner with the silicone resin appeared to be the major problem and could explain the fact that the highlight areas would not print after approximately 10,000 impressions. One explanation for this is that the mixing of the BXT-34 toner and zinc oxide-silicone coating into a complex chemical material allowed the gradual transformation of halftone dots to water-receptive surfaces by repeated and prolonged contact with the sodium ferrocyanide and acetic acid in the fountain solution. Such toner requirements would be necessary not only for charged area development using positive originals, but uncharged area development using negative originals. Finally, for reproducing 300 line halftones by the direct screening technique, toners of very small particle size, probably in the range of 1 μ would be required.

Another area requiring work relates to the adverse effect of moisture in the air on the process. As the relative humidity of the air increases, the air becomes a better conductor of electricity. The increased moisture in the air thus aids in removing the charge from the surface of the plate. In addition, if the zinc oxide particles are not completely covered with the silicone resin, the particles will absorb some atmospheric moisture lowering the resistivity of the coating. For these tests, the atmospheric moisture became a problem above approximately 50 per cent relative humidity at around 70°F. Under this condition, sufficient charge was removed from the plate surface to produce inferior images. The period of time between charging the plate, exposing it in the camera and developing the plate was 5 min. During this period and under these conditions the charge on the plate would drop to less than one third of the original charge. It would therefore appear necessary to utilize a photoconductor-resin combination that was insensitive to the effects of atmospheric moisture.

A further area requiring some effort is the development of satisfactory techniques for making deletions or corrections directly to the plate. Deletions can be made fairly easily before the toner is heated and thus fixed to the plate. However, after the toner is fixed to the coating surface, it becomes difficult to remove the toner, without damaging the coating.

Finally, it might be desirable to investigate the screening problem from the view point of designing a screen specifically for use in this process. The contact screens evaluated were designed specifically for use with silver halide emulsions, not photoconductive coatings. It might be expected that such an investigation could produce some very fruitful results.

DISCUSSION

ZETTLEMOYER: Contrary to what you suggested, I would expect zinc ferrocyanide to be hydrophobic, as ferriferrocyanide is. Perhaps a hydroxyferrocyanide is formed. Did you study the character of zinc ferrocyanide separately?

MYERS: Battelle Memorial Institute, in experimenting with the sodium ferrocyanide-acetic acid treating solution suggested that the zinc oxide in the coating reacted with the treating solution to form a water receptive zinc ferrocyanide complex on the coating surface. However, it is quite possible that some other ferrocyanide complex, such as a hydroxyferrocyanide may be formed in this reaction.

ADAMS: Have you considered making continuous tone plates for photo-gelatine printing using an electrostatic process?

MYERS: We have looked at the continuous tone possibilities of these coatings because they have application to the reproduction of photo images as part of our work in developing an electrostatic printing process. This resulted in reproducing 8–10 steps of a gray scale thus showing continuous tone possibilities.

YULE: If no flash gave too high contrast, and a flash exposure gave too low contrast, would an intermediate amount of flash give the correct contrast, without the necessity for using filters?

MYERS: Very likely it would—this should be tried.

BRUNO: (1) Have you tried dispersing materials other than silicones?
(2) Did you try liquid toners or developers?

MYERS: (1) We found one particular class of vinyl resins that showed considerable promise. They are normally water receptive and do not, therefore, require a chemical treatment.
(2) Yes, we did. However, the kerosene type liquids, such as varsol, leave a greasy and ink receptive residue. This residue causes the non-image areas to print. Metcalf and Wright in Australia must be mentioned for they have made some excellent contributions to liquid development.

BRUNO: A liquid developed electrophotographic process is being developed in the U.S.A. for making proofs from positive halftones.

WALKER: Did you have an opportunity to study the effect of changing the pigment to binder ratio? One might expect a definite effect on photographic speed and other properties.

MYERS: Yes. Battelle did some extensive work on the pigment to binder ratios, in which the ratio was varied from about 1:1 to 10:1. At the higher ratios, it was found that the coating would not adhere to the plate during printing; at the lower ratios, image quality was poor. It has also been found that the photographic speed was affected.

BANKS: Does not the peeling away of the contact screen introduce effects due to static?

MYERS: Yes, it does. Our experience using a vacuum frame for exposure indicates that a vacuum of more than 5 inches of mercury adversely affects image quality.

CHRISTENSEN: Can the finished plate be recharged as in xerographic printing?

MYERS: No, because the sodium ferrocyanide-acetic acid treatment adversely affects the photoconductive properties of the coating. In effect, this treatment poisons the coating and prevents its further use.

INK TRANSFER IN THE AREA OF HALFTONE DOTS

by KURT WAGENBAUER
Institut für Druckmaschinen und Druckverfahren der Technischen Hochschule Darmstadt

IN order to study the processes which take place during ink splitting, Zettlemoyer, Walker, Fetsko and Myers[1], Sjodahl[2], Howard and Jones[3] as well as Blokhuis[4] have used high speed photographic methods.

In this paper we describe briefly an ultra high speed method using a microscope. The essential part of this device is the circulating microscope connected to an ink splitting apparatus. The microscope is supplied with a rotating light by means of a suitable system from a controllable spark light source.[5] The arrangement is shown in Fig. 1, while Fig. 2 shows the optical details. In this way an isolated halftone dot corresponding to a dot area of a letterpress forme remains in the field of vision of the microscope during rotation of the cylinder. The testing apparatus which is connected to a printing press is further provided with an inking device and a means of measuring the surface temperature of the cylinder during operation. Some preliminary results are illustrated in Figs. 3, 4 and 5.

TESTING RESULTS

As can be seen, ink splitting procedures involve the formation and deformation of filaments. From a knowledge of the time intervals of the photographs and the possibility of varying these, the times taken to reach the maximum string length during break-off and for the re-formation of the broken string with different inks and varying test conditions, can be studied.

Such studies will be pursued in the near future. With the aid of this device the ink transfer process in rotogravure will also be studied.

I should like to take this opportunity of thanking all those who contributed to the success of this study. Special thanks are due to Professor Dr. Eschenbach and his staff, and to the Forschungsgesellschaft Druckmaschinen.

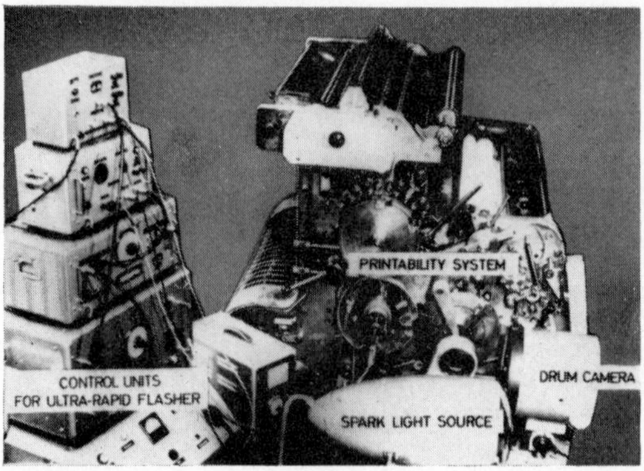

Fig. 1.

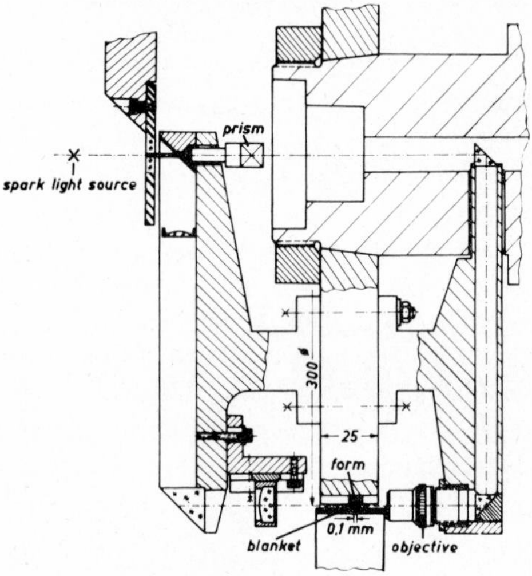

Fig. 2.

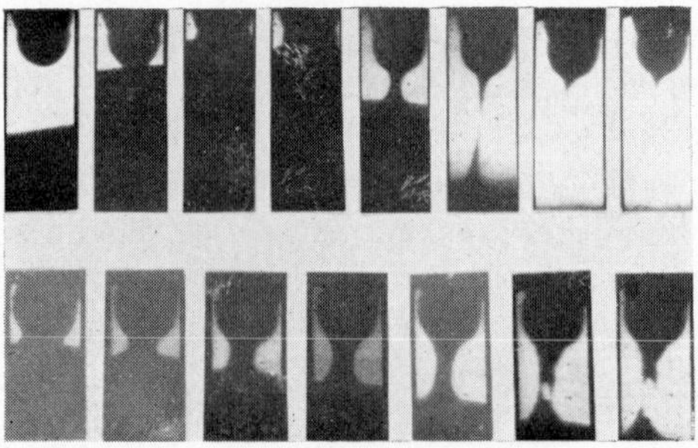

Fig. 3.

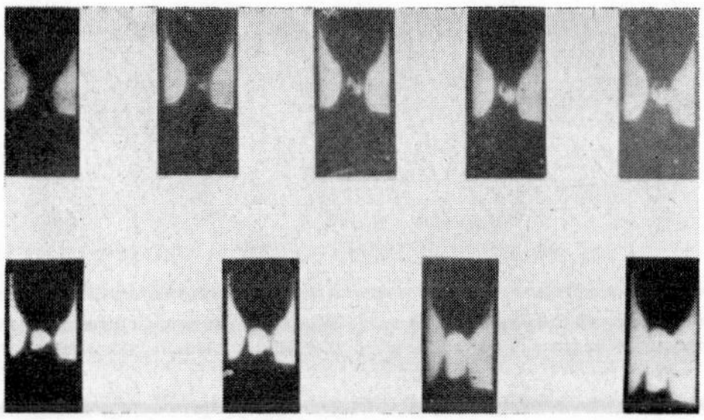

Fig. 4.

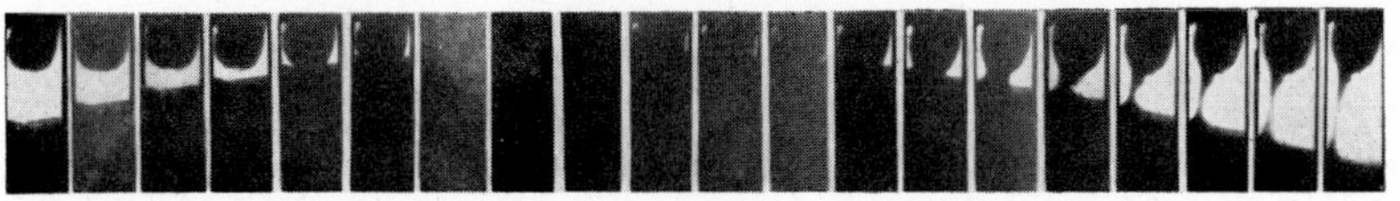

Fig. 5.

REFERENCES

1. A. C. ZETTLEMOYER, W. C. WALKER, I. M. FETSKO and R. R. MYERS, *The Transfer of Printing Inks*. International Bulletin No. 73, 60–64; 70, 1956.
2. L. H. SJODAHL, *Amer. Ink Maker* **29,** 31, 1951.
3. J. W. HOWARD and W. L. JONES, High speed camera studies of ink misting. *TAGA* part B, 153–162; 193–195, 1957.
4. G. BLOKHUIS, *Influence of certain factors on the printing results*. International Bulletin No. 73, 64–70, 1956.
5. F. FRUNGEL, Ein neues Hochfrequenz-Blitzgerat für lange Blitzserien (25000/sec) sowie Anwendungen gesteuerter Einzelblitze in der Spannungsoptik. *Z. Angew. Phys*, 8. Bd. 2. Heft, S.86–90, 1956.

DISCUSSION

MYERS: Your illustrations, in most cases, show the ink film as splitting into a single filament. Is this always so or do you sometimes obtain many filaments?

WAGENBAUER: During ink splitting in the area of halftone dots both forms of splitting occur.

BANKS: The behaviour shown in the series 4 photographs has been discussed by Banks and Mill (*J. Coll. Sci.*, 1953). It clearly shows that the extended "film" of ink is in reality roughly a cylindrical envelope enclosing a space due to cavitation. On further extensions the envelope thins and breaks down and the so called filaments are the remains of a much extended envelope. Filamentation is thus a much later stage in so called ink splitting.

FRØSLEV-NIELSEN: How will you use this technique in gravure printing?

WAGENBAUER: To study the ink transfer in gravure printing with the same apparatus, the printing form will be made of transparent Plexiglas.

WALKER: In the pictures you have shown us, what was the speed and ink film thickness?

WAGENBAUER: Printing speed and ink film thickness were not specified because the pictures I have shown were made purely with the object of demonstrating the possibilities of the method.

THE INFLUENCE OF PRINTING SPEED ON INKING AND PRINT QUALITY OF HALFTONE AND LINE IN SHEET-FED LETTERPRESS PRINTING

by HERBERT DÜRNER

Institut der Deutschen Gesellschaft für Forschung im Graphischen Gewerbe, München

Abstract—In the following report the inking of letterpress formes and printing of halftone and line etchings and the effects of printing speed are examined. The tests were conducted under practical conditions on a commercial sheet-fed cylinder/flatbed letterpress machine. Ink samples were taken from the running machine with the help of a removable plate base of special design.

Photomicrographs show that under normal roller setting, a complete utilization of the running speed of cylinder/flatbed machines is possible without detriment to the quality of inking.

The visual judgment of the prints, both with the unaided eye and by means of photomicrographs showed a slight reduction in the squeeze-out, characteristic of letterpress printing, at higher speeds. For line originals this has a positive advantage, but in the case of complicated, large sized halftones, a decrease in quality, even though of minor degree was noted, caused above all by the composition of the cylinder covering papers.

INTRODUCTION

MANY studies in the past have dealt with the problem of ink transfer from the printing forme to paper, a few with the transfer from roller onto the printing forme. The majority of these, however, dealt with transfer from solids only. It was relatively simple to assess gravimetrically or even photometrically, the amount of ink transferred to either plate or paper.

The present studies have been extended to printing from halftone and line areas since these constitute the greater part of printing formes used in practice. For this purpose, a test forme (see Fig. 1) was designed. Apart from gray step wedges and line plates, the following details are worth mentioning: One halftone and line plate each had continuously varying etching depth, and one line plate sensitive to ink fill-in formed by the intersecting spaces between tangentially touching lines and circles.

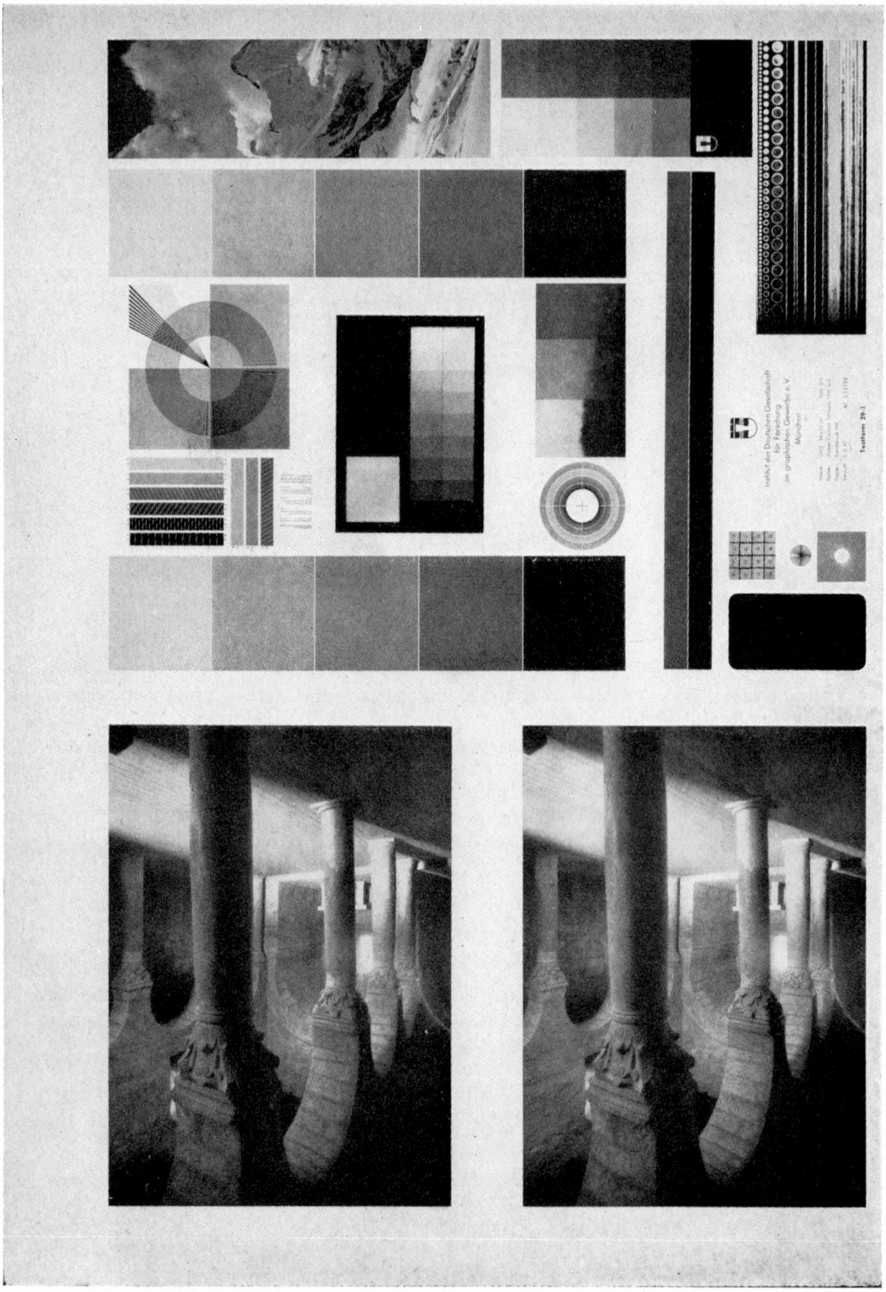

Fig. 1. Letterpress test forme.

INKING

For judgment of the effect of inking the test forme alone would not be sufficient. The momentum of a letterpress cylinder flatbed machine at top speed is too high to allow a sudden stop judgment of the ink distribution on the forme after either inking or printing, for it is inevitable that before the press comes to a complete stop the forme will be either completely or partially contacted by the forme rollers. At lower running speed this would, perhaps, be possible, yet the forme rollers would have to be tripped off the forme and re-adjusted each time a sample has been taken.

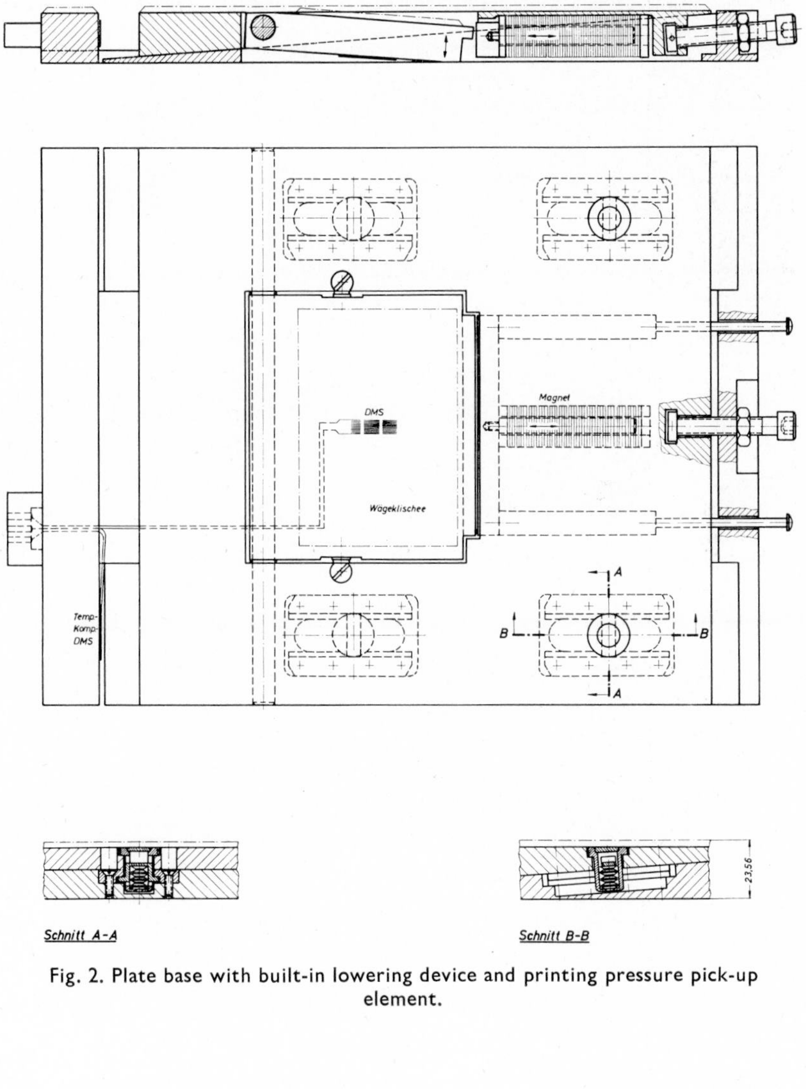

Fig. 2. Plate base with built-in lowering device and printing pressure pick-up element.

For this reason, a special mounting base was developed, consisting of two wedge-shaped plates, tensioned against each other (and therefore adjustable in height for varying plate thicknesses), the constructional details of which are depicted in Fig. 2. Figure 3 shows the plate base locked in the forme, bordered on its sides by the two five-step tone wedges. As becomes clear from the two figures, any chosen plate of size 70 × 100 mm and fixed to the

Fig. 3. Plate base locked in printing forme.

centre part of the base, may be tilted, parallel to its longitudinal axis, thereby lowering it below the printing plane for removal from contact with both rollers and printing cylinders.

Lowering of the plate is possible in practically any position of the cylinder or bed; in effect, however, just three positions (Fig. 4) are of interest, i.e. that after complete inking but before printing sets in (II), that immediately after printing (III) and, in certain instances, after partial inking (I) in the front dead position of the bed. Lowering is effected in this region by hand, in position II after hand release by a cylinder-controlled relay. After taking out the test plate the sinkable centre part of the plate base must be re-adjusted by hand into a printing position. For inking tests, instead of the solid plate

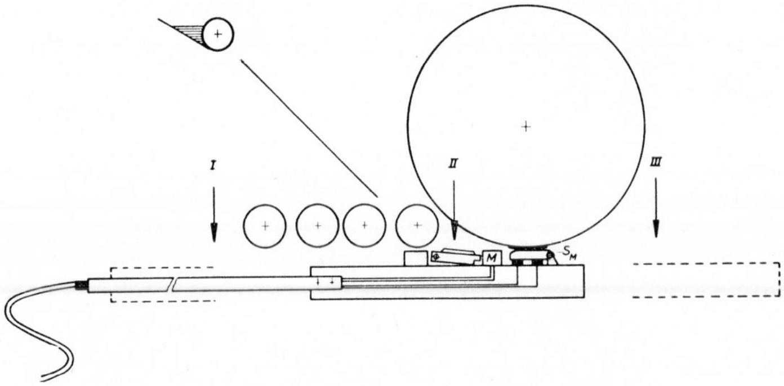

Fig. 4. Sketch showing lowering points of test plate.

shown in Fig. 3, a test plate consisting of a combination of type, line and halftone, the original of which is shown in Fig. 5, was used for microscopic evaluation. The plate was so arranged that printing elements of interest stood rather free, whereby above all smaller forme elements were unfavourably

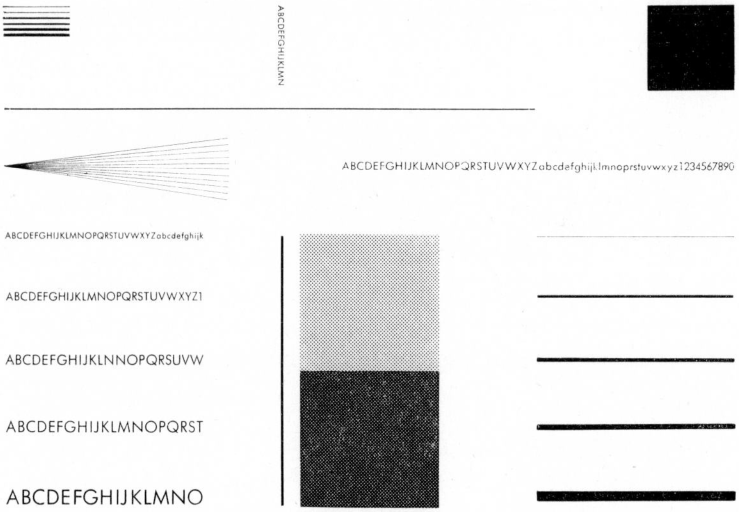

Fig. 5. Test plate for inking studies.

influenced by edge effects in the course of inking. For this reason, one of the large tone wedges of the test forme (Fig. 1) was also removed for these tests.

The test procedure was as follows: First the setting of the inking unit necessary to obtain equal printing results at 1700 and 4000 i.p.h. was determined. Printing was done on an "Original Heidelberg Cylinder", 54 × 72 cm.

Then according to the speed rhythm, the position of the forme rollers against the forme was adjusted with a mechanically functioning forme roller setting height tester, recently developed at FOGRA, at 0.05 mm (light), 0.2 mm (normal) or 0.7 mm (heavy). At these three roller settings and after thorough cleaning of the plate, a hundred prints were prepared each at a printing speed of 1700 and 4000 i.p.h. In the course of each hundredth printing action, the centre part of the test forme was lowered at position II, after inking had been completed but the printing cylinder not yet having been reached. The machine was stopped and photomicrographs were taken of the lowered test plate under inclined illumination outside the machine.

A group of such photographs for measuring position "AB" (see vertical row of letters in the test plate of Fig. 5) has been reproduced in Fig. 6. The left hand row shows the area when inked at low, the right hand row when inked at high printing speed. Closeness of roller adjustment increases from top to bottom.

Apart from the results depicted in Fig. 5, further test series have shown that the influence of speed upon the inking of a printing forme is not great. In general, this may be partially caused by the speed control range of the printing press used, which only slightly exceeded the ratio of 1 : 2. Furthermore, the inking speed, even at constant printing speed, varies in the ratio of 1 : 2.5 between forward and backward movement thus somewhat masking any influence of speed.

As previously noted in model tests, the closer squeeze of the rollers is affecting the inked forme. In connection with increased printing pressure this property brought about, as shown in Fig. 6, a slight broadening of the uninked plate edge (letter edges). This effect, of course, increases with closer adjustment of the rollers. It can be clearly seen on letter "A", which constitutes the outermost point of the test plate, thus carrying the full pressure of the roller. Although, in consequence of the above, the edges of the forme parts are not completely inked, printing results are perfectly satisfactory. The squeezed-off ink is replaced by excess ink in the centre of the printing elements.

As a result of the considerable squeeze-off at the edges, ink flows down to the bottom of the etching. At higher speeds, this effect is slightly larger, on the one hand, for the reasons explained above, and on the other, presumably on account of greater ink supply necessitated by the less favourable ink splitting which occurs at growing printing speeds. Because of the considerable enlargement the effects appear rather blurred in Fig. 6, and only contours can be recognized.

From the above findings an increased filling-in at growing printing would be expected. Extended printing tests, however, have proved the contrary, and a later example will serve to illustrate this.

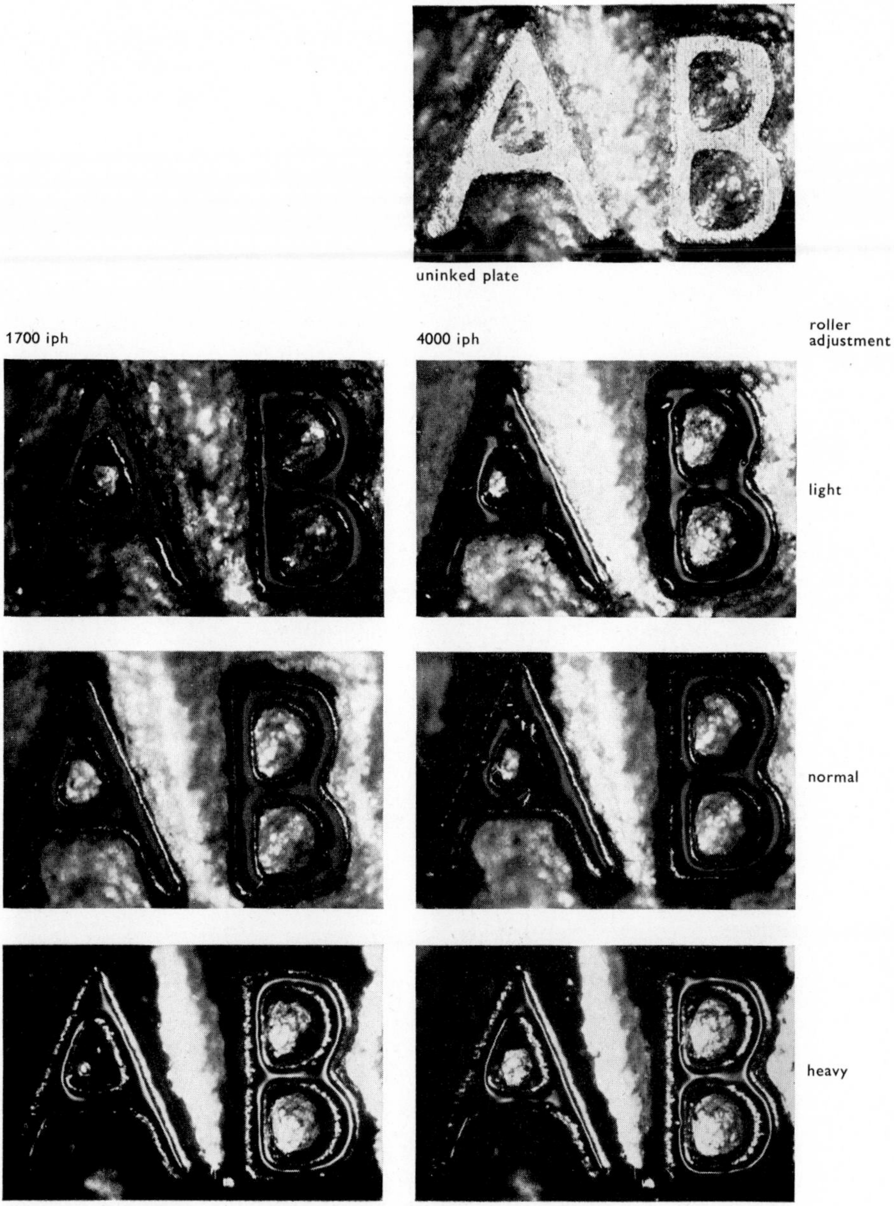

Fig. 6. Ink distribution on the plate (34 × enlarged).
(inked by a perbunan two-layer roller)

THE PRINT

In separate tests, with the same press and a similar test forme, extended printing experiments were conducted with varying stock and inks at different printing speeds, under controlled printing conditions (inking, printing pressure, speed).

As far as possible, the printing result was evaluated photometrically though mainly visually—either at original size or else enlarged to between 10- and 150-times the original.

The comparison was between a large number of sheets printed under equal conditions yet at varying speed. For the comparison of print areas such prints were chosen as had equal densities in a solid ahead of and to the rear of (as seen in the printing direction) the area to be compared. The results are illustrated in Fig. 7 onwards and are enlargements of two of the segments of the test forme. It should be pointed out that the studies were made at speeds lying between 0.9 m/sec (approx. 1700 i.p.h.) and 2.2 m/sec (approx. 4000 i.p.h.). Thus the differences are not very marked and this is why only extreme values have been compared.

1. Solid

In order to understand the observations on the prints from halftone and line areas, the influence of speed on solid printing areas will be briefly discussed. Visual judgment of the solid, without the aid of a microscope,

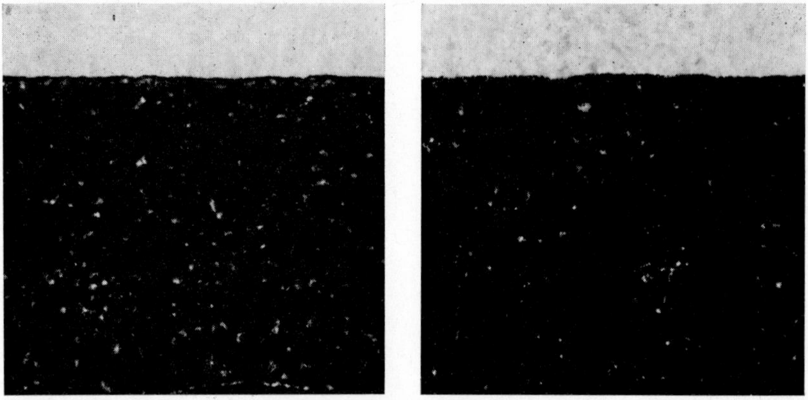

2000 iph 4000 iph

Fig. 7. Solid letterpress print on art paper (photomicrograph in transmitting light, 13 × enlarged).

showed, under the condition of equal density, that the uniformity of ink distribution increases with growing printing speed, up to the picking limit. In the speed range under test the printed solid optically appeared at higher print unrolling speeds slightly smoother and more even.

In the enlarged segment (× 13) reproduced in Fig. 7, the above becomes even clearer. The improved ink distribution or rather more uniform coverage obtained at high speeds gives the print produced at 4000 i.p.h. a smoother appearance, even when viewed under the microscope.

2. Halftones

With halftones, on the other hand, the situation is completely different. In the case of larger, sensitive tone values, the appearance to the unaided eye is—even though to a small degree—more grainy and non-uniform at increasing printing speed. When viewed under the microscope, however, the prints would appear rather contrary to the above. How can this be explained?

To start with, when comparing the segment of a 75 per cent tone reproduced in Fig. 8 under strong, i.e. approximately 130 times enlargement, the following general observation is made: Both speed steps very distinctly show the edge ink squeeze, characteristic of letterpress printing, the so-called squash. This means that the ink has been pushed towards the edges and hence is missing in the centre areas of the halftone dots, the reason being the variation in pressure from centre to edge centre. According to R. G. W. Croney* this pressure increases to a high value towards the edges. The tendency will be, therefore, to push the ink on the plate in the course of printing into areas of low pressure.

Ink squeezing, finally, requires a definite period of time. It follows that under constant conditions, i.e. application of uniform printing pressure and uniform ink viscosity, the ink would have to be pushed aside more, the longer the printing cylinder rests on the printing forme. Close examination of Figs. 8 and 9, provides evidence for this view. It appears that the squeezed edges on the print produced at low printing speed are stronger and more marked than those on prints produced at higher printing speed. Accordingly, with the latter the ink is concentrated in the centre of the dots, giving relatively uniform coverage. And yet, viewed macroscopically, the printed area appears more imperfect.

The following explanation is offered: Owing to the non-uniformity in the "formation" of cylinder covering papers, the printing pressure varies and its distribution is influenced by the compressional irregularities of cylinder dressing materials. These variations which can be clearly seen from Fig. 10, result from non-uniform pulp distribution in the production of the paper. Through strong calendering these varying pulp components may be smoothed down and the paper brought to uniform thickness, yet the difference in resilience will remain unchanged. If such pulp accumulations happened to be superimposed in a cylinder covering consisting of several sheets, the printing pressure may even be increased. These differences cannot be partially

* R. G. W. Croney, Measuring printing pressure, PATRA—Int. Report No. 40 (1950).

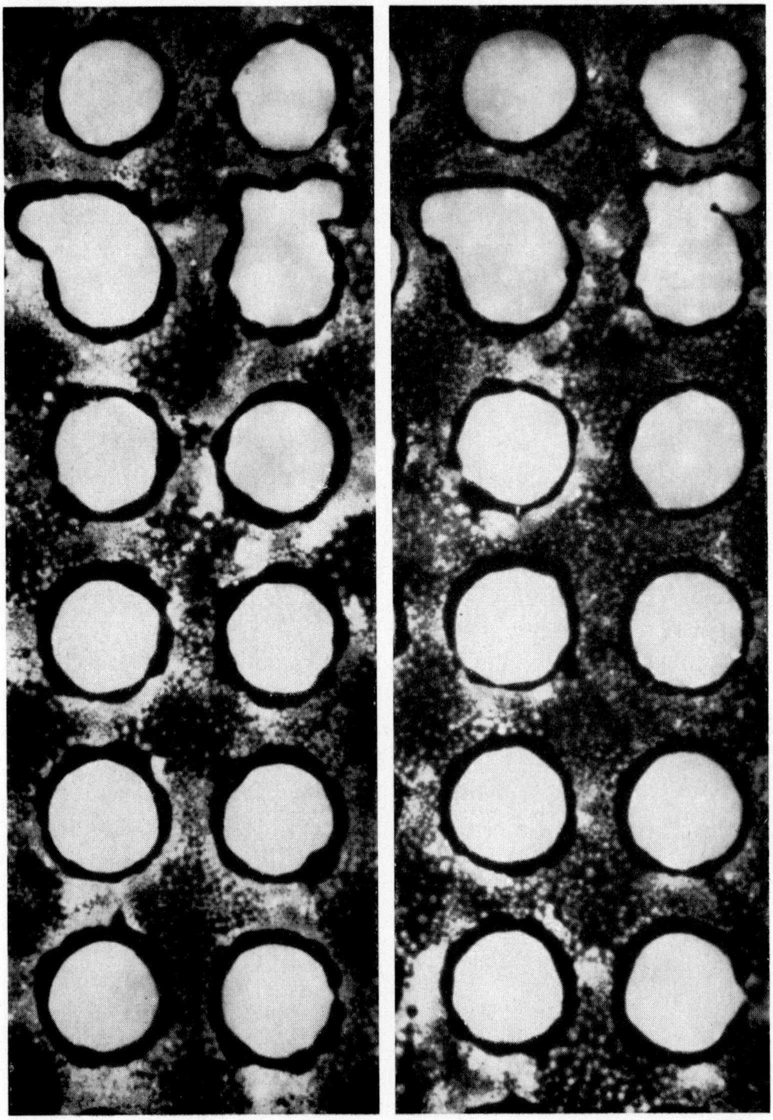

Fig. 8. 135-screen halftone letterpress print (photomicrograph in transmitted light, 130 × enlarged).

2000 iph

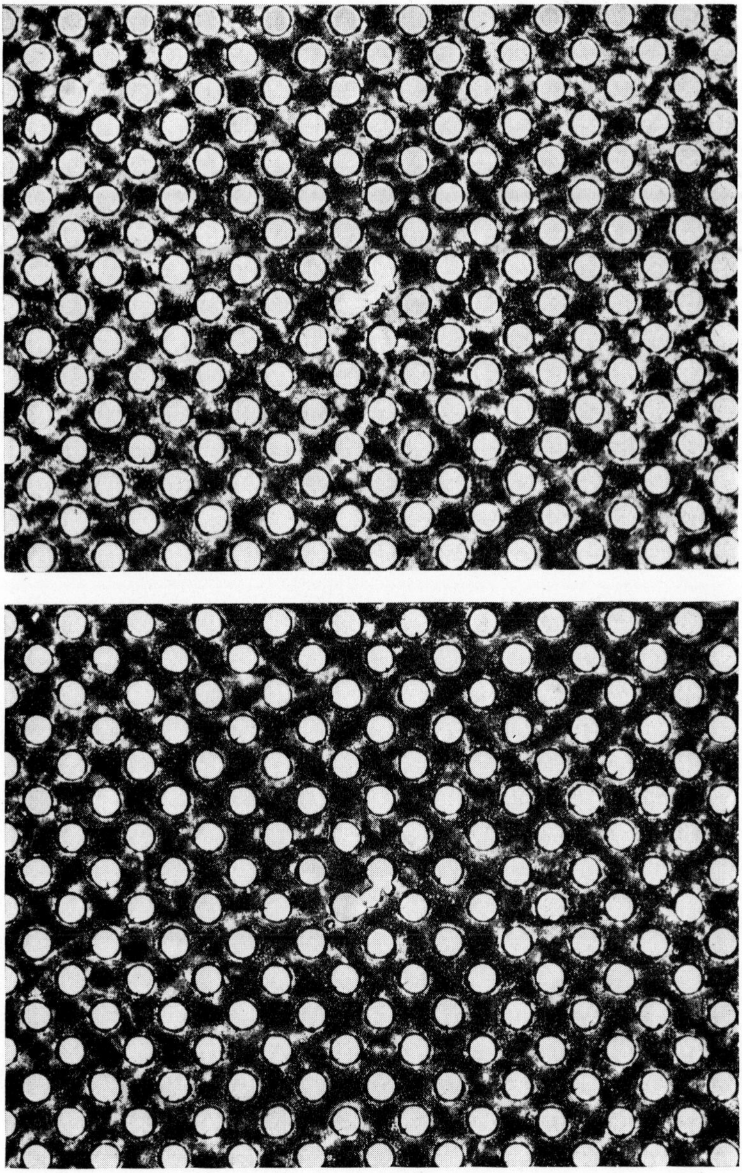

4000 iph

Fig. 9. 120-screen halftone letterpress print on art paper (photomicrograph in transmitted light, 32 × enlarged).

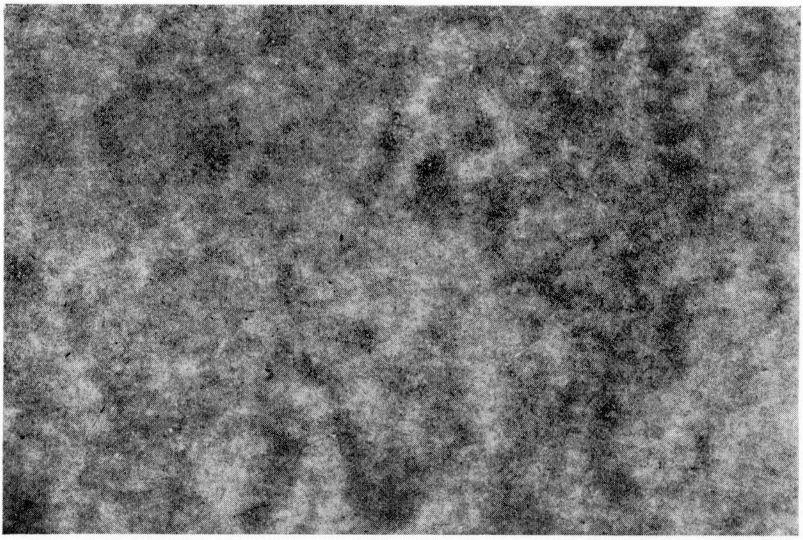

Fig. 10. Tympan sheet, photographed in transmitted light (1:1).

adjusted by the printer but will have to be suppressed in production printing by using pressures which affect the more compressive areas. The extent of the differences becomes clear from the print reproduced in Fig. 11 which, after complete hand-cut make-ready, was prepared before applying increased printing pressure. It shows the "formation" cloudiness of cylinder dressing mentioned above, which roughly corresponds to the density distribution of the cylinder covering paper of Fig. 10, photographed in transmitted light.

These variations undoubtedly affect the printing pressure and lead to non-uniform inking of the plate. At constant dwell time, areas of higher printing pressure will push ink to a greater extent towards the edges than those of lower pressure. On the other hand, in the case of solids, no disadvantages result, because of the absence of the edge effect and the increased rate of inking. The influence is confined to halftone areas. The non-uniform ink distribution resulting therefrom is clearly visible from the photomicrograph of a sheet printed at low speed shown in Fig. 9, which applies particularly to differences extending over large areas. Comparing, from this point of view, the halftone in Fig. 9 printed at high speed, we find here a somewhat less significant difference in the appearance of the halftones in the congruent areas of the print. At this enlargement, i.e. under microscopic view, the impression of a more uniform appearance of the halftone at higher printing speeds is gained. On the other hand as mentioned above, the impression under macroscopic viewing is to the contrary. This can only be explained by the differences in printing pressure caused by cylinder covering materials

Fig. 11. Gray wedge letterpress printed with too low a printing pressure (1:1).

having more influence at higher speed on account of the structural difference in ink distribution. The fact is that the total ink density and the optical impression gained in macroscopic view are not only determined by the ink distributed over the dot area but likewise by the ink squash, which is of annular appearance in our illustration. At low printing speed the latter

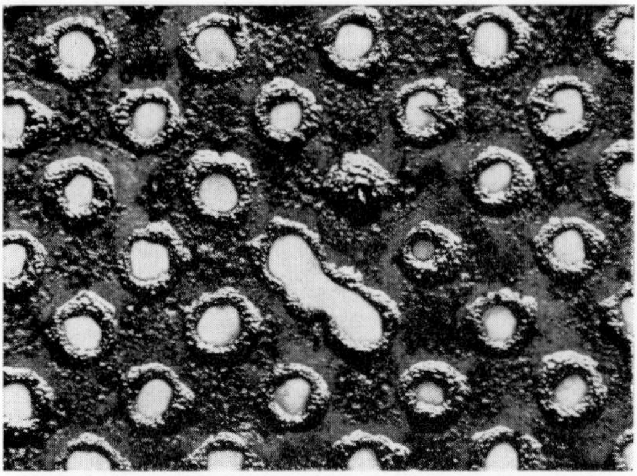

1700 iph

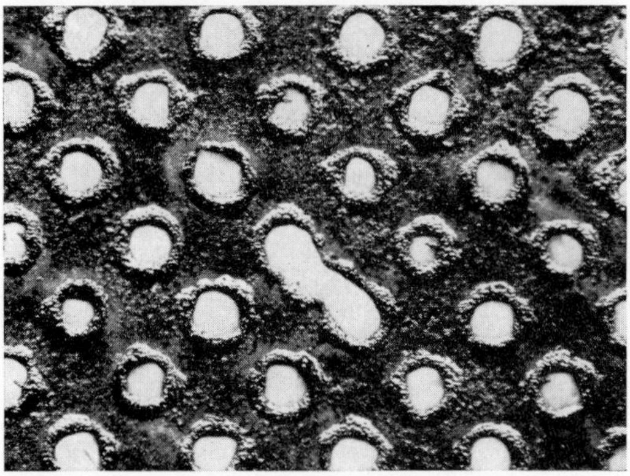

3400 iph

Fig. 12. 150-screen halftone letterpress print on art paper (photomicrograph in reflected light, 55 × enlarged).

becomes more distinct since, on account of the extended dwelling time more ink is pressed from the intermediate areas towards the edges. Thus the uniformity of a halftone area printed at low speed is largely determined by the uniformity of squash, whereas at higher speeds equal distribution of the ink over the complete area is decisive. This explains why in all parts of the printing segment obtained at 2000 i.p.h. (Fig. 9) areas are only partially covered with ink, whereas in the sample obtained at 4000 i.p.h. areas of complete coverage alternate with some showing partial coverage. This makes the uncovered areas particularly noticeable. Furthermore, the differences in printing pressure caused by both cylinder covering and stock are more easily accommodated at low speed whereas at high speed the dynamic stress on the cylinder covering is higher and the effect more marked.

Reference must be made to the comet-like ink splashes in Fig. 9, appearing in unprinted spaces. They result from the filaments caused by ink splitting. In our tests these defects occurred rarely and at sporadic intervals but were somewhat more significant at higher speeds.

These studies indicate that under absolutely equal conditions it is principally the dwell time and to a certain degree also the angular acceleration of separation of printing forme and printing cylinder, which influence the uniform appearance of halftones. The influence of cylinder diameter on print quality is often a matter of speculation. This work leads to the conclusion that with the inks and cylinder dressing materials in use today more uniform halftone prints will result from an increase in the diameter of the printing cylinder.

The frequent supposition, that, owing to the heavier inking required, fine detail will be lost by fill-in of the printing forme, was not confirmed by the tests conducted. With runs of up to 5000 prints, even the contrary could be established. Thus, for instance, the halftone dot above the mis-etched spot in Fig. 12 opened up at higher printing speeds whereas it kept on filling in at a performance of 1700 i.p.h. This was observed on sheets of uniform density even after repeatedly changing the speed. There are two possible explanations. On the one hand, the squeezing effect is lower at higher speed so that the amount of ink pushed beyond the edges of the plate and filling the non-printing areas, has hardly grown; on the other hand, the negative pressure which occurs in the etched areas and affects splitting is stronger at higher speeds. More ink, therefore, is pulled from the deeper parts of the plate than in the case of lower speed. This observation was made on both halftone areas and plates of finest line etching.

3. Line etchings

Depending on the area of printing elements the statements made on solids and halftones hold good for ink distribution in line areas. For demonstration two comparable enlarged prints have been reproduced in Fig. 13. Apart from the above both the sharpness of contour and detail which is resolved are of special interest with line etchings. The contour sharpness is particularly good owing to the squash common in letterpress printing. As explained in the section on halftones, they decrease with growing printing speed, without however, completely disappearing at high speed. The pressure on the edges of the printing area is so heavy that there will always be a certain ink squash, and this the more so the more isolated the printing element. Thus the squash in Fig. 13 is more distinct at the front edges of the lines than it is on the inner longitudinal edges. With type the situation is similar. In summary, it may be stated that the squash at higher speeds, even though reduced, ensures sufficient contour sharpness. There is no decrease in the detail printed.

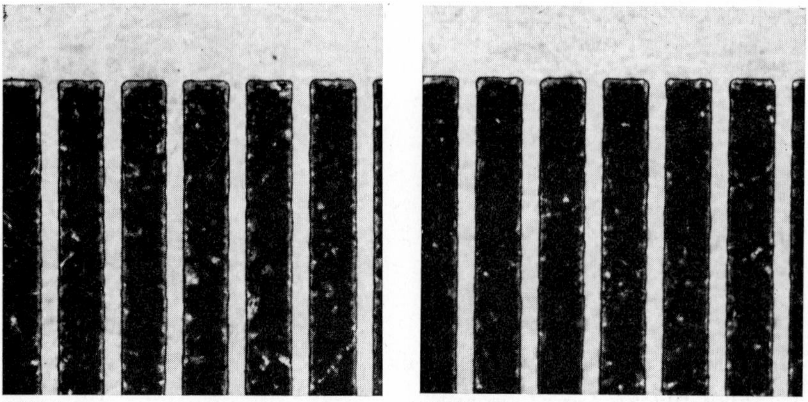

2000 iph 4000 iph

Fig. 13. Letterpress print on art paper (photomicrograph in transmitted light, 11 × enlarged).

PRINTING WITH MULTICOLOUR MACHINES

Apart from the problem of register, there remain problems of overprinting wet ink layers on top of each other. The squash common in letterpress printing becomes a critical problem both on the edges of the printing forme as also on halftone areas. When the squash happen to be printed one on top of the other, the resulting accumulation of ink will lead to a mixture effect. This effect, however, as shown by tests on a two-colour-Miller-press, leads to a slight improvement at higher printing speed. This can be clearly seen, from the enlarged printed areas shown in Fig. 14. The moiré resulting from overprinting two angled halftone areas, becomes more noticeable at high speed due to the more uniform distribution of ink over the entire area. When the danger of moiré arises, this effect will of course grow and detract from quality of the printing. In normal conditions, however, the effect is advantageous. Greater enlargement of the printed area as depicted in Fig. 14, shows a slightly larger non-printing area at higher speed, caused by less squash. Thus, in multicolour-wet-on-wet printing better results may be expected from higher speeds. Initial tests indicate that, apart from register accuracy, printing quality will at least not be impaired.

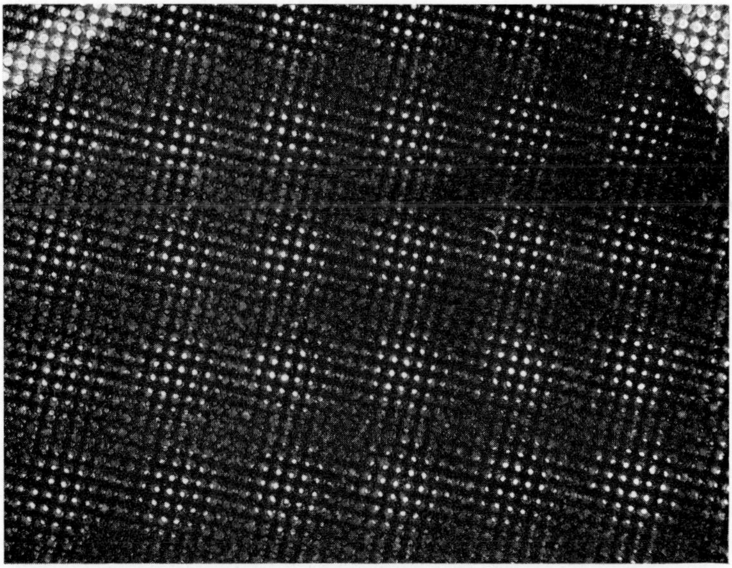

4000/4000 iph

1700/1700 iph

Fig. 14. Two-color, 135-screen halftone letterpress print on art paper (photomicrograph in transmitted light, 11 × enlarged).

SUMMARY

The effect of speed on differences in inking and print quality is small, certainly there is no significant deterioration of quality. The present somewhat grainy reproduction of sensitive large-sized halftone areas which can be improved with improved cylinder dressing materials will be hardly noticeable and is compensated by better printing of solids. The bad effect of the "formation" of printing paper, however, cannot be avoided. In multicolour printing, too, apart from register errors, increased speed seems to bring no quality deterioration.

It should be pointed out, however, that higher printing speeds necessitate increased accuracy on the part of the printer, above all in the preparation of cylinder coverings, setting of rollers, and adjustment of both feeder and delivery.

DISCUSSION

CHRISTENSEN: I should like to ask Mr. Dürner how he maintained the rollers at constant temperature when working at different speeds. Our own investigations have shown that the transfer of ink to the forme depends on temperature and this complicates any interpretation of the effect of speed.

DÜRNER: The arrangement of our tests ensured that the temperature variations were within small limits. In practice, of course, a machine running at a higher speed will also run at a higher temperature and our interests were the effects of speed under practical conditions.

TOLLENAAR: Your explanation of the differences in uniformity of density have been made on the assumption that the ink film on the forme is uniform both at high and low speeds. However, the ink films are always reticulated and this effect will be superimposed on other sources of non-uniformity like the paper and the packing. This reticulation is likely to be affected by speed and since it may well be of the same order of dimension as the screen dots, it is likely to influence the evenness of the print.

DÜRNER: I quite agree that the inklayer surface structure on the forme is not even and varies as a function of time. Thus the reticulation of the inklayer will change with speed on transference from the forme roller to the plate. I do not think, however, that these differences in inklayer-surface structure are responsible for the effects shown, especially if we consider the high pressures operating during transfer.

As to the order of magnitude, I would like to point out that—as photomicrographs of halftone prints have revealed—the ink distribution within one halftone dot cannot itself determine print quality. Otherwise a halftone printed at high speed should appear more uniform, and this is not the case. I therefore believe that in the first place the differences in printing pressure distribution are of importance.

BANKS: I support Dr. Tollenaar in believing that the interpretation of the print pattern is complicated by the effect of speed on reticulation. Higher speeds will, I think, reduce the scale of this reticulation. This reticulation arises, I believe, through acceleration of the ink during stretching of the film in the so-called splitting stage. It is a particular form of instability which arises in accelerated liquids and has been discussed by Sir G. Taylor.

CARLSSON: I must compliment Mr. Dürner on his very interesting work. Regarding the non-uniformity of the cylinder packings, some years ago we studied the uniformity of caliper of the tympan sheets commonly used in Sweden. Under a pressure of 35 kg/cm^2 we found a variation of ± 0.0003 mm for the best and ± 0.008 mm for the worst. When these facts were presented to a manufacturer, he pointed out that over a period of 30 to 40 years no complaints had ever been received!

Regarding the dynamic behaviour of the cylinder packing we have observed that when printing a hard magazine coated paper with a packing consisting of a rubber blanket the pattern of the textile backing showed up in the print at very high speeds but not at low.

BRUNO: We have these problems in lithography and have been experimenting with plastic sheets like Mylar and metal foil as packing materials.

EFFECT OF PLATE MATERIAL ON SOLID AND HALFTONE PRINTING QUALITY

by J. M. Fetsko, D. E. Young, and A. C. Zettlemoyer

National Printing Ink Research Institute
Lehigh University, Bethlehem, Pa., U.S.A.

INTRODUCTION

The effect of plate composition on printing results has been a subject of long standing dispute. It is frequently heard, for example, that one type of metal gives higher transfer and coverage than another, or that a certain plastic is superior to metal. Controversial opinions have also been expressed as to the relative performance of halftones compared with solids.

Reliable answers to such questions can be derived only through suitable quantitative measurements made under carefully controlled printing conditions, and a start in this direction has been effected in the work reported herein. Two sets of plates were investigated, one consisting primarily of the metals and a few plastics commonly used in printing practice and the other of synthetic rubber varying in hardness. The rubber series comprised a halftone along with the corresponding solid, whereas the majority of the metal plates were solid-faced only. The principal numerical yardsticks were ink transfer, optical density, and dot diameter where appropriate.

This work introduced the printing plate as a new variable in the printability research program of this Laboratory. Since the plate is an integral part of the printing process, an awareness of the plate contribution to printing results was considered germane to the overall program. It was also thought likely, and results subsequently confirmed this suspicion, that different inks and/or papers would exhibit different sensitivities to changes in plate material and surface area. Most of all, an appreciation of the many problems involved in quantitative halftone printing research was obtained.

EXPERIMENTAL WORK

Printing plates

The first group of plates consisted of solid-faced hard plates made from five different metals and two plastics as follows: magnesium, chrome plated magnesium, copper, nickel, zinc, nylon, and vinyl. To study the effects of surface smoothness, a magnesium plate was rubbed with fine grain sand paper and another with coarse grain sand paper. This series had dimensions *ca.* 3.5 × 6 in. (21 in.^{2}) × 0.065 in.

The second group of plates consisted of Buna N Synthetic rubber in four degrees of hardness: 20, 30, 40, and 50 Durometer-A (soft to hard respectively). Each hardness was provided both as a solid-face and as a 20 per cent tone 30 line screen halftone. A similar magnesium pair was included for comparison. The top face dimensions of this series were 2.5 × 4.5 (11 in.^{2}). They were 0.085 in. thick and were mounted on a 3.5 × 5.5 × 0.055 in. metal base; that is, the total thickness was 0.140 in.

Papers and inks

All plates were used to make prints with two inks and two papers having widely different properties. The inks selected were a black oil-based letterpress and a blue comic news with plastic viscosities of 90 and 15 poises respectively at 73°F. One of the papers was a brush coated stock and the other was a rougher more porous uncoated stock.

Printing techniques

The printing experiments were conducted entirely by the letterpress process on a Vandercook No. 4 Proof Press. Besides the plate, the only press variable was ink film thickness, which ranged from 0.5 to 15 μ carried on the plate, and up to 25 prints were made over this range with each ink-paper-plate combination.

Other press conditions were held constant: speed at 200 f.p.m., pressure at 100 pli (5 mils interference), room temperature at 73°F, and relative humidity at 50 per cent. The plate hold-down and pressure measuring techniques, however, differed for the two series of plates. The Huck pressure-sensitive base, which incorporates a vacuum system for holding the plates firmly in place, was conveniently used for the 0.065 in. hard solid series. Unfortunately, the 0.140 in. thickness of the rubber series was about twice that which could be accommodated on the Huck Base. A special wooden base with a dovetail clip arrangement was therefore constructed, and printing pressure had to be controlled by the static "interference" measurements. Since the rubber series comprised both a solid and a halftone, the base was designed to hold two plates so that the corresponding pair could be inked and printed simultaneously.

Other problems with the rubber series were the considerable amount of makeready required to achieve a uniform impression and the inability to clean the plate with solvent as desired. To minimize changes with use, the plates were first equilibrated with the ink. The inking procedure adopted during printing was to start with low ink film thickness and gradually build up by small additions of ink to the distribution system. When excessive lint accumulated on the surface of the plate, the ink was removed from the plate by successive impressions with a high grade smooth coated paper. When the plate had to be cleaned with solvent (petroleum ether 60–100°BP), the experiments were stopped until the next day to allow the plate to dry thoroughly.

Measurements

The ink film thicknesses originally on the plates and transferred to the paper were determined by weighing the plate before and after each printing. Optical densities of the prints were measured with a Welch Densichron using a green filter for the black prints and a yellow filter for the blue prints; six determinations were averaged per print. The dot diameters on the halftone prints were also measured and twelve dots per print were averaged; this phase was greatly facilitated by use of a Graphic Arts Inspector, which projects the print onto a ground glass screen at a magnification of 23×.

In addition, print quality was evaluated visually from the uniformity standpoint. The chief numerical parameter was the lower practical limit (LPL), defined as the minimum amount of ink required for full coverage without visual breakup. The solids were observed at a distance of 12 in., and the halftone dots were observed under a low power (1.5 ×) viewing glass. The solid prints in the practical range were also evaluated qualitatively for mottle, defined as the nonuniformity of prints having full coverage.

The printing results from all ink-paper-plate combinations were compared principally from plots of the average numerical measurements as a function of ink film thickness either on the plate or on the paper. In all cases, the LPL's were represented on the graphs as solid circles for the solid prints and thin dashed lines for the halftones. Whenever the results from both inks were plotted within the same graph, the letterpress ink was indicated by solid curves and the news ink by broad dashed curves.

PRINTING RESULTS WITH SOLID PLATES

Ink transfer to paper

In the first series of experiments, which involved principally smooth solid-faced metal and plastic plates, it was found that transfer of a given ink to a given paper was essentially identical irrespective of the plate material. There were of course differences among the inks and papers, as is illustrated in Fig. 1A with the magnesium plate. The letterpress ink on the coated paper gave a relatively sharp transfer peak and then levelled off, whereas this ink on the uncoated paper and the news ink on both papers gave much wider peaks indicative of systems where surface absorbency should be relatively high.

With the roughened magnesium plates, the percent transfer curves were displaced 1 or 2 μ to the right of the comparable curve for the smooth

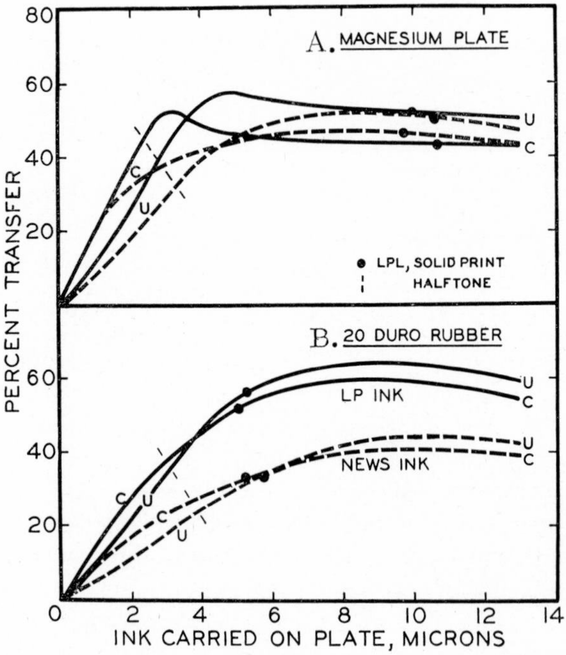

Fig. 1. Transfer of inks to papers from solid faced plates.

magnesium. The major effect was that transfer in the thin ink film region was reduced due obviously to the fact that ink trapped in the cavities on the plate surface was unavailable for transfer to the paper.

Whereas all of the smooth hard plates performed in a similar manner with respect to ink "release" to the papers, nothing can be said from these experiments regarding other performance characteristics such as halftone etching properties, wear with use, and dimensional stability under different humidity conditions. The results of the work described here suggest only that the transfer properties of hard-solid faced plates do not depend on material but that they are affected by the initial state of smoothness. A similar conclusion has been reached recently by Carlsson[1].

A different situation was observed with the rubber plates. First, the transfer differences between the coated and uncoated paper were greatly minimized. Note in Fig. 1B that the softest plate (20-Durometer) produced similar curves for both papers with either ink. Although this plate represented the extreme case, the harder rubbers tended toward this situation.

The major interest in these experiments, however, was to compare the relative performances of the plates with particular ink-paper combinations,

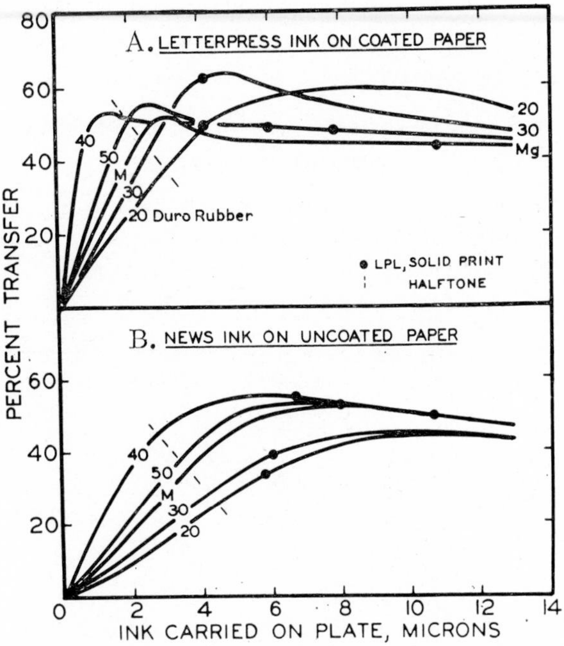

Fig. 2. Effect of plate material on ink transfer to paper.

and the situation is summarized in Fig. 2. Irrespective of the ink and paper, transfer in the thin ink film region was always higher with the 50-Durometer rubber than with the magnesium plate, reached an optimum with the 40-Durometer, and was lower with the 30 and 20 plates. Since transfer in the thin film region is generally associated with printing smoothness, it can be presumed that the different plates effected differences in area of the paper surface in contact with the ink film. It is postulated that, under the same external pressure, the 40 and 50 plates compressed to produce a widened nip just enough to accommodate the surface roughness of the paper, but the softer 30 and 20 plates absorbed the pressure in the nip to such an extent that little smoothing out of the paper surface occurred.

At higher film thicknesses, no change in transfer order due to the plates occurred with the news ink with either of the papers, but a complicated situation arose with the relatively non-penetrating letterpress ink. Note in Fig. 2A that the 40 and 50 plates merely shifted the peak to the left of the magnesium, but the 30 and 20 plates gave the high wide peaks and the high practical film thickness transfer normally obtained with porous systems. The explanation offered is that the absorption of the pressure by the softer plates caused not only less surface smoothing, but also less deformation of the paper capillaries. Consequently, despite the lower contact area in the thin ink film region, more ink uptake in the contact region could occur than with the harder plates.

OPTICAL DENSITY

The objective of the printing process demands, in the long run, that prints of the desired quality be produced. In the case of solid prints, the principal quality criterion is normally that the desired color density be

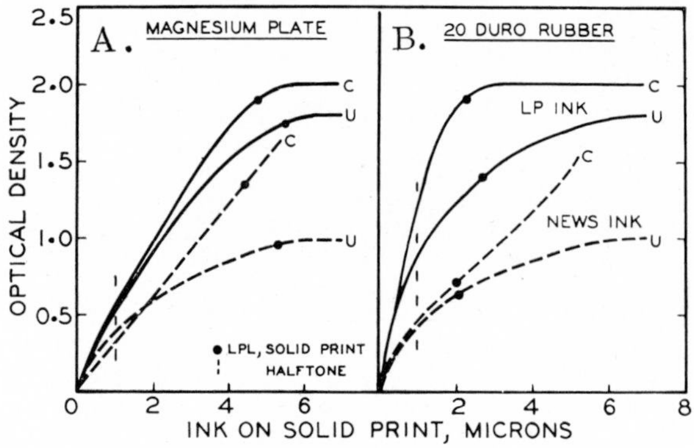

Fig. 3. Optical density of solid prints versus ink film thickness.

achieved with a minimum of ink consumption. The various ink-paper-plate combinations were therefore compared for optical density as a function of film thickness; print rather than plate film thicknesses were used for this purpose on the basis that the actual ink used up by the paper controls ink mileage rather than how much ink must be carried on the plate.

Irrespective of the plate material, the maximum optical density obtainable with either ink definitely depended on the paper. Figure 3 illustrates the results with the two extremes in plates. Note that the black letterpress ink reached a maximum optical density of 2.0 on the coated paper but only 1.80 on the uncoated paper in agreement with expectations based on relative capacity of the papers to hold up ink. A rather curious phenomenon was observed with the blue news ink. On the uncoated paper, optical density levelled off at a value of 1.0, but it increased continuously and essentially linearly on the coated paper. Examination of these prints revealed an irregular mottle consisting of small dark blue areas. Since this effect was much more noticeable on the coated paper prints than on the uncoated paper prints, it was theorized that the cause was agglomeration or flocculation of pigment particles on the surface rather than accumulation of pigment around the paper fibers.

As was the case with ink transfer, there were no differences in the optical density curves of the prints made from the various smooth hard solid faced

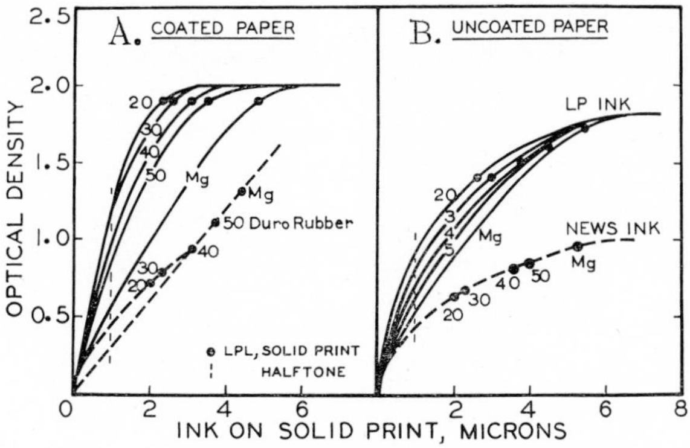

Fig. 4. Effect of plate material on optical density of solid prints.

metal and plastic plates. That is, curves identical with those illustrated in Fig. 3A for the magnesium were obtained. On the other hand, the roughened magnesium plates reduced the rate at which the curves reached maximum optical density, whereas all rubber plates increased the rate. Figure 4 shows the effects with the various rubber plates in comparison to magnesium. In the case of the letterpress ink on either paper, the softest plate (20-Durometer rubber) always gave the highest optical density at lower film thicknesses than the other plates. As plate hardness increased, the ink film thickness requirements to achieve a given optical density progressively increased.

It should be noted that the order in which the plates are rated by optical density results, where the 20 rubber is the best, is in direct contrast to that established by thin film transfer, where 20 rubber is the poorest. Although both types of measurements are used as printing smoothness parameters, it is obvious that different mechanisms control the two aspects. Whereas thin film transfer is based on fraction contact, the fact that higher optical densities at comparable film thicknesses on the print were achieved by the softer plates suggests that ink in a deformed nip can spread out more on the surface of the paper at the moment of impression than can an ink in a relatively undeformed nip.

Visual examination of the prints confirmed this suggestion. At the same film thicknesses on the paper, the breakup of the prints made from the magnesium plate took the form of distinct inked and non-inked areas, but the rubber plate prints exhibited a fine scale breakup consisting of diffuse gray and white areas which apparently resulted from a flow-out of ink over the paper surface. Comparable prints made from the magnesium and the softest rubber plate (20-D) are reproduced in Fig. 5. The two prints selected for

$x = 8.7\ \mu$	$D = 1.6$	$x = 6.5\ \mu$	$D = 1.6$
$y = 3.8\ \mu$	$D_\infty = 2.0$	$y = 3.8\ \mu$	$D_\infty = 1.8$
Magnesium Plate, Coated Paper		20-Duro Rubber, Uncoated Paper	

Fig. 5. Appearances of prints having the same average ink film thickness and average optical density.
(Black Letterpress Ink. x = ink carried on plate; y = ink on print.)

the illustration are particularly interesting because both have identical average ink film thickness and average optical density, yet the distribution of ink on the surface makes the one print entirely useless and the other one acceptable. Because of the relatively large area viewed by the densitometer, black and white areas gave an average integrated density which was the same as a uniform print of lower brightness.

From the optical density results obtained in this study, two conclusions can be drawn. First, optical density measurements are in themselves meaningless without some measure of the deviation from the average. Secondly, they are suspect as a fundamental parameter for printing smoothness because they do not necessarily evaluate coverage due to fraction contact but rather that due to surface flow of ink.

Returning to optical density results, comparison of Fig. 4A and B shows that the differential between plates was much more marked on the coated paper than on the uncoated paper. Coated papers are the less porous and less compressible and therefore should be expected to respond more to effects of nip deformation. Rather curiously, the plate material had no effect on the average optical densities of the news ink prints; but the distributions of densities were affected as will become apparent from the LPL's.

Minimum coverage

As indicated previously, printing quality properties such as average optical density may be misleading. Consequently, a uniformity measurement should be included. Barring suitable instrumentation, the criterion used in this study was the minimum amount of ink required to provide a fully covered print without visual breakup; this quantity, which is selected by visual observation, is referred to as the lower practical limit (LPL).

The LPL's of the solid prints are listed in the left side of Table 1 and have been represented on all graphs as solid circles. In Figs. 1 and 2 illustrating transfer, it may have already been noticed that with the harder plates the LPL's occurred after the peak, but with the softer plates they occurred before the peak. Furthermore, in Figs. 2 and 4, it is obvious that, with all ink-paper combinations, less ink was definitely required for full coverage as plate softness increased. In the case of the coated paper/letterpress ink combination, illustrated in Fig. 4, it is interesting to note that the LPL occurred at the same optical density (1.90) irrespective of the plate despite the different rates to achieve full coverage and the maximum density. The LPL's with the other ink-paper combinations, however, generally occurred at lower optical densities as plate softness increased.

The significance of these observations is that rubber plates not only give better ink mileage at the desired density level, but they also can produce acceptable prints at far lower densities than metal plates. While it has always been known from practical experience that rubber plates improve coverage, the fact that they resulted in lower thin ink film transfer indicates that the reason for their effectiveness is not an improvement in fraction contact as had once been thought, but is due to an enhancement of ink spreading out on the surface of the paper at the moment of impression.

Mottle

The different ink–paper–plate combinations also exhibited different degrees of nonuniformity, called mottle, in the full coverage range. The black letterpress ink/coated paper/metal plate prints tended toward a mottle having a definite periodic pattern which was completely absent on the rubber plate prints. This observation provides further evidence for the hypothesis that nip deformation enhances ink spreading.

The uncoated paper prints with the letterpress ink exhibited a random type of mottle due to soft and hard areas on the paper surface, and the nature of the plate made no discernible difference. As was mentioned previously, the news ink prints were nonuniform because of the random dark blue areas. This situation was more deleterious on the coated paper than on the uncoated prints, and here also the nature of the plate made no difference. The news ink/coated paper prints scratched and were easily damaged when handled because of the lack of drying coupled with the low degree of penetration into the relatively nonporous surface.

TABLE 1. PRINT QUALITY DATA FOR INK-PAPER-PLATE COMBINATIONS

Plate	LPL of solid print				LPL of halftone			Dot diameter	
	Ink on		Transfer	Opt. dens.	Ink on plate*	Transfer	Opt. dens.	at LPL of	
	Plate	Paper						Solid	Halftone
	μ	μ	%		μ	%		mm	mm
Letterpress ink on coated paper									
Mg	10.8	4.8	44	1.90	2.3	45	0.15	0.46	0.39
50	7.9	3.4	45	1.90	2.0	50	0.20	0.46	0.42
40	6.0	2.8	48	1.90	1.9	52	0.22	0.47	0.43
30	4.2	2.5	61	1.90	2.5	40	—	—	—
20	4.2	2.1	50	1.90	2.8	35	0.24	0.47	0.43
Letterpress ink on uncoated paper									
Mg	10.0	5.5	55	1.75	2.7	38	0.15	0.48	0.39
50	7.8	4.5	58	1.65	2.5	40	0.20	0.45	0.41
40	6.3	3.8	60	1.50	2.4	44	0.22	0.45	0.41
30	5.9	3.0	51	1.45	2.8	36	—	—	—
20	5.4	2.7	50	1.45	3.0	34	0.24	0.44	0.42
News ink on coated paper									
Mg	9.6	4.4	44	1.33	2.7	38	0.13	0.47	0.41
50	8.7	3.7	44	1.08	2.6	39	0.15	0.48	0.43
40	6.6	3.1	47	0.95	2.4	43	0.16	0.50	0.46
30	5.9	2.3	39	0.80	3.5	29	—	—	—
20	5.4	2.0	37	0.72	3.8	26	0.19	0.56	0.48
News ink on uncoated paper									
Mg	10.6	5.3	50	0.98	3.2	32	0.13	0.45	0.40
50	8.0	4.0	50	0.85	3.0	33	0.15	0.49	0.43
40	6.7	3.6	54	0.80	2.4	41	0.16	0.51	0.46
30	6.0	2.3	38	0.70	3.9	26	—	—	—
20	5.8	2.1	38	0.65	4.1	24	0.19	0.56	0.48

* Ink on solid plate required to transfer 1μ to solid print (established as LPL of halftone).

Transfer versus print quality

It is obvious from the foregoing discussion that the plates were rated in two different orders by various results involving solid-area printing. The order 40, 50, Mg, 30, 20 (to be designated hereafter as *A*) was established by transfer at low film thicknesses. The order 20, 30, 40, 50, Mg (to be designated hereafter as *B*) was established by the LPL's and by the film thickness necessary to achieve a desired optical density. The major discrepancies involved the two softest plates, 20 and 30 Durometer, which

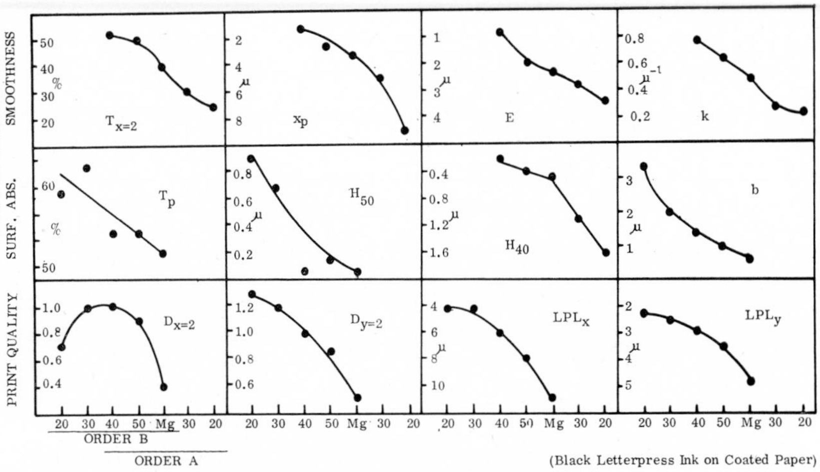

Fig. 6. Printing parameters vs. plate durometer.

transferred less ink than the other plates but provided better coverage. The lack of correlation found between transfer and print quality, either of which is frequently used as smoothness parameter, was considered worthy of further exploration, and the approach adopted was to examine various parameters which have been suggested for describing printing properties. The letterpress ink on the coated paper was selected for this purpose.

In Fig. 6, various transfer and print quality parameters are plotted versus Durometer of the plates. The sequence of the numbers of the left hand coordinate in each square was always arranged so that the top represents the highest values for the respective parameters. As for the bottom coordinates, the points associated with the 20 and 30 Durometer plates were purposely plotted either before or after 40–50–Mg, the choice depending on which sequence gave the best progression of points.

In the top section of Fig. 6, it can be noted that every smoothness transfer parameter agreed in following order *A* (40–50–Mg–30–20). Included here are respectively $T_{x=2}$, the percent transfer at a plate ink film thickness of 2 μ; X_p, the film thickness at which the peak of the transfer curve occurs; *E*, the film thickness at which 50 percent transfer first occurs, from Ginman[2] and k, the smoothness transfer constant from the NPIRI equation[3].

In the middle section are plotted transfer parameters which have been proposed for describing surface absorbency: T_p, percent transfer at the peak; H_{50}, the ink transferred at the peak in excess of 50 per cent, from Ginman (1957); H_{40}, the same but based on an actual 40 per cent ink split found from the NPIRI equation; and b, the ink immobilization transfer constant, also from the NPIRI equation. Although the progression of points for T_p and H_{50} do not line up exactly, their tendency is to follow order B rather than A, but the observation that H_{40} agreed with order A suggests that this parameter might be better related to smoothness.

In the bottom section are print quality parameters derived from optical density and the lower practical limits based on either plate or print film thicknesses. All agree with order B (except for $D_{x=2}$, which indicates this measurement arises from a combination of effects). The most striking feature in Fig. 6 is the excellent correlation of print coverage results with the transfer parameters for absorbency, especially b, rather than with the smoothness parameters. This finding suggests that, under the conditions of these experiments, the factors affecting coverage of the paper were more related to those which induced a greater ink acceptance at the moment of impression rather than fraction of area in actual contact as established from thin film transfer measurements.

It has already been proposed that lateral flow of ink in the nip contributes significantly to optical density and coverage, and now it is apparent that this type of flow also contributes to b, as was recently concluded by Schaeffer[4]. Originally, it had been thought that b was descriptive principally of surface absorbency due to penetration of ink into the paper during nip contact, but this concept may have to be altered to take into account horizontal as well as perpendicular flow, and methods should be found for separating the two aspects. Similarly, print coverage, which has usually been associated principally with printing smoothness, also involves ink flow over the paper surface, and it is not illogical for the lateral flow phenomenon to be the more important of the two. Material factors must therefore be examined in light of their influence on lateral flow.

Proposed mechanism for rubber plates

Based on the observations made in this work, the reasons why the rubber plates produced one order for printing contact smoothness and another order for covering power can now be traced basically to events occurring in the nip region. Proceeding from hard to soft plates which are subjected to the same external pressure, the soft plates start to absorb the pressure and deform to produce a widened nip. At first the widened nip serves to accommodate the paper roughness and to overcome effects of the reduced pressure so that contact area, which controls thin ink film transfer associated with printing smoothness, actually increases. Simultaneously, the paper capillaries are less compressed under the reduced pressure, so that, coupled with the effects of the widened nip, ink flows both into and across the paper and thereby increases ink takeup in the contact areas as well as coverage.

A point is reached, however, at which further widening of the nip reduces the pressure maximum to the point that contact area is decreased. With the plates studied, the optimum in printing smoothness was apparently reached at a plate softness of 40-Durometer. Nevertheless, the softer plates continue to absorb more of the pressure so that the paper capillaries are compressed even less, and the nip region continues to widen. Under these conditions, ink immobilization and coverage are increased further as plate softness increased despite the lower printing smoothness.

PRINTING RESULTS WITH HALFTONE PLATES

Ink transfer to paper

Unfortunately, it was impossible to evaluate percent transfer of ink to the paper from the halftone plates with any degree of accuracy. Although the amount of ink deposited on the plate and transferred to the paper could be

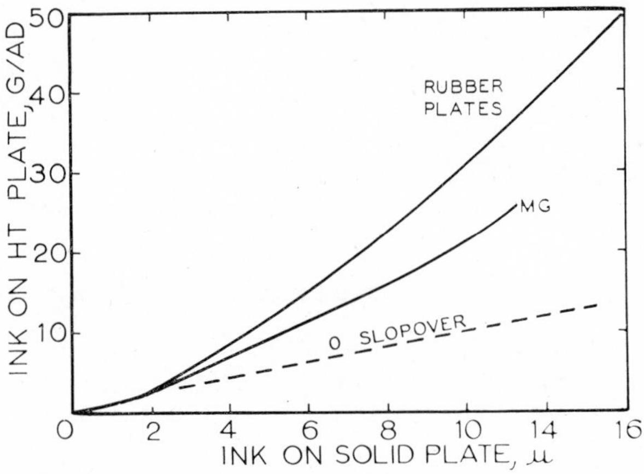

Fig. 7. Excessive ink deposited on halftone plates due to slopover.

determined from appropriate weight differences, conversion to microns of ink thickness based on dot area and ink density were found to be meaningless.

Despite careful roller settings, slopover occurred; consequently, an unknown portion of ink deposited on the halftone plate was unavailable for transfer to the paper. As seen in Fig. 7, the slopover was especially large in the region of practical interest for the solids (4–10 μ) but it was also significant enough in the minimum region for the halftones (2–4 μ) to create problems in quantitative work. The greater slopover which occurred on the rubber plates compared with the magnesium is attributed to their sloping shoulders evidently formed during the molding process.

Problems also arose in estimating the film thicknesses on the print. The main difficulties were that neither the dot shapes nor the ink distribution across the dots were uniform from case to case. Because of the inability to calculate accurate film thicknesses, it was decided to compare halftone print properties at equivalent film thicknesses on the corresponding solid print. It might be mentioned that, in the low ink film region where slopover was at a minimum, estimates assuming perfectly circular and uniformly covered dots indicated that the film thicknesses on the halftone prints were of the order of magnitude of one and a half times those on the corresponding solids. The greater transfer can be assumed to be due to the greater pressures on the dots (20 percent surface area) at equal force applied to the solid plate. In the heavier ink film region, the film thicknesses on the halftone prints were generally about twice those on the corresponding solids probably because of the compounding effects of greater pressure and the transfer of "slopover" ink.

QUALITATIVE OBSERVATIONS

Figure 8 illustrates the dot structures obtained with various ink–paper–plate combinations. The film thickness used for the comparison is more appropriate for solid than for halftone printing, but it was purposely selected to show the variety of effects obtained.

The most distinct nonuniformities were observed with the news ink on the coated paper; hollowed centers occurred on the magnesium plate prints, and white rings frequently appeared on the rubber plates prints due undoubtedly to the transfer of slopover ink. These effects did not occur at all film thicknesses; they were not apparent at minimum coverage (2–4 μ of ink carried on the corresponding solid plate), but generally set in at about 6 μ and disappeared at about 10 μ, after which the nonuniformity was no longer visible due probably to the excessive ink. Although the same effects could be seen on the black letterpress/coated paper prints, they were not nearly so pronounced. The uncoated paper showed no distinct signs of squash out and rings; however, fibers on the paper surface were clearly visible even at excessive film thicknesses, again much more so with the news ink than with the letterpress ink.

The distinct nonuniformities of dots of the news ink on the coated paper are attributed to a number of causes, mainly the low viscosity of the ink

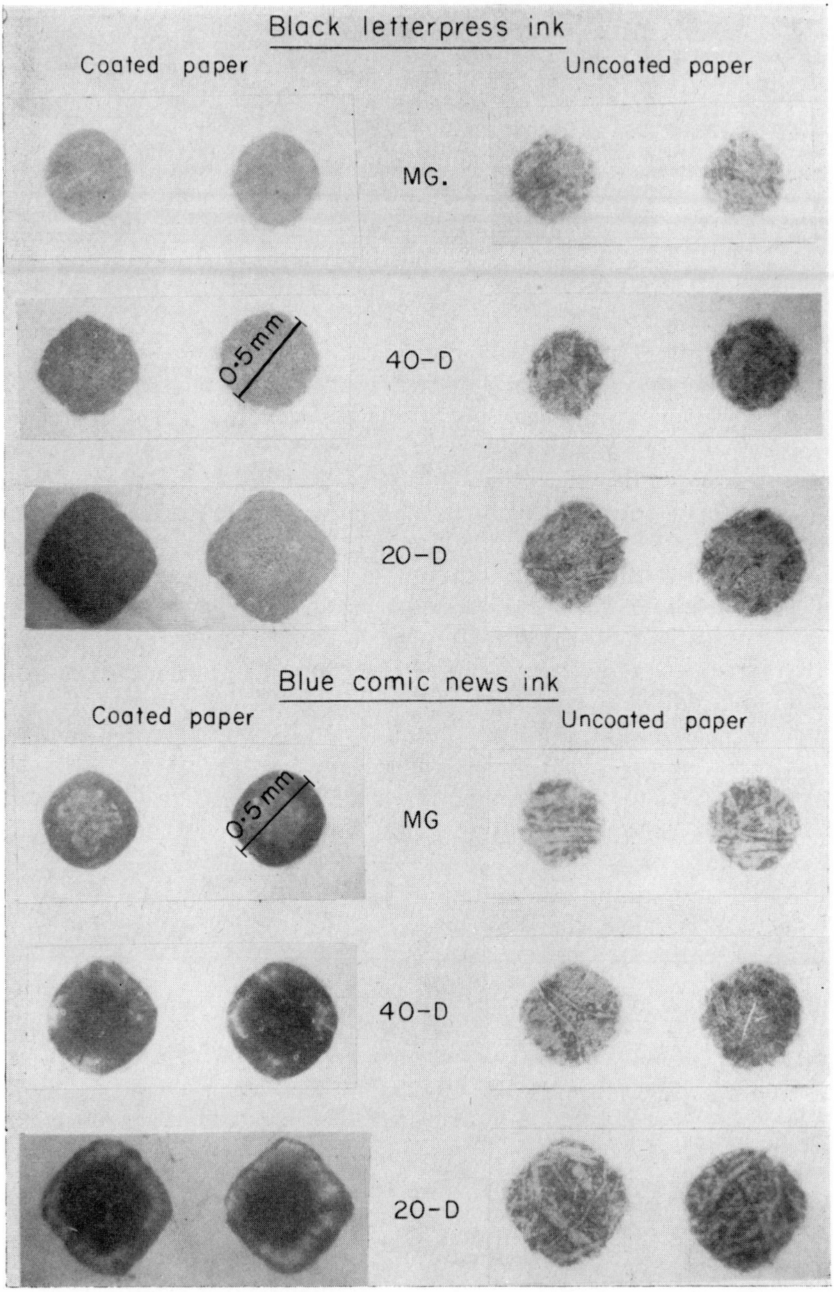

Fig. 8. Dot structures of various ink–paper–plate combinations. (Magnification 33 ×; 8 μ ink on corresponding solid plate.)

and nonporous nature of the paper, either of which contribute to lateral spread of ink over the paper surface. Another factor which might be involved is the greater sensitivity of the blue color to variations in film thickness compared with that of the black color.

It should also be mentioned that, although the dots on the bare plates resembled squares with somewhat rounded corners; the printed dots generally became circular with increasing film thicknesses. The dot edges of the 30 plate were so irregular and varied within a print that the results were completely discounted.

Minimum dot coverage

In selecting the film thickness required for the presence of all dots and for apparent complete coverage, it was noted that irrespective of ink, paper, and plate, the LPL for all halftones occurred at about 1.0 ± 0.1 ink on the corresponding solid print. The LPL's were therefore based on the ink on the solid plate required to transfer one micron of ink to the solid print. The values are listed in appropriate columns in Table 1 and were designated by thin dashed lines on all figures.

The similarity of the LPL, expressed as ink on the paper, for all combinations is probably due to the assumption that the high pressure on the individual dots minimizes the differences among the material variables. On the other hand, different film thicknesses were obviously required on the plate to transfer the desired thickness, and in this case, since the film thickness region is low, the effectiveness of the plates correlated well with thin film transfer, which is associated with printing smoothness. It can be seen in Table 1 that 40 rubber was the best, magnesium was in the middle, and 20 rubber was the poorest. The uncoated paper and the news ink required more ink on the plate than the uncoated paper and the letterpress ink respectively. It can also be noted that the solids required 2–4 times more ink than the halftones; this point will be discussed again later.

Dot diameter and optical density

Figures 9 and 10 illustrate the dot diameters of the various ink–paper–plate combinations as a function of ink film thickness on the corresponding solid print. Optical densities of the halftones are plotted on the same graphs on the basis that a relationship with dot diameter ought to exist.

Whereas all the rubber plates had initial dot diameters of 0.41 mm, the magnesium plate diameters were only 0.39 mm. To make the results comparable to the rubber plates, 0.02 mm were added to each dot value from the magnesium plate prints. No effort was made to correct the density values accordingly. Another problem with the magnesium plate was that the dots printed at low film thicknesses were always smaller by about 0.05 mm than those on the plate and this is attributed to an unsharp edge on the dot. The rubber plates, however, gave low film thickness dot sizes approaching those of the plate.

Figure 9 compares dot enlargement as a function of the inks and papers on various plates. Several general trends are immediately obvious. First,

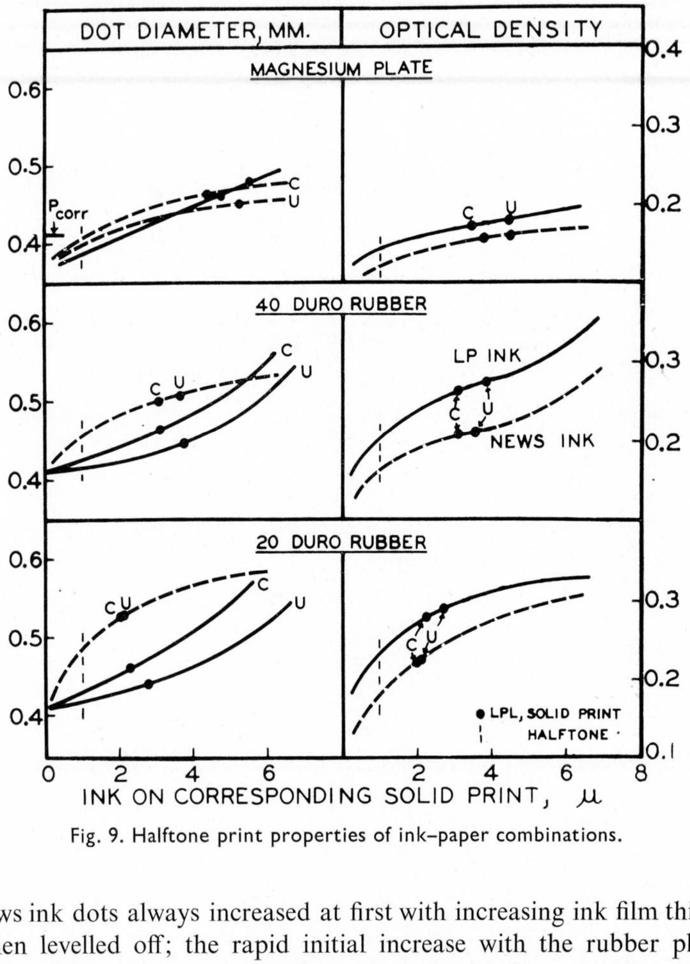

Fig. 9. Halftone print properties of ink–paper combinations.

the news ink dots always increased at first with increasing ink film thickness and then levelled off; the rapid initial increase with the rubber plates is especially striking. An opposite effect occurred with the more viscous letterpress ink; here dot enlargement increased essentially linearly at first, but then in the case of the rubber plates, increased very rapidly at higher film thicknesses. It is interesting that dot spreading, whether due to squashout and/or pick up of slopover ink, should reach a saturation point with the news ink but becomes increasingly more extensive with the letterpress ink.

Generally, the dot spreading was greater, as would be expected, on the nonporous coated paper than on the uncoated paper. Note that the rubber plates minimized the differences between the papers with the thin news ink, but magnified the differences between the papers in the case of the viscous letterpress ink. Note also the similarity in dot diameters provided by the magnesium plate irrespective of paper and ink, whereas differences due to ink as well as paper were much more marked with the rubber plates.

Surprisingly, optical density of the halftone prints showed no difference between the papers with either ink. One might have expected the density to be greater on the coated paper because of the greater dot enlargement combined with the greater density observed on the solids. On the other hand, the lower density of the news ink compared with the black letterpress print is expected from the comparative solid print density results. The flat middle section of the 40-D optical density curves, which also occurred with the 50-D prints, is attributed to the white ring observed on the printed dots in the medium film thickness range.

Figure 10 illustrates the comparison among the plates. In all cases, the softer the plate, the more extensive was the dot enlargement. Despite the corrected values for the magnesium, the dot diameters were always smaller than with the rubber plates at comparable film thicknesses. Note again the large differences among plates with the news ink on either paper. In the case of the letterpress ink, larger differences in dot diameter from plate to plate occurred on the coated paper than on the uncoated paper. Recalling that a similar situation existed with respect to optical density, it is again surprising that the halftone print optical densities from both papers produced essentially the same spread from plate to plate.

Optical density measurements are sometimes employed to estimate dot diameter. The different curve shapes as a function of film thickness found in these experiments makes it apparent that no overall correlation between dot diameter and halftone optical density or solid print optical density existed among all the material variables studied.

It should also be pointed out from perusal of Fig. 10 and the halftone data listed in Table 1 that the tendency of dot size and halftone print density to increase as the plates became softer is the same trend which had been observed in the case of print coverage and optical density of the solid prints. Apparently the softer plates caused lateral spreading of ink with halftones as well as solids, a condition which is advantageous only for solids.

Halftone versus solid print quality

In the discussion of the solid plate results, it was suggested that the effectiveness of rubber plates in improving solid print coverage involves an ink spreading mechanism rather than printing contact smoothness. In considering the situation for halftones, it may be recalled from examination of appropriate columns in Table 1 that the plates were again rated in two different orders. The ink on the plate required for minimum dot coverage followed smoothness order *A*, that is, optimum conditions were obtained with the 40-Durometer

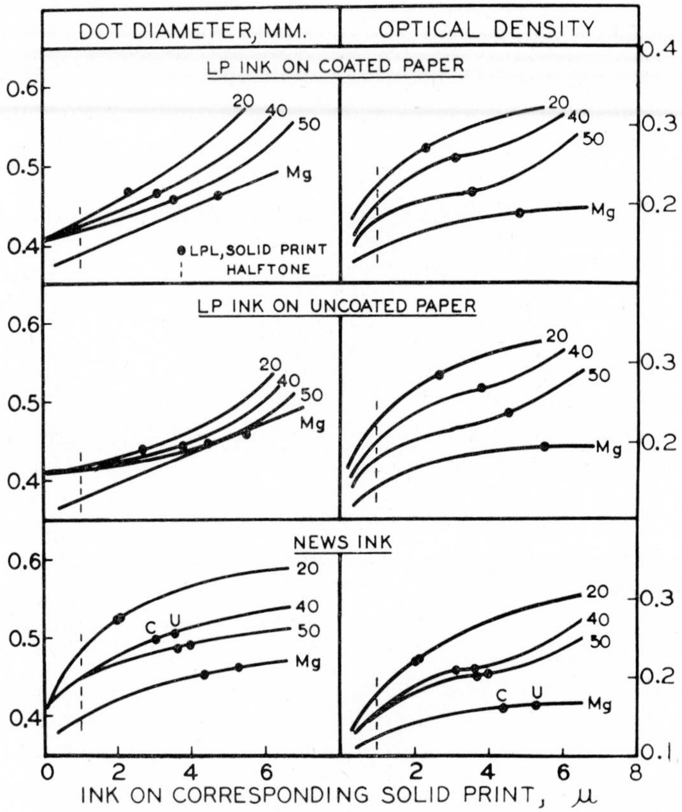

Fig. 10. Effect of plate material on halftone print properties.

plate, whereas dot enlargement followed coverage order *B*, that is dot size increased with increasing plate softness.

The printing smoothness and lateral flow mechanisms remain the same as with printing, but with opposite desirability. Successful halftone printing requires both the presence of all dots with a minimum of ink carried and a close approximation to the dot size on the plate. The softer the plate, the greater is the failure in both requests. It can therefore be concluded that factors, such as lateral flow, which are advantageous for solids may well be deleterious for halftones.

In comparing the LPL ink requirements with LPL dot sizes, it can be noted that the dots from 40-Durometer rubber halftone plate printed completely with slightly less ink than the magnesium plate, but that the magnesium plate provided the smaller dot diameter at the LPL. On the basis that fidelity is the most important aspect, hard plates are to be preferred over soft plates for halftone printing.

Comparisons of practical printing conditions

One of the questions which can be partially answered from this work concerns whether solids and halftones can be both run successfully side by side. Reference to Table 1 reveals that, depending on the ink–paper–plate combination, the solids required 4–11 μ of ink carried on the press, whereas the halftones required only a range of 2–4 μ.

Obviously, the solids cannot be run at the minimum film thickness of the halftones. The suitability of the vice versa situations requires examination of the dot sizes at the LPL. With the letterpress ink on the coated paper, all the plates, despite the wide variance in ink which had to be carried, produced a dot increase of 0.05 or 0.06 mm over the bare plate, which represents a 13 per cent average increase in diameter, and a tone value of about 25 per cent instead of the desired 20 per cent. With this ink on the uncoated paper, the range in dot increase was 0.07 mm for the magnesium plate and to 0.03 mm for the softest rubber. But the news ink on either paper averaged 0.06 mm for the magnesium up to 0.15 mm for the softest plate.

The general tendency indicates that, at the same plate heights, dot enlargement is likely to occur when halftones are run at the same film thickness necessary to cover a corresponding solid. With magnesium plates, about the same degree of squashout occurred irrespective of the ink and paper, but with rubber plates, the news ink printed excessively large dots compared with the letterpress ink. The systems studied to date are of course too limited to draw definite conclusions.

SUMMARY

1. The same ink transfer and print quality were observed with seven hard smooth solid-faced plates irrespective of the metal or plastic material. Roughened metal plates transferred less ink and provided poorer coverage than the smooth plates.
2. In the case of rubber plates, an optimum in plate softness (40-Durometer) was found with respect to ink transfer in the thin ink film region where breakup of the solid prints occurred. In the higher ink film region where acceptable solid prints were obtained, the rubber plates improved transfer, coverage, optical density, and print uniformity to a degree proportional to the plate softness.

3. Breakup on halftone prints disappeared at $\frac{1}{4}$–$\frac{1}{2}$ the ink film thickness required for solid print coverage, and an optimum in plate softness was found (at 40-Durometer). On the other hand, the softer rubber plates caused more extensive dot enlargement than the hard plates.
4. The thin ink film transfer results with the solid rubber plates and the breakup results with the halftone plates correlated well with transfer parameters for printing smoothness. The coverage results with the solid plates and dot enlargement results with the halftone plates correlated well with transfer parameters for ink immobilization by the paper.
5. The coated papers gave higher coverage and optical density, but greater dot enlargement than the uncoated paper. The dot enlargement was more extensive with the news ink compared with the letterpress ink especially when rubber plates were used.

CONCLUSIONS

1. The printing quality of hard solid plates depends on initial surface smoothness of the plate but not on its material.
2. The effectiveness of rubber plates in improving solid print quality is due to enhanced lateral flow of ink in the deformed nip rather than to increased contact area.
3. Different optimum printing conditions and material variables apply to solids than to halftones. Halftone printing requires good contact between the paper and inked plate without lateral flow of ink over the surface of the paper. For coverage of solids, however, lateral ink flow contributes more than does printing contact smoothness.

RECOMMENDATIONS

1. For practical printing, soft rubber plates can be recommended for solid work on the basis that they improve coverage even though contact area is reduced. Although an optimum in printing contact smoothness occurred in these experiments with a 40-Durometer rubber plate, hard plates are recommended for halftone fidelity because they minimize dot enlargement.
2. For printability testing, low ink film thickness transfer measurements with solid plates should be useful for predicting breakup results from halftone plates on the basis that both aspects are associated with printing contact smoothness. Average optical density measurements integrate a variety of causes and effects and therefore should not be used as a fundamental parameter for printing smoothness without a measure of the deviation from the average.

ACKNOWLEDGEMENTS

The authors are indebted to W. D. Schaeffer, J. J. Hammel, C. E. Grund, and A. M. Butto for extensive assistance with the experimentation and calculations. They also gratefully acknowledge the long range support of basic research sponsored by the National Printing Ink Research Institute with the assistance in this case of the Louis Calder Foundation and several individual company contributions.

REFERENCES

1. G. E. Carlsson, Swedish Graphic Arts Research Laboratories.
2. R. Ginman, A. Svedlin, and L. Norman, Estimating the printability of paper by proof printing. *Norsk Skogindustrie* **11,** No. 1, 14 (1957).
3. W. C. Walker and J. M. Fetsko, A concept of ink transfer during printing. *Am. Ink Maker* **33,** No. 12, 38 (1955).
4. W. D. Schaeffer, A. B. Fisch and A. C. Zettlemoyer, Transfer and penetration aspects of ink receptivity, *Tappi* **46,** No. 6, 359 (1963).

DISCUSSION

Bruno: There is an interesting case of the lateral flow effect of soft rubber in offset printing. This effect is especially noticeable in the reproduction of solids from conventional blankets and the new compressible Polyfilm blanket which consists of a thin coating of rubber on a fibrous base. The compressible material reproduces all imperfections in the surface whereas the conventional blanket with its thicker rubber surface flows laterally in the impression and covers over the defects, resulting in a better transfer of ink in the solids.

Zettlemoyer: I am pleased that you pointed out the relation to offset printing. It would be helpful to have a method of separating this lateral flow from the total ink transfer in both offset and letterpress printing.

Walker: The differences in ink distribution over the dots shown in Fig. 8 for the Blue Comic Ink on coated paper with various plates is very interesting. For the magnesium plate the dots have a heavy edge, while for the soft rubber plate the dots have a thin edge. Do you have any suggestions for differences in mechanism of squashout that might cause this effect?

Zettlemoyer: The rubber dots had a considerable shoulder so that the light rings they produced were due to slopover and squashout. The magnesium dots, at least at low ink film thickness, printed a smaller diameter than indicated by their size. Apparently, there was a slight depression around their edges which would explain the heavy annular rings produced at the edges.

Frøslev-Nielsen: You have found the best coverage with soft plates, and the best dot printing with the hard ones. Do you think that it is possible to combine these properties and get optimum qualities by making plates of two materials, a hard surface layer on a soft base, for example?

Zettlemoyer: There may indeed be some practical advantages to the printing of solids with soft plates and halftones with hard ones, but the arrangement would presumably have to be side-by-side. Inking requirements, for one thing, would be different. It seems doubtful that the same results could be achieved by backing up a hard plate with a very soft base.

Carlsson: I understand that your experiments are carried out at the same printing speed, but I would like to ask if you eventually investigated the same difference between the behaviour of the various plates at a substantially higher printing speed?

Zettlemoyer: We have not had the opportunity to extend the work to higher speeds. Differences would be expected to decrease somewhat as the printing speed is increased.

A NEW METHOD FOR MEASURING THE SURFACE ROUGHNESS OF PAPER

by P. C. van der Vloodt
Stichting Instituut voor Grafische Techniek—T.N.O. Amsterdam

1. INTRODUCTION

The printing quality of a paper depends on many factors, but undoubtedly the surface smoothness is of first importance. Many different methods and instruments have been devised for assessing smoothness.

Among current methods are:

1. Air flow methods, as introduced by Bekk, Gurley, Sheffield, Bendtsen, Williams and others.
2. Optical contact methods, due to Chapman.
3. Surface profile measurements, using a moving probe.
4. Ink and oil transfer and coverage methods.
   1. Proof press, micro-contour test, printing smoothness, reflectance measurements (Baysung Hsu).
   2. Nip spreading and other filling-in methods[1].
5. Subjective evaluation of magnified surfaces; visual or photographic.

All the methods have their own particular limitations.

1.1 By using these methods one gets an assessment of the surface irregularities by indirect measurements. The roughness is determined by the rate of air *passage* through the voids formed between the paper surface and an optically flat surface. Most air-flow instruments use relatively low contact pressures in comparison with those applied in printing. Furthermore, with smooth papers large errors can enter into the results, because of air passing laterally through the sheet.

1.2 With Chapman's optical contact instrument the paper is pressed against a glass prism and the sample is illuminated. The amount of reflected light is related to the smoothness. A possible drawback is that optical contact is not needed in printing, because a fluid ink film is used. Very shallow depressions can prevent optical contact and yet not be of practical significance.

1.3 The conversion of the readings to actual printing performance is difficult.

1.4 (1) In most cases these methods do not give a definite figure, but provide only a subjective comparison with other papers.

(2) Most of the procedures are very time-consuming.

1.5 The results can be misleading, unless extreme care is exercised in selecting a representative area of the surface.

Skill in interpretation and comparison with standard samples is required.

When introducing a new method we must bear in mind that it has to fulfil certain conditions.

In measuring the roughness of a paper one has to take into account the following:

(1) during printing, mechanical forces are exerted on the paper, causing deformation of the surface structure. Therefore it is important to measure the paper under pressure, preferably under circumstances closely related to the (dynamic) printing conditions.

(2) For practical use it is important that the method is rapid and simple.

(3) The value of a method decides its usefulness; this is increased by expressing the smoothness in a practical figure, making it unnecessary to compare the papers with standards.

In the present report a nip-spreading method is described, giving the roughness as an average of the hole depths. This method satisfies the previously mentioned conditions.

2. GENERAL PRINCIPLE

In the application of this method, with the aid of the IGT printability tester, a small, accurately determined, quantity of water is spread over the paper, forming an oval spot by filling the surface irregularities. With this nip-spreading method water is used instead of the usual organic liquid[2,3].

It was found that when the water was applied very quickly, i.e. when the time of interaction between paper and liquid was short, the water ($\gamma = 72.8$ dyne/cm at 20°C, $\eta = 1$ cpoise, $\cos \theta < 1$) had no opportunity to penetrate into the capillary spaces of the paper. So the results of the measurement refer only to the roughness.

Absorption within the body of the paper after the spot is formed has no influence on the subsequent measurement of the surface of the spot.

The brief duration of the application was realized by using the spring drive of the printability tester.

So as to know the exact quantity of liquid with which to form the spot the water is spread between two identical paper strips to each of which half of the volume is applied.

3. EXPERIMENTAL

Two strips of paper are placed in the clamp of the IGT printability tester with identical sides facing each other.

One strip is mounted over the 2 cm wide aluminium disk, the other over the rubber blanket on the sector.

On the strip first mentioned a drop of lacquer is placed in order to prevent the water from penetrating into the paper in the time interval between applying the drop and spreading it.

By means of a micro-syringe 3.00 ml of distilled water stained with trypane blue (1 g/100 ml) is placed on the (dry) lacquer. With the spring tension

Fig. 1. Testing the roughness of a paper with the IGT printability tester.

adjusted to 20 kg and the spring drive in position B, the water is spread out over the paper, producing an oval spot.

The surface of the spot is determined planimetrically.

The volume per surface unit (X in ml/cm^2) is calculated and represents the average depth of the irregularities of the paper surface.

With very smooth papers the area of the spot becomes so large that a quantity of 1.5 ml of water is enough; with very rough papers it is preferable to take a greater volume.

Every measurement is carried out in triplicate and the average given.

4. RESULTS

As the new roughness measurement is given in the same unit as the roughness which can be calculated from Sweerman's[4] roughness-porosity test, it is obvious to compare both (Table 1).

TABLE 1

Description	Side	R (roughness measured by Sweerman's method) in ml/cm²	X (roughness measured by new method) in ml/cm²
Wood-free machine	1	0.18	0.12
coated paper	2	0.18	0.11
Woody machine	1	0.19	0.15
coated paper	2	0.20	0.14
Wood-free machine	1	0.16	0.16
coated paper	2	0.18	0.19
Wood-free machine coated paper		0.20	0.17
Woody chromo paper		0.10	0.15
Wood-free chromo	1	0.08	0.09
paper	2	0.32	0.31
Wood-free art paper	1	0.05	0.06
	2	0.06	0.07
Low woody art paper*	1	0.08	0.09
	2	0.09	0.09
	1	0.04	0.07
	2	0.01	0.07
Esparto art paper	1	0.07	0.11
	2	0.11	0.12
Wood-free one-sided cast-coated paper		0.14	0.09
Wood-free one-sided cast-coated paper		0.10	0.09
Wood-free writing	1	0.40	0.40
paper	2	0.44	0.45
Stencil paper	1	0.80	0.84
	2	1.16	1.08
Wood-free Foudrinier	1	0.29	0.48
Bristol paper	2	0.32	0.43
Wood-free type-writing	1	0.64	0.63
board	2	1.16	0.85
Uncoated box board		0.52	0.51
Lithographic paper		0.32	0.42
Wood-free offset paper	1	0.83	0.60
	2	0.55	0.55
Wood-free offset paper		0.68	0.74
Wood-free halftone	1	0.22	0.32
paper	2	0.31	0.35
Newsprint	1	0.77	0.65
	2	0.76	0.64
Gravure paper	1	0.28	0.29
	2	—	0.33
Gravure paper	1	0.16	0.16
	2	—	0.27
Gravure paper	1	0.35	0.28
	2	—	0.31
Gravure paper	1	0.36	0.34
	2	—	0.28
Gravure paper		0.32	0.33

* It was found that two different batches of different roughness were mixed.

Using Sweerman's method, the paper is drawn along a rectangular slit filled with an organic liquid. During this movement the liquid fills the holes in the paper surface and at the same time penetrates into the paper.

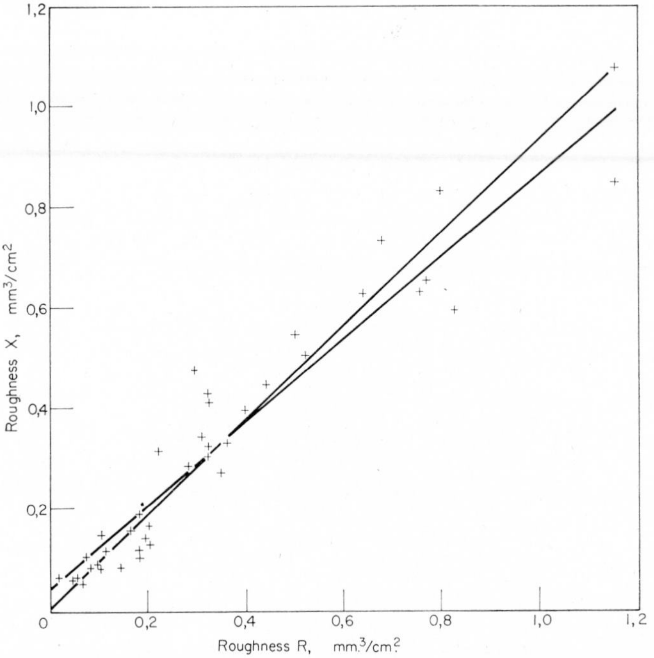

Fig. 2. Regression lines for the correlation between *R* (roughness values calculated from Sweerman's roughness-porosity test) and *X* (roughness values determined with new method).

The roughness is determined with the aid of the formula:

$$Y = R + K\sqrt{\frac{\gamma t \cos \theta}{\eta}}$$

in which:

Y = total quantity of liquid transferred to the paper per square centimeter.

R = quantity of liquid that fills the holes per square centimeter.

$K\sqrt{\frac{\gamma t \cos \theta}{\eta}}$ = quantity of liquid that penetrates per square centimeter.

With some exception, the correlation is significant.

All measurements were carried out at a relative humidity of ± 65 per cent and a temperature of ± 20°C.

The high degree of correlation between both measurements is shown in Fig. 2, indicating the regression lines.

The correlation coefficient is 0.96; the expressions for the regression lines are:

$$R = 1.09\ X - 0.02$$

$$X = 0.84\ R + 0.05$$

5. REPRODUCIBILITY

To test the reproducibility of the method the roughness of three sorts of paper was measured ten times on two different printability testers.

The following results were found:

TABLE 2

	Printability tester 1			Printability tester 2		
	Average surface in mm²	Average roughness X in ml/cm²	Standard error in %	Average surface in mm²	Average roughness X in ml/cm²	Standard error in %
Lithographic paper	350	0.43	4.3	335	0.45	2.4
Machine coated paper	885	0.17	1.6	865	0.17	0.7
				880	0.17	1.1
Cast-coated paper	795	0.095	2.4	730	0.100	1.4

6. EFFECTS OF VARIOUS FACTORS ON THE RESULTS

6.1. Effect of the duration of application

The influence of the duration of application on the measured roughness was obtained by testing the paper at various velocities. This was done by using the printability tester with the pendulum drive and with the spring drive.

By allowing the pendulum to fall and by using the spring drive in position A, M or B, the average time of interaction between paper and liquid is $\pm 3\frac{1}{2}$, 8, 9 or 10 times as brief as when the spot is made by controlling the pendulum by hand with a constant velocity of 20 cm/sec.

At low velocity the spots become elongated and irregular and it is not so easy to measure the surface.

TABLE 3

	Pendulum drive		Spring drive		
	$v = 20$ cm/sec X in ml/cm²	Weight acceleration X in ml/cm²	Position A X in ml/cm²	Position M X in ml/cm²	Position B X in ml/cm²
Lithographic paper	0.35	0.39	0.43	0.45	0.45
Machine coated paper	0.23	0.19	0.17	0.17	0.17
Cast-coated paper	0.073	0.080	0.090	0.100	0.100

We see that at higher velocities the roughness values found do not show significant differences, so we may conclude that the surface of the spot determines the roughness and during this short time none or very little of the water penetrates into the paper.

6.2. Effect of the pressure

The influence of the pressure is determined by measuring the roughness at different spring tensions.

TABLE 4

	Spring tension				
	5 kg/2 cm	10 kg/2 cm	20 kg/2 cm	40 kg/2 cm	70 kg/2 cm
Cast-coated paper	0.106	0.103	0.091	0.086	0.081
Lithographic paper	0.43	0.42	0.42	0.40	0.41
Newsprint	0.74	0.73	0.65	0.60	0.59
Machine coated paper	0.20	0.20	0.17	0.15	0.15
Machine coated paper	—	0.17	0.17	0.17	0.16
Machine coated paper	—	0.17	0.16	0.15	0.14

The smoothness increases at higher pressures. The degree of variation of the smoothness is an indication of the compressibility of the paper.

This method enables us to measure the roughness at values of pressure closely related to practice.

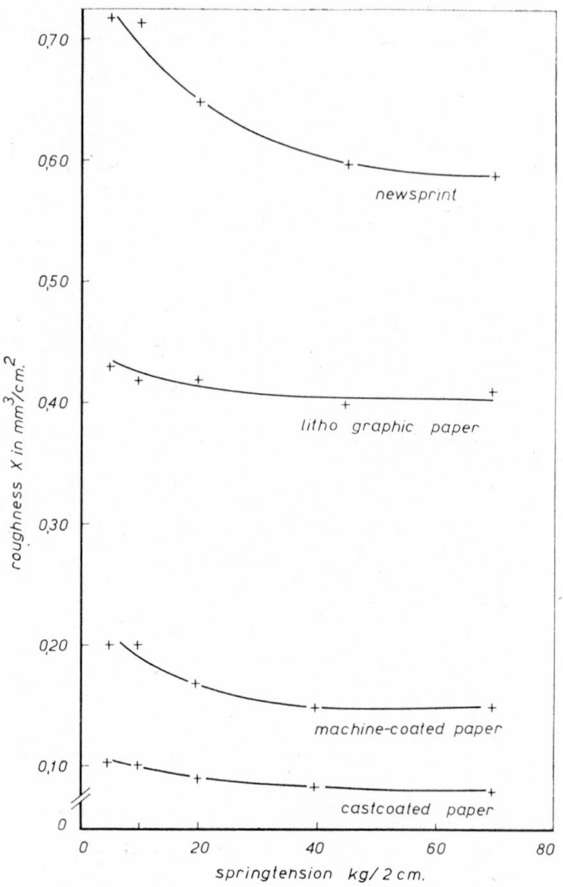

Fig. 3. Effect of the pressure on the measured roughness.

6.3. Effect of the surface of contact

It is well known that the smoothness depends on the nature of the surface of contact[5].

To investigate this, the roughness was measured by using different backing materials. For that purpose the rubber blanket normally used was replaced by a paper layer, or no layer at all was used (metal backing). In another test the metal disk was replaced by a rubber one.

The influence of the backing material is not only evident in the figures mentioned above, but shows still more in the uniformity of the patterns of the spots. The test enables the backing to be chosen in agreement with practical conditions.

TABLE 5

Blanket	Rubber	Rubber	Paper	Metal (none)
Disk	Rubber	Metal	Metal	Metal
	X in ml/cm^2	X in ml/cm^2	X in ml/cm^2	X in ml/cm^2
Cast-coated paper	0.113	0.100	0.111	0.104
Chromo paper	0.10	0·10	0.11	0.10
Lithographic paper	0.41	0.45	0.46	0.48
Machine coated paper	—	0.17	0.19	0.17

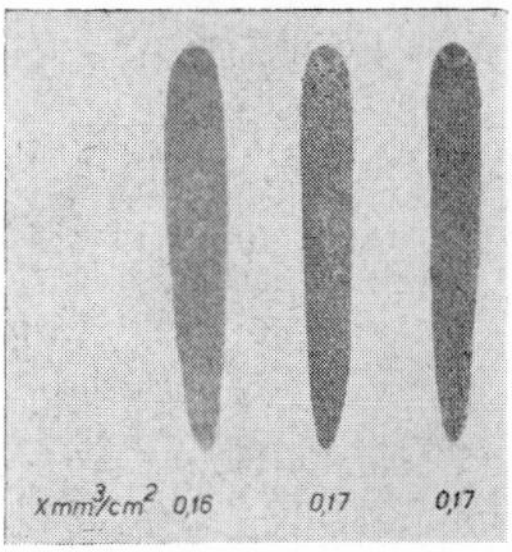

Fig. 4. Characteristic patterns of three machine coated papers showing the differences in distribution of the surface irregularities.

7. UNIFORMITY OF THE SPOTS

The majority of smoothness tests describe the surface configuration as an average degree of roughness.

In actual printing, shape and distribution of the irregularities are of great importance.

The method described above also expresses the roughness by an average figure. When looking at the spots, however, it is evident that they show a certain pattern by which it is possible to get an idea of the shape and the frequency of the irregularities.

Though it is not possible to describe the uniformity by a parameter, one can differentiate between certain papers by comparing them.

If we have three machine coated papers with identical roughness values, we see that even if they have the same average depths of holes, the surface patterns are quite different.

The investigation on the effects of pressure and backing has already shown that they influence not only the measurement of the roughness, but especially the uniformity of the appearance of the spot. For one machine coated paper we have compared this appearance with the surface structure which can be obtained by printing the paper with a small quantity of ink[6].

This has been done with increasing spring tensions and different backings. There is agreement in the pattern of the spot and the print.

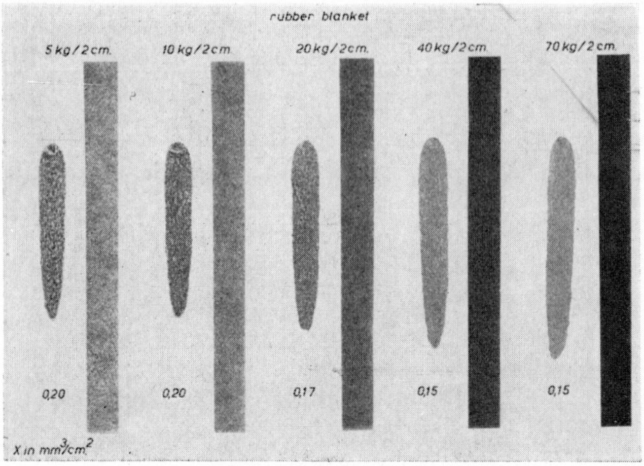

Fig. 5*a*. Correlation between appearance of spots and prints and the effect of pressure and backing on the measured roughness and surface structure of a machine coated paper.

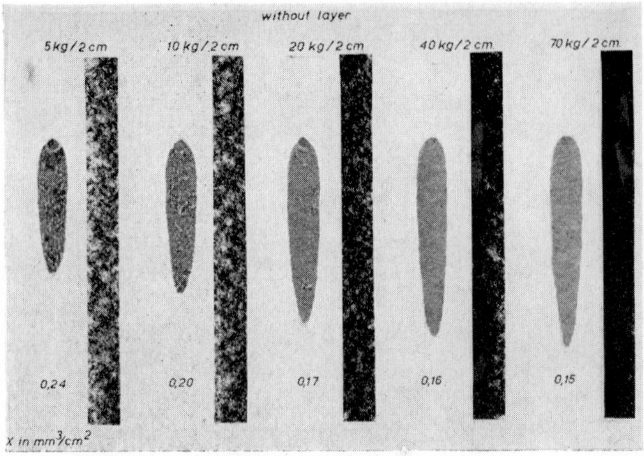

Fig. 5*b*. Correlation between appearance of spots and prints and the effect of pressure and backing on the measured roughness and surface structure of a machine coated paper.

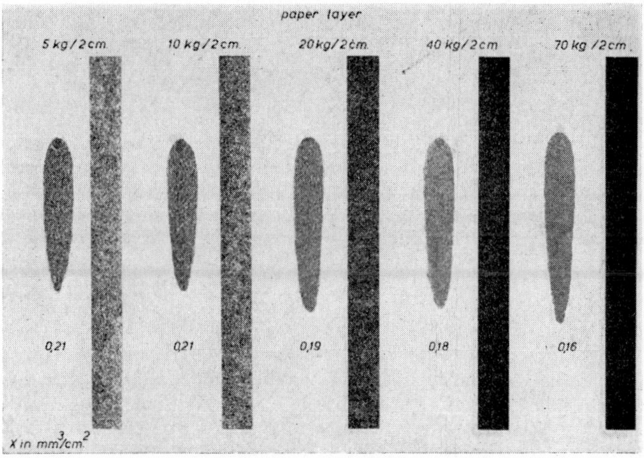

Fig. 5c. Correlation between appearance of spots and prints and the effect of pressure and backing on the measured roughness and surface structure of a machine coated paper.

8. SUMMARY

A new method is described which makes it possible to measure the roughness of a paper in a simple and rapid manner, under circumstances closely related to printing conditions.

By means of the IGT printability tester, the surface cavities are filled by spreading a measured quantity of water at great velocity over the paper.

By measuring the filled area, the average depths of the holes can be calculated.

The results are in agreement with the roughness figures found by Sweerman's roughness-porosity method.

The effects of pressure, velocity of application and backing on the measurement are examined.

It is shown that besides the roughness index the distribution of the irregularities can be determined visually.

This characteristic surface pattern is related to the pressure applied and the layer used.

The correlation between this pattern and the surface structure visible when the paper is printed with a small quantity of ink, is obvious.

REFERENCES

1. J. A. Hart, J. Verhoeff and W. Gallay, *Pulp and Paper Magazine of Canada* **63,** T-387 (1962).
2. W. A. Wink and J. A. Van den Akker, *Tappi* **40,** 528 (1957).
3. L. A. van Gastel, *IGT-Nieuws* **11,** 176 (1958).

4. A. J. W. Sweerman, *Tappi* **44,** 172A, No. 7 (1961).
5. G. Blokhuis, *IGT-Nieuws* **8,** 81 (1955).
6. Application of the IGT-printability tester, IGT-publication 12 (1962), p. 15.

DISCUSSION

Mme Benedite: All well known methods of measuring surface smoothness do say something about the printing smoothness we are interested in, but none tell the whole story. Even with a correlation coefficient of about 0.8 (which is generally considered reasonably high in paper testing) this is not enough to predict with accuracy the probable behaviour of paper, especially in gravure printing, and particularly in light and middle tones. Do you believe that your method offers anything new in this respect?

Miss van der Vloodt: The purpose of our work was to compare the results of our new method with those of Sweerman's method. To find the correlation with actual printing, further investigation will be required. With this new method, however, it is not only possible to find the average roughness (as in most smoothness tests) but at the same time you get information about the surface structure. If you consider both, I think you will have more success in predicting the behaviour of a paper. You also have the possibility of varying the pressure and packing and to use conditions closely related to the printing process you are concerned with.

Banks: Is there a particular reason why you use water?

Miss van der Vloodt: Because it has a high surface tension and is easy to apply.

Yule: Do differences in surface tension of the water with different papers affect the results?

Miss van der Vloodt: We made measurements on a few papers with water of a low surface tension (*ca.* 30 dyne/cm), and we got results which were different from those with water of a surface tension of 72 dyne/cm. This is caused by penetration.

Ginman: Will a great difference in water absorbency between samples influence the measured smoothness value? You have shown that for lithographic, machine coated, and cast-coated paper the speed of application does not influence the roughness value, but all these papers have a rather low water absorbency. If you take two papers with about the same smoothness but very different water absorbency, for example, lithographic paper and newsprint, would you, in that case, get an error due to absorbency effects?

Miss van der Vloodt: I do not think so. As you can see in Table 1 the roughness figure for newsprint found with this new method is even lower than the roughness which can be calculated from the roughness-porosity test of Sweerman, and in the case of lithographic paper we have found just the opposite.

Miss Pritchard: Have you compared the patterns given by the K and N and Microcontour tests with those given by your method? This should show whether penetration is involved.

Miss van der Vloodt: We have only compared them with the Microcontour test for some papers, and we found the same sort of distribution pattern.

THE PRINTING SMOOTHNESS OF PAPER

by WILLIAM C. WALKER and ROBERT F. CARMACK
West Virginia Pulp and Paper Company

Abstract—The printing smoothness of paper is a measure of how well it conforms to the plate surface and accepts a full ink image under printing conditions. Since the usual bench tests for smoothness give inadequate correlation with the press performance of papers, proof press tests have been devised to simulate the performance behavior. The proof press test prints are commonly evaluated by reflectance measurements which confuse smoothness with ink holdout.

More meaningful analysis requires separation of these two properties. The ink holdout can be evaluated from a full coverage print, while the printing smoothness can be obtained from the amount of break. Prints were scanned with a modified Scan-a-graver to produce strip chart traces of reflectance variations. Several functions of these data were studied for correlation with visual evaluation of break. Correlation of greater than 0.90 was obtained with "out-of-limits reflectance." An integrating scanner was successful in measuring this quantity directly and in correlating with break obtained in halftones.

THE "printability" of paper is recognized as a subject of prime importance to both the graphic arts and the paper industry. As such it has received considerable attention from this and other technical groups.

One logical starting point for discussion of printability has been the problem of defining the term in a concise and useful manner consistent with its use in the industry. Many attempts have been made to do this, and a number of conflicting results have been published[1–5].

In our opinion the following three definitions form an accurate and practical basis for discussions in this field. They are in agreement both with proper etymology and widely accepted usage in the field. They are slight modifications of definitions developed over a period of years by the Subcommittee on Printability of the TAPPI Graphic Arts Committee.

1. *Print Quality*, or the quality of a print, is the degree to which the appearance characteristics of the print approach those of the desired result.

2. *Printability*, or printing quality, of a surface is the degree to which its properties enhance the production of high quality prints by a particular process.

3. *Runnability* of a material on a printing press is the degree to which it can be printed on that press without operating difficulties.

Since these definitions were made as concise as possible, a brief discussion may be helpful to clarify their implications.

The term "print quality" refers to the judgment of the merits of the finished product in terms of the objective, regardless of how it was produced. High quality is highly dependent upon the desired results. Therefore, a more specific statement of what constitutes quality in the wide variety of printing jobs produced today is very difficult to make. For instance, high gloss on a label may be desirable to catch the eye of a prospective customer, while less gloss is desirable in a textbook to minimize eye strain for the reader.

Print quality is not a single property that can be expressed meaningfully in terms of a single number. It is a composite of many contributing factors whose relative importance may vary from case to case. Focusing of attention on the quality factors of greatest significance in the particular case makes a discussion of print quality specific and practical. Quantitative measurement of these individual quality factors is often achievable, as in the work of LTF,[(6)] but their combination to a single value for print quality, as discussed by Rupp[(5)], must involve arbitrary decisions.

After the discussion of print quality, it is apparent that the printability of a surface is likewise a composite of many properties. It includes any properties that will have an influence on the quality of the prints made on that surface. As in the case of print quality, printability cannot be handled as a single entity, but technical discussions must deal with specific properties. In most cases of letterpress printing the most significant of these properties is "printing smoothness" which is the primary subject of this paper.

The runnability of a material on a printing press is essentially its freedom from defects which interfere with the mechanics of the printing operation. Any paper property which prevents the paper from passing smoothly through the press, reduces press speed, causes frequent washups, requires special press adjustments, or reduces production in any way reduces the runnability of the paper. Some deficiencies detract from both runnability and printability. Picking may reduce printability by producing blemishes on the prints and may reduce runnability by necessitating frequent stopping of the press for extra washups.

Against this background we can now come to grips with the concept of "printing smoothness," undoubtedly the most important of the properties contributing to the printability of papers for letterpress and gravure printing. The softness of offset blankets and rubber plates reduces its significance greatly when they are used.

The printing smoothness of paper may be defined as the facility with which full contact can be attained between the ink image and the paper surface by the printing process in question. A paper of high printing smoothness gives full coverage with a minimum of pressure and ink film thickness.

Insufficient printing smoothness results in breaks in the printed pattern so that unprinted paper shows through and interferes with the desired effect. Printing smoothness is quite different from the smoothness of a free sheet. It is concerned with the contour of the paper surface under the impression pressure of the printing process.

In this and other discussions, it is frequently convenient to speak of the roughness of a paper surface instead of its smoothness, especially when the scale increases with decreasing smoothness. Roughness is understood to be the reciprocal of smoothness.

Bench tests for smoothness

As you are well aware, a considerable number of bench tests have been devised and used for measuring the smoothness of paper. Several excellent surveys of these instruments and their performance have appeared recently.[7,8] The best known approaches and instruments are the following:

1. Air leak under smooth ring
   Bekk, Bendsten, Gurley, Sheffield, Brecht
2. Stylus tracing for contour
   Brush, Talysurf, Metrosurf, Proficorder
3. Optical contact with glass prism
   Chapman
4. Low angle shadowing
   Scheid

All of these measurements have been useful to a degree but have definite limitations when attempts are made to use them for precise prediction of the printing performance of paper. They may be very helpful in the control of papers within a given type, but any unusual change may be erroneously evaluated. Among the more obvious deficiencies of these methods are the following:

1. Air leak smoothness testers operate at compression pressures far less than those encountered in printing. They are influenced by the degree to which the surface depressions of the paper are interconnected and by flow of air through the body of the paper.

2. Stylus tracing gives the contour of an essentially uncompressed paper or one where the pressure is exerted equally on hills and valleys in a fashion quite different from that found in printing.

3. While the optical contact method examines the paper under high pressure, it is concerned generally with only the highest 50 per cent of the paper surface which is the easiest to print. It ignores the deep valleys that cause the most serious printing smoothness problems.

4. The low angle shadowing technique of Scheid examines a completely uncompressed sheet and is quite unrealistic for prediction of printing properties.

Printing tests

In the face of these deficiencies and difficulties, many paper testing laboratories have gone directly to printing tests.(9) While printing tests are difficult to set up and control with adequate precision for meaningful results, they aim most directly at the heart of the matter. With press testing one has a chance to measure performance directly rather than trying to establish reliable correlation with performance.

A number of such press tests have been used and described. Perhaps the most carefully considered are those published recently by the Sub-committee on Printability of the TAPPI Graphic Arts Committee.(10) RC 312 is based on the use of the IGT Print Tester and RC 313 on a proof press.

The proof press test for printability used by West Virginia is fairly typical but should be described here briefly. The procedure was developed by Hunt and Carmack at the Williamsburg Mill in 1955 and has been extensively used there, at other West Virginia mills and at the Institute of Paper Chemistry. It has been discussed briefly by Carmack in a paper on ink roller problems encountered with it.(11)

Essentially, the test consists of the production of black solid prints with a proof press under controlled conditions and the analysis of their reflectance to give a "printability value." The press used is a Vandercook No. 4 equipped with means for careful control of ink film thickness, pressure, and speed and operated in a room with controlled temperature and humidity. The ink used is IPI tack graded black No. 2. The ink film thickness and pressure used are lower than those for normal letterpress printing. As a result, the prints show considerable break which is quite sensitive to the printing smoothness of the paper.

After printing and drying, the paper and prints are measured for diffuse reflectance with a Photovolt reflectance meter to arrive at a "printability value" according to the following formula:

$$\text{Printability} = 100\left(\log\frac{Ru}{Rp} - 0.25\right)$$

Where Ru = Reflectance of unprinted paper

Rp = Reflectance of printed paper

The "printability values" from this test are similar to those calculated in TAPPI RC 312 except that the term 0.25 has been introduced here to keep results from exceeding 100. RC Method 313 which suggests reporting the results simply as reflectance values for the prints as a per cent of paper reflectance would line up papers in the same way. These measurements have served well in predicting the letterpress printing characteristics of coated papers. Unfortunately, the value obtained in this way is not a measure of a single property. It appears to be primarily a combination of printing smoothness and absorbency, the two properties of greatest importance in the problem at hand.

The difficulty with such tests lies in the fact that the result is based solely on the measured average reflectance of the print. The reflectance of the print can be lowered by either or both of two different effects. The first is the amount of "break" in the print or the area not covered by ink and showing the white of the paper surface. The second effect is the blackness of the areas bearing an ink film. This blackness is a function of the ink holdout of the paper surface and its gloss. These two effects are blended in this "printability number" and cannot be distinguished.

It is important to distinguish between these two effects, however, if one is to understand what is happening and take effective corrective action. This point was made particularly clear by the comparison of prints quite different in appearance with the same "printability values." Typically, one would have a rather uniform gray appearance with little break while the other would have sharply contrasting black and white areas with the same average reflectance.

Qualitative scanning

Prints showing the above differences with the same "printability value" were studied on a modified Fairchild Scan-a-graver. This equipment was an early model of the Scan-a-graver which was designed to scan original copy on a rotating cylinder and reproduce it as a plastic letterpress plate. The platemaking part of this machine had been removed, and the signal from the scanner was fed to a strip chart recorder.

Thus, the diffuse reflectance of small areas of the print could be traced as a function of distance across the print. The spot was illuminated at an angle of 45° and viewed normal to the surface. The area being viewed at any instant was about 0.0066 in. in diameter. The sample print was moved axially at a speed of only 0.3 in./min so that the variation could be picked up readily with the Brown recording potentiometer.

Typical traces for the two different types of prints are shown in Figs. 1 and 2. Qualitative examination of these traces shows readily that they are quite different in character. The trace in Fig. 1 shows very black regions but a large number of very sharp peaks. The trace in Fig. 2 is not nearly as irregular; its low reflectance areas are not as low, and it has much fewer peaks.

It was quite apparent from examination of these curves that they contained information concerning the differences between these papers and that proper analysis of them should result in a quantitative method for differentation

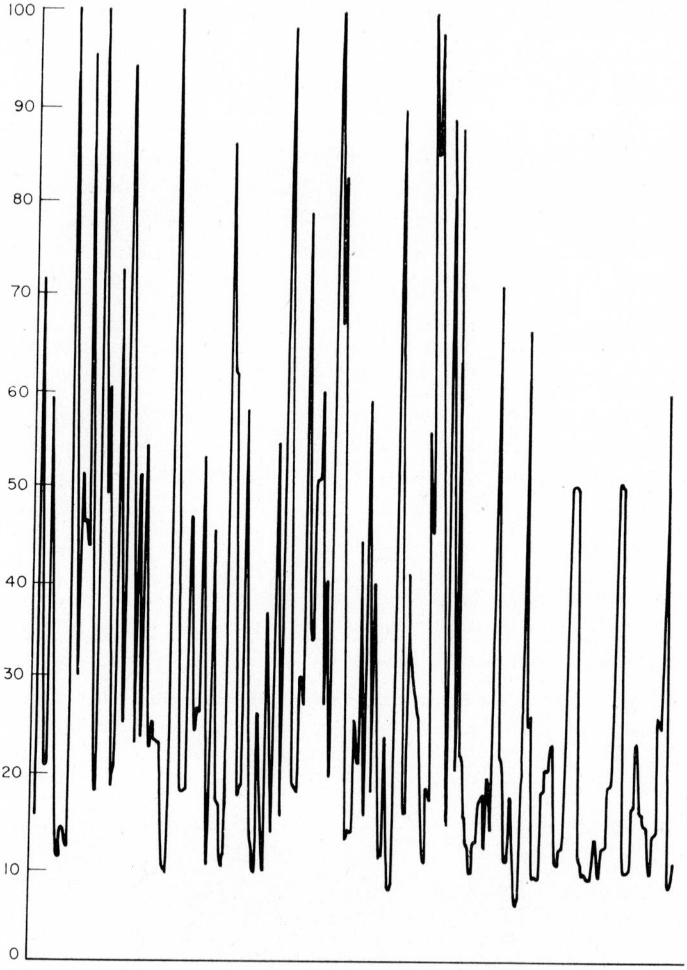

Fig. 1.

of the roughness and ink holdout of the paper surfaces. Some measure of the variations should indicate the amount of break in the print and hence its printing roughness.

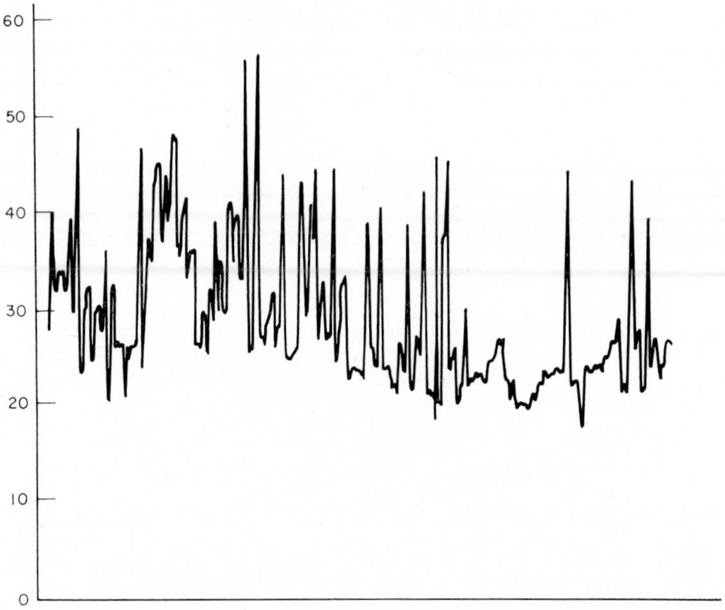

Fig. 2. Reflectance trace for one inch of smooth absorbent sheet.

Quantitative studies

The next investigation centered on a series of nine coated papers of widely different characteristics. These samples were first printed and evaluated by the proof press printability test. Visual ratings for amount of break were determined by three observers using the pair comparison method;[12] their results are shown in Table 1. The papers are listed in Table 2 with their proof press and visual examination results for comparison. The sum of the results obtained by the three observers in visually ranking the sheets is recorded as the visual evaluation rating. The samples are arranged and lettered from best to worst on the basis of the visual ratings as a primary standard.

Examination of the "printability values" indicates poor agreement with visual judgment and resulted in a rank correlation coefficient of only 0.25. Examination of the postcoated sheets, D and H, clearly emphasizes this difference. D was rated best by "printability." The ink was held up on the surface of this sheet giving these prints by far the glossiest and blackest appearance of any in this series. However, closer examination revealed a large number of breaks. Ink holdout was also good on H. "Printability" rated this sample third, but the print again showed a great deal of break.

Prints were scanned in the same areas measured by the Photovolt meter for the "printability" tests. Figures 1 and 2 are typical traces. The Y-axis is numbered in units of ten from 0 to 100 and measures reflectance. The instrument was standardized to give a chart reading of 90 when viewing a standard chip having a reflectance of 30. Thus, reflectance values are obtained by dividing chart scale by three. The X-axis is the base line measuring time or length of scan.

These traces were analyzed by a number of approaches in an effort to find a characteristic number which ranked the samples in the same order as visual rating. The first of these approaches was analysis of the reflectance distribution.

TABLE 1. VISUAL EVALUATION RESULTS OF THREE OBSERVERS ON FIRST SERIES OF PAPERS

Observer	Sample scores									Correlation with totals
	A	B	C	D	E	F	G	H	I	
1	16	14	13	11	9	7	7	3	1	0.97
2	17	15	13	9	11	7	5	3	1	0.94
3	17	15	13	11	9	7	5	3	1	1.00
Total	50	44	39	31	29	21	17	9	3	

TABLE 2. BASIC PROPERTIES OF FIRST SERIES MACHINE COATED PAPERS

Sample number	Source	Type	Basis weight No.	"Printability"		Visual evaluation
				%	Rank	
A	Compet. I	C1S	60	71	5	50
B	W. Va.	C2S	60	72	4	44
C	Compet. I	C2S	70	69	6	39
D	Exper.	C1S-PC*	60	81	1	31
E	Compet. II	C1S	60	74	2	29
F	W. Va.	C1S	70	65	8–9	21
G	Compet. III	C2S	70	66	7	17
H	Exper.	C1S-PC*	60	73	3	9
I	Compet. IV	C2S	70	65	8–9	3

* Postcoated sheets with exceptional ink holdout.

Reflectance distribution

Reflectance distribution analysis involved recording the reflectance at regular intervals along the traces from the Scan-a-graver. These data were plotted in the form of reflectance distribution curves for further study. About four hundred points were required for each trace to get a reasonable distribution curve. Curves for three samples are illustrated graphically in Fig. 3. As may be seen there, these curves have a very characteristic shape;

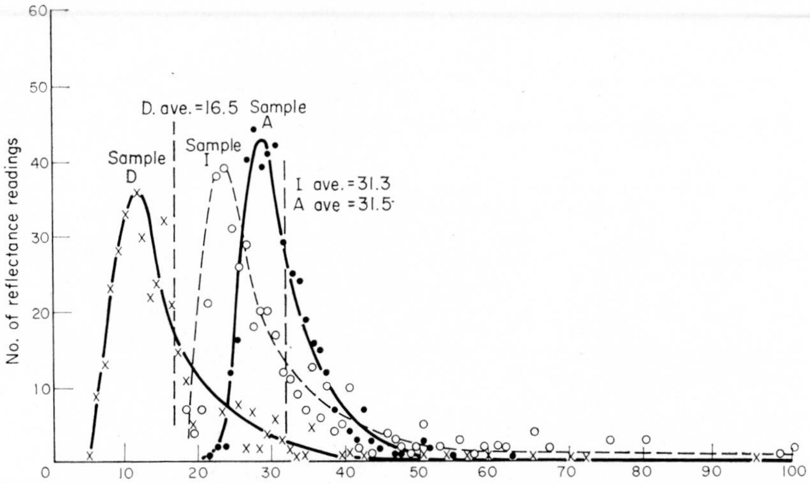

Fig. 3. Reflectance distribution curves for three typical curves.

a sharp peak with abrupt drop off at low reflectance and a long tail or skew at high reflectances.

It was apparent that a large number of methods had possibilities for calculating a roughness value. Visual comparison of the curves for these papers indicated differences in height, breadth, and degree of skew. The samples were ranked on the basis of average reflection and average deviation, and the results are shown in Table 3. The average reflectance showed no correlation with visual examination, but average deviation showed a very good correlation of 0.78, three times as high as that for the "printability value."

It was apparent that the high reflectance ends of these distribution curves were most directly dependent upon the breaks in the prints and hence the roughness of the sheet. The aim throughout the investigation was to find a method which correlated with the eye and could be measured instrumentally. It was hypothesized that the eye might tolerate small reflectance variations near the average for the print and that the reflectance variations beyond some limit might be objectionable. Therefore, a method was sought for expressing the amount of this "out of tolerance" reflectance.

Reflectance distribution curves were too irregular for noting directly the area in the skewed high reflectance ends of these curves. Therefore, integral curves were drawn in which the per cent of surface beyond a given

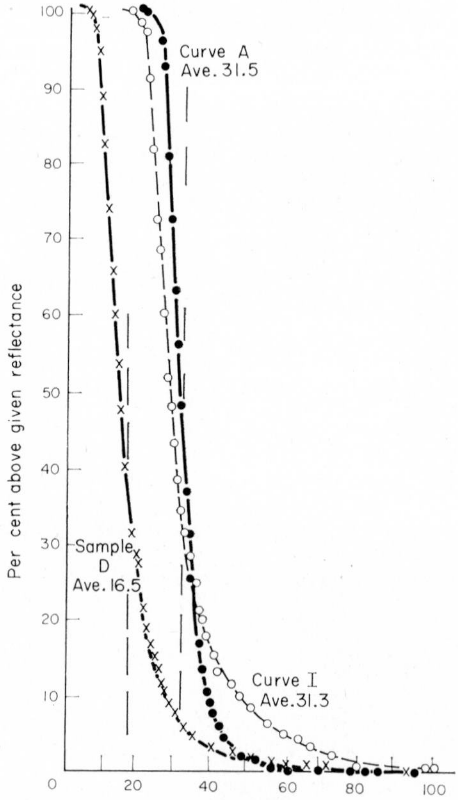

Fig. 4.

reflectance was plotted against that reflectance. Integral curves for three samples are illustrated in Fig. 4.

Visual examination of the integral curves showed distinct differences to the right of the average. The per cents of surface more than 5, 10, 15, 20, and 30 units above the mean were calculated for each sample. This method is illustrated in Figs. 5 and 6. As is indicated in Fig. 6, this value is essentially the area under the peaks in the scanning traces but above the selected limit. Samples were ranked according to these figures as shown in Table 3.

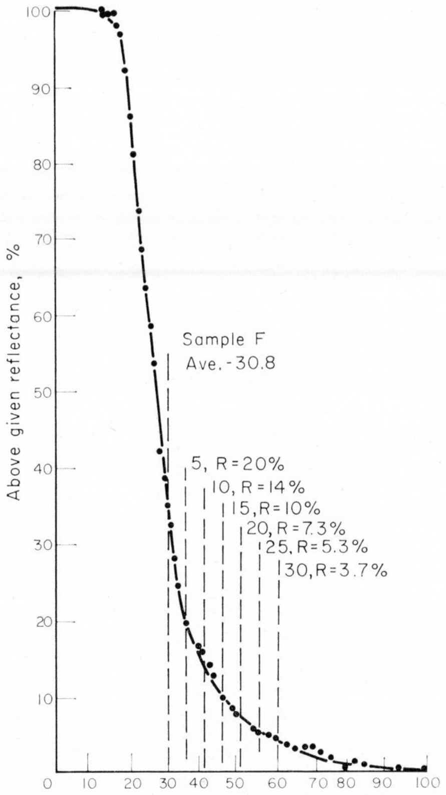

Fig. 5. Out of limit reflection from integral distribution curve.

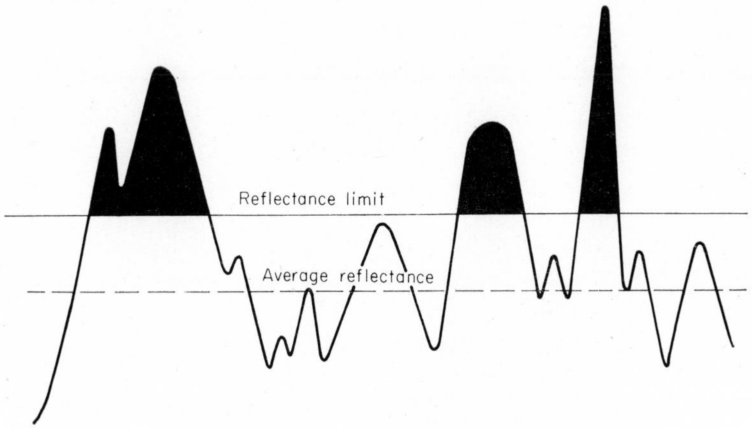

Fig. 6. Significance of out of limit reflectance.

TABLE 3. REFLECTANCE CURVE RATINGS FOR FIRST SERIES

	Order of Rank									Correlation with visual
	1	2	3	4	5	6	7	8	9	
Visual examination	A	B	C	D	E	F	G	H	I	
Printability ..	D	E	H	B	A	C	G	F	I	0.25
Ave. reflectance ..	D	H	E	B	C	G	F	I	A	0.00
Ave. dev. reflectance	A	B	C	E	D	G	H	I	F	0.78
% surface at										
5 above mean ..	A	B	E	C	D	G	I	F	H	0.78
10 above mean ..	B	A	C	E	D	I	G	F	H	0.67
15 above mean ..	A	B	C	D	E	F	G	I	H	0.94
20 above mean ..	A	B	C	D	E	H	G	F	I	0.83
25 above mean ..	A	B	C	D	H	E	G	F	I	0.78
30 above mean ..	A	B	C	D	E	H	G	F	I	0.83
% surface at										
15 above median	A	B	C	D	E	G	I	F	H	0.83
20 above median	A	B	C	D	E	G	F	H	I	0.93
25 above median	A	B	C	D	H	G	E	F	I	0.73
30 above median	B	A	C	D	H	E	G	F	I	0.73

Correlation coefficients ranging from 0.67 to 0.94 were obtained by comparing these rankings with visual judgment. The correlation coefficients passed through a maximum when the limit was about 15 units above the mean. This appears then to be a critical value that may correspond to the point where the eye starts to note the existence of break. It may also be related to the size of break and its relationship to the size of area viewed during scanning. At any rate, its correlation with visual judgment is very striking.

Another reference point for surface measurements which might have some significance is the median. The median is, in this case, the reflectance level where half the surface has less and half has more reflectance. It is the 50 per cent point on the integral distribution curves. Per cents of the print surface more than 15, 20, 25 and 30 units above the median were also calculated and the correlations for these values are shown at the bottom of Table 3. As indicated in Table 3, the best correlation was found at 20 units to the right of the median. Since it was found that the median averaged three reflectance units below the mean, this position approximates the 15 units above the mean.

The correlation data in Table 3 clearly indicate that the scanning technique presented here measures printing roughness. The surface areas measured for ranking the samples are the areas of the print beyond the acceptable tolerance of reflectance set by eye, namely the area of break in the print which the eye holds most objectionable. The correlation coefficient of 0.94 based on the area above 15 units beyond the mean shows that the scanning technique and visual judgment agree quite closely in evaluating printed papers for surface roughness.

The work done on this first series of samples was considered to be most significant. These samples were selected to represent papers differing widely in printing characteristics and methods of manufacture. An instrumental method which will differentiate printing roughness among papers in this group should work very well on series of more similar papers if it has enough sensitivity.

Frequency analysis

A great deal of work was also done with "frequency analysis" of the scanning traces. Frequency analysis involved recording the number of times the trace crossed each level from 0 to 100. This type of data was much easier to take than the reflectance distribution data and could be readily handled with instrumentation by triggering a counter at a given reflection level.

The fundamental significance of the frequency data is not as clear as that of reflectance distribution. Nevertheless, distribution curves and a variety of functions were calculated from these data. The distribution curves were smoother and calculations easier, but the correlations with visual examination were poorer than for reflectance distribution as shown in Table 4. Therefore, this approach was dropped.

TABLE 4. FREQUENCY CURVE RATINGS FOR FIRST SERIES

	Order of rank									Correlation coefficient
	1	2	3	4	5	6	7	8	9	
Visual examination	A	B	C	D	E	F	G	H	I	
"Printability value"	D	E	H	B	A	C	G	F	I	0.25
Peak total left ..	A	B	H	I	C	E	G	D	F	0.28
Peak total right ..	A	B	C	E	G	I	F	H	D	0.56
% skew right ..	C	F	B	G	A	E	I	D	H	0.28
Total freq. count	A	B	C	E	I	G	H	F	D	0.44
Ave. reflect. level	D	B	H	C	E	A	G	F	I	0.33
Ave. dev. ref. level	B	A	C	D	G	H	I	F	E	0.56
Frequency count at										
5 above mean ..	A	B	C	E	I	D	G	H	F	0.60
10 above mean ..	A	B	C	E	G	D	I	H	F	0.67
15 above mean ..	A	B	C	G	D	E	I	H	F	0.67
20 above mean ..	B	A	C	G	D	I	E	H	F	0.60
25 above mean ..	B	A	C	G	D	H	I	E	F	0.56
30 above mean ..	B	A	C	G	H	D	I	F	E	0.44

Poisson distribution for roughness determination

The skewed characteristics of the distribution curves suggested a possible conformation to a Poisson distribution. The distribution curves obtained here terminate abruptly on their low reflectance end at a value that corresponds to the reflectance of a full film on the paper. The Poisson distribution has the same type of a termination at zero and a tailing off at high values. Thus, if the reflectance scale is shifted to place its zero at this point, there is a strong resemblance to a Poisson distribution.

A Poisson distribution was plotted for each sample using the average frequency level as a basis and computing the points from statistical tables.

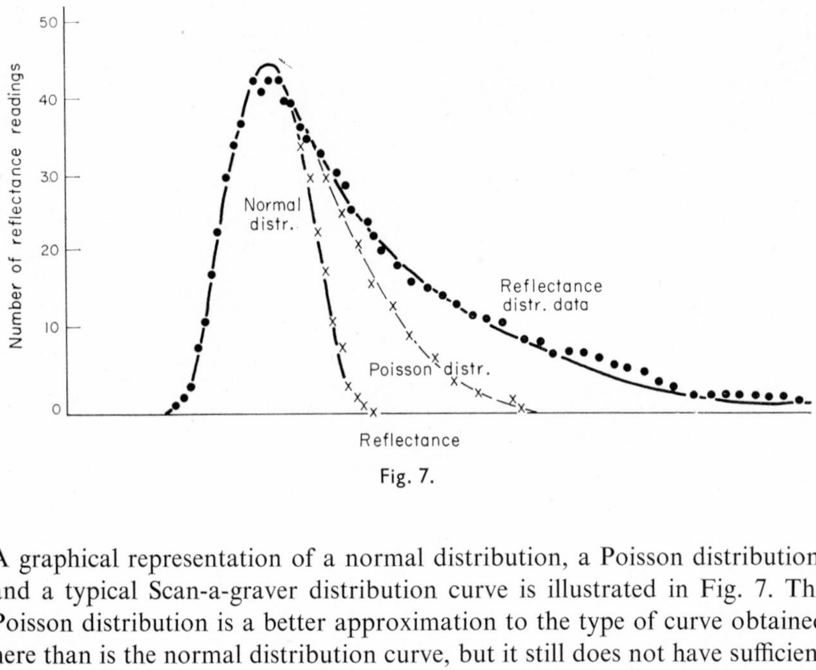

Fig. 7.

A graphical representation of a normal distribution, a Poisson distribution, and a typical Scan-a-graver distribution curve is illustrated in Fig. 7. The Poisson distribution is a better approximation to the type of curve obtained here than is the normal distribution curve, but it still does not have sufficient skew.

Consideration of the Poisson distribution led to a simple and rapid test and technique for calculating roughness. The press procedure was modified slightly by overpacking the cylinder to give a 1 in. band of high pressure and full coverage along one side of the print: Photovolt reflectance measurements were taken on the underprinted area, on the band at full coverage, and on the unprinted sheet. These values were substituted in the following equation.

$$\% \text{ Roughness} = \frac{R \text{ print} - R \text{ ink}}{R \text{ paper} - R \text{ ink}} \times 100$$

where R print = average reflectance of the print as made by the standard method at low pressure.

R paper = average reflectance of the unprinted sheet.

R ink = average reflectance of the solid image at full coverage.

In the Poisson distribution the variance is equal to the mean. In the above equation the numerator corresponds to the mean for the Poisson distribution, and the denominator makes the final result a percentage of the possible difference for the particular ink-paper combination.

Table 5 summarizes the results obtained by this method. The correlation coefficient between roughness and visual examination (0.61) was much better than between printability and visual judgment (0.25).

TABLE 5. POISSON ROUGHNESS RATING FOR FIRST SERIES

	Order of rank									Correlation coefficient
Visual examination	A	B	C	D	E	F	G	H	I	
% Printability ..	D	E	H	B	A	C	G	F	I	0.25
% Roughness ..	B	A	E	F	D	C	G	I	H	0.61

This method of measuring roughness was seriously considered as a control method since the technique and instrumentation are so simple and the correlation so much better than that of the regular proof press printability test. It was abandoned, however, since much better correlations had been obtained through reflectance analysis.

Printegrator

The results discussed above indicate that the per cent of the surface with reflectance above the mean gave the best correlation with visual evaluation. An integrating scanner was constructed, therefore, that would integrate the area under the curve above any preset level. Thus, it could be used to measure this function directly and permitted this function to become a useful tool in paper evaluation.

An integration with the gate set at zero gave a measure of the average reflectance as seen by this instrument. With this value the gate could be set at the threshold level above average, and a second scan and integration could be made to give the desired measure of out of limit reflectance and hence the amount of break in the print.

The sample holder for this instrument was a flat turntable with the scanning head slowly moving out from center as the sample turned. Thus the scan path was a spiral similar to that of a phonograph record. Two paths of 10 and 50 turns/in. of radius were available. Reproducibility studies indicated standard deviations for the first integral for average reflectance level of 0.75 and 0.67 per cent, respectively. The second integral for out-of-tolerance reflectance was much smaller and the standard deviations were 9.78 and 5.98 per cent, respectively.

Unfortunately, the Printegrator could not be checked on the same series of prints used in the previously discussed work. Those prints were made from a plate that outlined in white the four areas of the solid where the reflectance measurements are made in the proof press "printability" test. These white outlines had to be crossed by the scanner and made a large contribution to the integral.

Therefore, a second series of papers was used for the evaluation of the Printegrator. This series contained 179 samples of much more closely related papers than were used in the first series. These papers were all machine coated with roll coaters and supercalendered. They represented the production variations in a single grade and weight as produced at three of our mills over a period of several months.

These papers were evaluated for printing smoothness with the Printegrator, with the proof press printability test, by visual evaluation of break in solid prints and by visual evaluation of break in halftone prints. The results are summarized in Table 6.

TABLE 6. CORRELATION OF PRINTEGRATOR WITH OTHER ROUGHNESS MEASUREMENTS

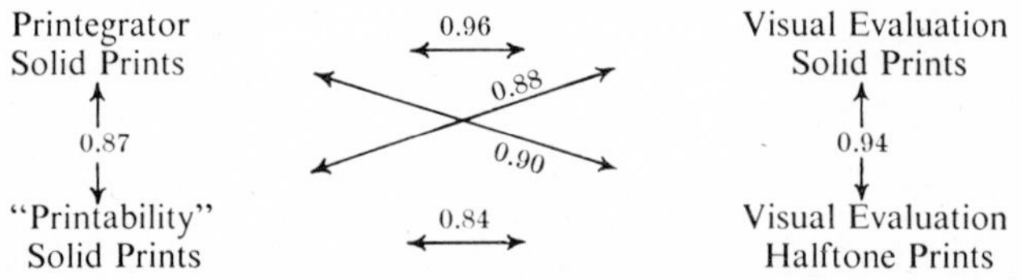

1. There was very good correlation between visual evaluation of solid prints and of halftones printed on the same papers.

2. The Printegrator showed excellent correlation with visual evaluation of the same solid prints but somewhat poorer correlation with visual evaluation of the halftones.

3. The proof press "printability" test showed much higher correlation with this series of papers than with the first series of more diverse papers. It did not do as well as the Printegrator, however.

REFERENCES

1. J. Homer Winkler, *Tappi* **39** (3), 195–7A (1956).
2. R. M. Schaffert, *7th TAGA Proceedings*, 92–5 (1955).
3. G. L. Riddell, *International Bulletin* (67) 53 (1954).
4. Appa, *The Dictionary of Paper*, 2nd Ed., 287 (1951).
5. E. Rupp, *International Bulletin* (80) 52–55 (1958).
6. G. W. Jorgensen and M. H. Bruno, *International Bulletin* (80) 13–19 (1958).
7. E. Beyer, *Das Papier* **13** (5/6) 85–92 (March 1959).
8. W. Brecht and H. Greenen, *Das Papier* **13** (21/22) 519–30 (1959).
9. H. Benedite, *Assoc. Tech. Ind. Papetiere*, Bull. 16(1) 73–81 (1962).
10. Tappi RC Methods 312 and 313, *TAPPI 45* (11) 141A–145A (1962).
11. R. F. Carmack, *TAPPI 42* (1) 71–3 (1959).
12. M. G. Kendall, *Rank Correlation Methods*, 2nd Ed., pp. 144–154, Hafner, New York (1955).

DISCUSSION

Jaschek: The diameter of the scanned area seems to be rather large. A smaller area would give perhaps a better agreement with the visual evaluation.

Walker: The minimum spot size distinguished by the eye at normal viewing distance is about 4 mils. The 6 mil diameter used here is close to this limit, but it is possible that a slightly smaller spot might be better.

Sweerman: (1) Is the the light spot in the paper imaged by a lens on the photomultiplier?

(2) Are there no difficulties with low frequency variation in the reflectance because the paper is scanned twice and then a certain limit is taken above the mean value?

(3) Is it possible to count the number of intersections with the reflectance level and to use this quantity as a measure of the smoothness, for this would be easier to do?

Walker: (1) Illumination is applied to an area of the paper much larger than the viewed area. An image of the paper surface is focused on a metal sheet containing a small hole. The light from the portion of the image falling on the hole passes through the hole to the photomultiplier.

(2) The path length of the scan is long, and the variation in repeat scans over the same path is small. The second scan is made over precisely the same path as the first one to minimize errors.

(3) A great deal of work was done by counting the number of times the traces crossed a given reflectance level since it was easier, as you mention. This is mentioned briefly in the paper. It was not pursued, however, since it did not give as good a correlation and its basic significance was not as well understood.

Zettlemoyer: Printability, and printing smoothness, depend also on the ink used. It would be interesting to know, therefore, whether you studied different types of ink.

Another question concerns the possible correlation of your results with other smoothness parameters such as *k* (in the well-known transfer function). Furthermore, some years ago we showed that subjective evaluation of smoothness from photographs of boxboard under glancing light (Chicago Boxboard technique) at a magnification of 23 times, and which is somewhat related to the Scheid test, gave surprisingly good agreement with printing results. Since this method would be much cheaper and simpler than your approach, I wonder whether it has been tried with papers?

Walker: Our work on the use of different types of inks in our method for printing smoothness has veen very limited, but we have recognized the significance of ink as a variable. The ink initially used in the proof press tests was I.P.I. Tack Graded Black No. 2. It was found, however, that this ink did not give a strong black colour; it tended to spread and fill the breaks, and varied in colour strength from batch to batch. It was, after all, formulated only to meet rigid tack specifications. We switched, therefore, to a black ink specially formulated to resist spread into the breaks and to be consistent and strong in colour. In these respects it was a marked improvement. We do not yet know the correlation between our smoothness method and other methods, such as you mention. It would be interesting to learn more about this point.

SMOOTHNESS AND SOFTNESS OF PAPERS AND THEIR SUITABILITY FOR PRINTING FINE HALFTONES

by E. Paszkiewicz

Institut professionnel de recherches et d'études des Industries graphiques, Paris

This report is concerned with the tests performed in the IPREIG laboratory on a relationship between the surface characteristics of paper and its suitability for printing fine halftones.

The best and most accurate method of assessing the quality of the paper and of testing, at the same time, its ability to print well-defined dots of uniform density, is to print with a series of correctly etched halftones and carefully examine the results. In this way one obtains realistic results, which are obviously of great importance, but they fail to bring out the respective influences of paper properties and their individual importance in the production of a good screened image. One would thus not be able to establish a direct correlation between the qualities of paper and the obtained results.

That is why it is essential to study the correlation between practical results and certain laboratory tests carried out on various types of paper.

We should like here to draw particular attention to the influence of the average density of each dot on the final result of a halftone reproduction.

This average density is, in fact, as important as the size of dot and if the average densities are irregular in some parts of the halftone, the effect is more important than that due to irregularities in the size and surface of printed dots in the granular appearance of the screened image.

We have noted that the properties of the paper corresponding to an acceptable regularity in size of dot are different from those corresponding to a perfect regularity in the surface of dots on the assumption, that a well etched halftone block is used.

We have observed that of two papers giving dots of the same sharpness and cleanness of outline the surface of the one is quite uniform in density, whilst in that of the other, a notable weakness appears, especially in the centre, which corresponds to an observable dot area reduction of 30–50 per cent.

We believe that, if smoothness is a preponderant factor in the contour of a printed dot, then the softness of the paper, determines, in practice, the evenness of the small surface of each dot thus ensuring a uniform density.

The suitability of papers for fine halftone reproduction thus seems to depend on the combined influence of smoothness and softness.

We have attempted to find how these properties, smoothness and softness, could be combined in such a way as to correlate with the suitability of the papers for the printing of fine halftones.

To this end, comparative tests were made on eleven kinds of paper which differed in the following characteristics:

Bekk smoothness.
Density with IGT printability tester and light inking.
Softness.
Microcontour test.

The data corresponding to the 22 sides of the papers are shown in the table where in column I the papers are arranged in order of decreasing Bekk smoothness. Column II shows the density of IGT print made with a force of 20 Kg on the impression cylinders and an inking of 0.2 g on the inking roller. The three figures represent the densities measured at the beginning, the middle and the end of the inked band.

Column III lists the softness determined by a method which depends on the extent of surface deformation of paper pressed against a thin metal blade in which there is a series of tiny perforations of decreasing diameter. The greater the softness, the easier the penetration of the paper through the holes under pressure. A thin strip of bronze or steel (4/100 mm) is fixed on the blanket of the IGT tester (Fig. 1). In this strip are two parallel series of holes, the diameter of these holes increasing progressively by 0.22 mm from one group of two holes to the next from 0.40 to 0.80 mm.

The paper to be tested is put between the blanket, and the metal strip.

When the roller, correctly inked, is pressed against the blade, the surface of the paper will penetrate through the holes and become inked by the roller. This will show as a black point on the paper.

In this way, it is possible to gauge the deformability of the paper over very small areas, that is to say, of its softness. Tests have been made with an applied force (roller against blade) of 50 kg.

The number of printed points varies between 0 and 30 thus affording adequate precision. The results of this test are given in column IV.

Columns VI, VII show the order of the papers based on printing from a 133 line screen with a Vandercook proof press.

TABLE 1. CHARACTERISTICS OF PAPERS EXAMINED

	I	II			III	IV	V (II + III)	VI	VII
	Bekk Smoothness	IGT Density			Softness	Microcontour test	Order of Classification of Paper sides		
		Beginning	Middle	End	Number of points Mean value of six measures	(Density)			
(1)	1952	1.04	0.83	0.85	22.25	0.10	126.25	3	4
(2)	1686	1.00	0.77	0.80	20.25	0.10	120.25	4	6
(3)	922	0.97	0.77	0.82	27.5	0.09	124.5	1	5
(4)	841	1.10	0.91	0.90	29.75	0.09	139.75	2	1
(5)	777	1.10	0.84	0.89	26.5	0.08	136.5	6	2
(6)	755	1.04	0.84	0.82	24.5	0.08	128.5	5	3
(7)	739	0.68	0.61	0.63	33.5	0.39	101.5	7	10
(8)	565	0.70	0.65	0.61	34	0.42	104	8	8
(9)	344	0.58	0.53	0.52	20	0.34	78	16	16
(10)	340	0.58	0.53	0.52	20.5	0.33	78	15	15
(11)	340	0.58	0.49	0.50	31.5	0.23	89.5	9	13
(12)	334	0.70	0.62	0.62	36	0.59	106	11	7
(13)	332	0.61	0.53	0.51	31.5	0.34	92.5	13	11
(14)	328	0.69	0.58	0.56	31.5	0.32	90.5	14	12
(15)	315	0.59	0.48	0.52	30.75	0.23	84.75	12	14
(16)	294	0.68	0.65	0.63	36	0.77	102	16	9
(17)	33	0.26	0.18	0.20	34.5	0.57	60.5	17	17
(18)	22.8	0.28	0.20	0.24	21	0.70	49	18	21
(19)	19	0.24	0.18	0.20	22.5	0.60	46.5	20	22
(20)	17.4	0.20	0.20	0.20	33.75	0.49	53.75	19	18
(21)	6.8	0.14	0.11	0.11	37.5	0.84	51.5	21	19
(22)	6.7	0.14	0.11	0.11	37	0.84	51.5	22	20

Column VI—Classification by observers.
Column VII—Classification resulting from addition max. density × 100 + softness.

The following conclusions can be made:

(*a*) The order of classification of decreasing qualities judged by the Vandercook printing is very close to the classification by Bekk smoothness.

(*b*) The density of the IGT prints decreases in the same way as Bekk smoothness. However, if the Bekk smoothness is the same, or very nearly the same, IGT density depends on softness (paper numbers: 12, 16).

Arrangement of metal strip on I.G.T. tester

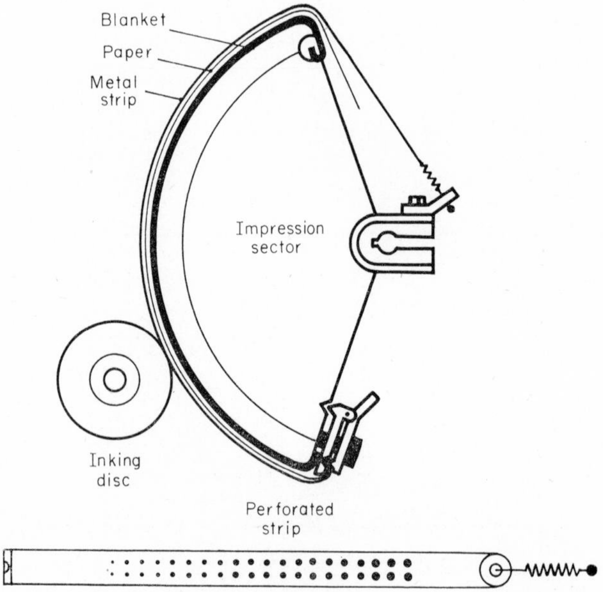

Two parallel sets of 20 perforations decreasing regularly between 0·4 m/m and 0·8 m/m

Fig. 1.

(*c*) Softness and microcontour test density decrease in the same way.

(*d*) For typography, which we have studied here, softness will not exceed 30 (30 marked points) since in excess of this, there is a loss in the quality of the print.

As there is a good correlation between IGT print density and Bekk smoothness, we consider that a good assessment of the suitability of paper for printing with fine halftones may be obtained by taking into consideration IGT smoothness (density) and IGT softness.

Until further work has been done it would be premature to formulate a precise expression of these correlations.

We can, however, observe a real correlation between the order of classification by figures obtained by addition of the *IGT densities* × 100 and the *values of softness* measured by the metal strip method (number of holes marked) and order of classification by observers, especially if we eliminate instances where the softness exceeds 32. This correlation is shown in Fig. 2.

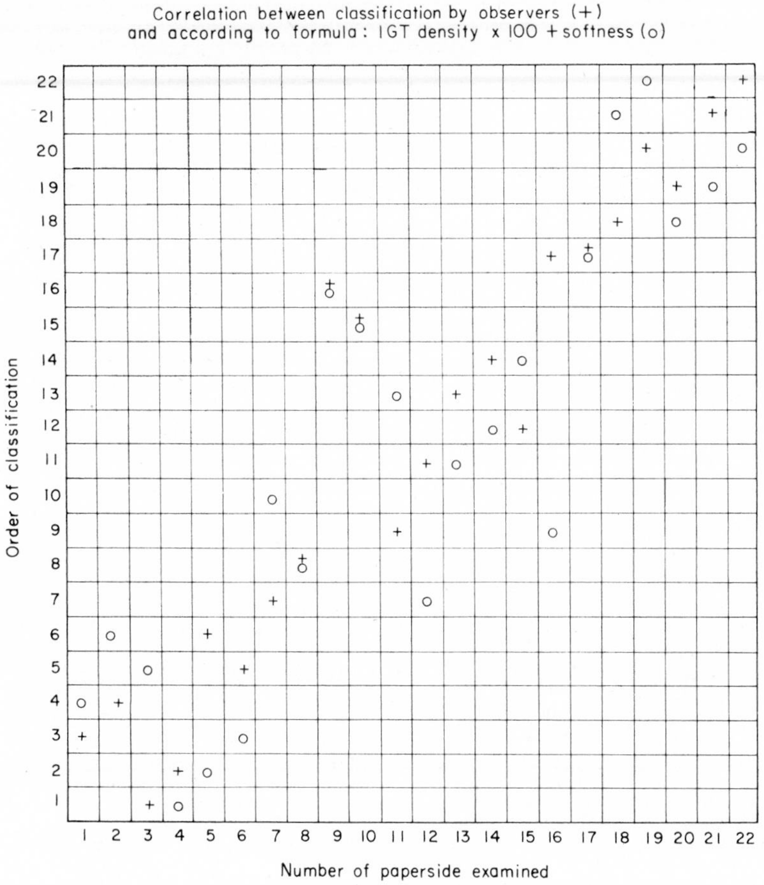

Fig. 2.

DISCUSSION

LARS O. LARSSON: From what you have told us, your method of measuring softness is a comparative one. Nevertheless, I would ask two questions. Firstly, can you tell us a little more about the packing you use and secondly, did you ever use several sheets of paper under the strip at one time? I think such would help us to obtain a clearer idea of the scientific basis of this test.

PASZKIEWICZ: We tried different kinds of packing in addition to having none. The greatest reproducibility was obtained with rubber 1 mm thick and of 70° Shore hardness. No systematic experiments were made with several sheets of paper, though I agree it would be interesting to do so.

MME. BENEDITE: Since the softness of the packing material also influences the results, have you tried to put the paper directly on the metal sector, without any packing at all?

PASZKIEWICZ: Yes, but so far as I can recall, we obtained less reproducibility.

DÜRNER: What kind of roller did you use for inking and impression and at what speeds did you work?

PASZKIEWICZ: The roller was of anodized aluminium. The work was done at constant speed. It would, however, be interesting to work at different speeds.

GINMAN: (1) Did the 11 paper samples you tested include both coated and uncoated papers?

(2) Will not the speed influence the result when testing the micro-compressibility because of the visco-elastic properties of paper? Perhaps it would be of interest to study this aspect.

PASKIEWICZ: (1) Yes, because our immediate concern was to explore the possibilities of the method.

(2) Yes I expect so, but further investigations are clearly necessary.

YULE: Did the papers vary much in thickness?

PASZKIEWICZ: The papers varied from 0.08 mm to 0.15 mm in thickness.

CHRISTENSEN: We have made some studies with Mr. Laraignou's disc method of measuring compressibility and have found that when all three rings are inked, those films on the outer rings influence the results. In fact the method measures a combined effect of film thickness and paper hardness. The method may, however, be adequate if after inking the disc, the ink is cleaned from the two outer rings.

PASZKIEWICZ: I agree that it is better to free the outer rings of ink before operating; however, in some comparative studies we obtained interesting results with the outer rings inked. We think, however, that the paper surface characteristic which we evaluate with the perforated strip method will give a better correlation with practical printing results, and especially with gravure printing.

MISS PRITCHARD: With regard to the Laraignou method of measuring compressibility, we have found that the ink-film thickness correction is in error, as the brass disc compresses during the measurement. If the disc is rolled along a metal surface without pressure, the correct film thickness is obtained, because it agrees with direct weighing of the ink. However, calculation shows that with a load of 45 g, the centres of the disc and sector are brought together by a distance of about 11 μ. This accounts for the inaccuracy found in the measurement.

REIMANN: Have you ever compared your compressibility figures with those obtained with the Bendtsen instrument?

PASZKIEWICZ: Yes, but the correlation is poor.

ROUGHNESS DISTRIBUTION IN POROUS SURFACES UNDER STRESS

by BAYSUNG HSU

The Printing, Packaging & Allied Trades Research Association,†
Leatherhead, Surrey, England

INTRODUCTION

IT is known that in halftone reproduction the choice of screen ruling, which affects the retention of detail in the reproduction, is limited chiefly by the surface roughness of paper. The rougher the paper, the thicker must be the ink film applied in order to ensure reasonable print density and tone range. But with a heavier film there is more likelihood of filling-in of holes, which can be avoided only by using a coarser screen. Monroy(1) reported that the optimum screen ruling for a paper bore a simple relation to the print density achievable on the paper at a certain film thickness. This observation, which was later confirmed at PATRA,(2) shows indirectly the importance of paper roughness in tone reproduction, as the optical density of dry print depends on, among other factors, the roughness of the paper used. Direct confirmation was, moreover, provided by Carlsson(3) who found correlation between optimum screen ruling and roughness as measured on the Bendtsen tester.

The roughness of a porous surface like that of paper is not, however, absolute. There is no natural distinction between recesses, which constitute roughness, and pores, which do not; any discrimination between them can only be arbitrary. It was pointed out(4) that exactly how large a pore must be to contribute to roughness depends entirely on the method of evaluation and the medium used.

Pores determine primarily the permeability of the material, in which roughness has no role. This leads to the author's suggestion(5–7) that the time factor in the flow of fluid into porous surfaces may be taken as the criterion by which pores are distinguished from surface recesses. The latter may be regarded as those which can be filled up with fluid instantaneously on

† Now at Department of Physics, New Asia College, Chinese University of Hong-Kong, Kowloon, Hong-Kong.

contact, whereas the filling of the former will take some definite time. If "instantaneous" means in zero time, the type of fluid and the magnitude of fluid pressure should make no difference to the roughness so defined. In fact however, as zero time is unattainable, the roughness evaluated will vary with both fluid and pressure, and these must be specified. The fluid pressure is not necessarily the same as the stress exerted on the surface; the former can be kept small to make its effect negligible even when the latter is quite appreciable, as will be discussed later. As to the type of fluid used as the medium of evaluation, the choice depends really on the particular requirements for roughness. Obviously it should be ink, so far as printing roughness is concerned; evaluation with any other fluid will not necessarily give a roughness identical with the printing roughness required.

A porous surface is generally compressible, so its smoothness varies with the stress applied. Naturally, it is the roughness under stress which matters most in a process like printing where high pressure is employed. Furthermore, on any surface, roughness varies from one point to another if roughness means the distance between the surface and a given reference plane. A roughness distribution rather than an average is really what is important. To meet these three major requirements a new method of roughness measurement has been developed primarily for porous materials like paper, though it is also suitable for other materials such as plastic films and metal sheets.

THEORY

In transferring a uniform film of ink from a plate to a porous surface, there are two alternative arguments regarding the depth which the film reaches in the surface. It can be said that this depth depends not only on the initial film thickness but also on the contour of the surface, because ink will be forced to conform with the surface contour. The argument is certainly justified if the transfer is between two flat surfaces, e.g. in platen printing. This case has been fully treated by the author elsewhere[5,6] and it is sufficient to mention here that, from the fractional areas covered, the roughness distribution can be calculated.

If, however, the transfer is between two cylinders, especially those of small diameter, the above argument may no longer be valid. As the actual contact region is now only a narrow nip, the ink displaced by the elevated parts of the surface during contact may flow laterally out of the nip and contribute little to the depth reached. In such a case the depth reached by the ink may be assumed to be equal to the initial film thickness. By comparing the results of ink coating on an aluminium surface with those of direct profile tracing, this assumption has in fact been found to be true.[8] As most printing processes are rotary in nature this second case is of more general interest and will be considered in some detail.

Let x be the distance between any point of the surface and the plane in contact with the three highest points of the surface. x may be called the depression or the roughness at that point. There is, of course, generally more than one point with this roughness x, and the frequency will be denoted by $\phi(x)$ per unit area. If l is the initial thickness of the ink film on the plate, which is impressed onto the surface, then any part of the surface whose depth is less than or equal to l will be covered with ink. The fractional area A so covered is

$$A = \int_0^l \phi(x)\,\mathrm{d}x \tag{1}$$

whence

$$\phi(x) = \frac{\mathrm{d}A}{\mathrm{d}l}. \tag{2}$$

Thus, on a plot of A versus l the slopes at various l's give directly the frequency distribution of roughness.

In the case of paper,[8] and some other materials, the distribution has been found to be normal logarithmic:

$$\phi(x) = \frac{1}{(2\pi)^{\frac{1}{2}}\sigma x} \exp\left[-\frac{1}{2}\left(\frac{\ln x - \ln M}{\sigma}\right)^2\right] \tag{3}$$

in which σ is the standard deviation of $\ln x$ and M the median of x. Equation (1) then becomes

$$A = \frac{1}{(2\pi)^{\frac{1}{2}}} \int_{-\infty}^{U} \exp\left(-\tfrac{1}{2}t^2\right) \mathrm{d}t \tag{4}$$

in which $U = (\ln l - \ln M)/\sigma$. U for any given A can be found in mathematical tables, and from a plot of U against $\ln l$, which should be a straight line, the parameters M and σ can be determined.

The minimum volume of ink necessary to fill surface recesses per unit area to the level of the reference plane has been called the recess volume m and is given by

$$\begin{aligned} m &= \int_0^{\infty} x\phi(x)\,\mathrm{d}x \\ &= \exp\left(\ln M + \tfrac{1}{2}\sigma^2\right) \int_{-\infty}^{\infty} \exp\left(-\tfrac{1}{2}y^2\right) \mathrm{d}y \\ &= M \exp\left(\tfrac{1}{2}\sigma^2\right) \end{aligned} \tag{5}$$

where $\quad y = (\ln x - \ln M)/\sigma - \sigma.$

This is the same as the average roughness, given by volume divided by area which is unity. It is also the same as the German roughness standard[9]

"Glattungstiefe" (R_p) used in the engineering profession. The corresponding British standard,[10] on the other hand, is "Central Line Average" (*CLA*). Expressed mathematically in our case,

$$CLA = \int_0^m (m - x)\phi(x)\,\mathrm{d}x + \int_m^\infty (x - m)\phi(x)\,\mathrm{d}x. \tag{6}$$

Substituting for $\phi(x)$ and m from equations (3) and (5), and letting

$$t = (\ln x - \ln M)/\sigma,$$

$$CLA = \frac{m}{(2\pi)^{\frac{1}{2}}}\left[\int_{-\infty}^{\frac{1}{2}\sigma} \exp(-\tfrac{1}{2}t^2)\,\mathrm{d}t - \int_{-\infty}^{-\frac{1}{2}\sigma} \exp(-\tfrac{1}{2}t^2)\,\mathrm{d}t\right.$$

$$\left. + \int_{-\frac{1}{2}\sigma}^{\infty} \exp(-\tfrac{1}{2}t^2)\,\mathrm{d}t - \int_{\frac{1}{2}\sigma}^{\infty} \exp(-\tfrac{1}{2}t^2)\,\mathrm{d}t\right]$$

$$= 4M \exp(\tfrac{1}{2}\sigma^2) \cdot \frac{1}{(2\pi)^{\frac{1}{2}}} \int_0^{\frac{1}{2}\sigma} \exp(-\tfrac{1}{2}t^2)\,\mathrm{d}t. \tag{7}$$

The American standard was formerly the "Root Mean Square" (*RMS*), but *CLA* is now becoming increasingly accepted. Mathematically *RMS* is expressed as:

$$RMS = \left[\int_0^\infty (m - x)^2\phi(x)\,\mathrm{d}x\right]^{\frac{1}{2}}. \tag{8}$$

Putting $u = (\ln x - \ln M)/\sigma + 2\sigma$, we have

$$RMS = \left[m^2\int_0^\infty \phi(x)\,\mathrm{d}x - 2m\int_0^\infty x\phi(x)\,\mathrm{d}x + \int_0^\infty x^2\phi(x)\,\mathrm{d}x\right]^{\frac{1}{2}}$$

$$= \left[m^2 - 2m^2 + \exp(2\ln M + 2\sigma^2) \cdot \frac{1}{(2\pi)^{\frac{1}{2}}}\int_{-\infty}^{\infty} \exp(-\tfrac{1}{2}u^2)\,du\right]^{\frac{1}{2}}$$

$$= M \exp(\sigma^2 - \tfrac{1}{2}). \tag{9}$$

One further roughness index is the most frequent roughness r, i.e. the mode of the distribution, which can be shown to be

$$r = M \exp(-\sigma^2). \tag{10}$$

It is seen that these roughness indices (m, r, R_p, *CLA*, and *RMS*) can all be calculated from the parameters M and σ, if the roughness distribution of the surface is normal logarithmic. An index is useful for the purpose of ranking different surfaces. The choice of a particular index depends on the requirements for the surface and, in the last resort, will be limited by the agreement with practical printing results.

The fractional area A coated with ink may be determined by diffuse reflectance measurements taken immediately after coating. The amount of light reflected from uncoated spots or speckles is proportional to their total area, $1 - A$, while the reflectance R_a from the coated parts A will depend on the thickness of the coating layer, but is generally very small if an optically dense ink is used. As an approximation, the coating layer may then be assumed equal to $\frac{1}{2}l$ everywhere. Let R_0 be the original reflectance of the surface and R_∞ the limiting reflectance of the ink, and we have

$$R_a = R_\infty + (R_0 - R_\infty)R_f \tag{11}$$

where R_f is a function of the thickness $\frac{1}{2}l$ only and can be determined independently. If R_1 is the reflectance of the surface immediately after coating, then defining $R = (R_1 - R_\infty)/(R_0 - R_\infty)$ we have

$$A = \frac{1 - R}{1 - R_f}. \tag{12}$$

EXPERIMENTAL METHOD

Three art papers, three process coated papers, and five uncoated papers, whose specifications are listed in Table 1, were measured for roughness distribution. The ink film on the plate, whose thickness l had been determined by weighing, was transferred to the paper on an IGT tester, run at 45 cm/sec and 18 kg/cm. The reflection was then measured with a Baldwin reflection densitometer, within 5 sec or in some cases within 30 sec after ink transfer. An average of four readings was generally taken from each strip of paper. The fractional area A coated with ink was calculated according to equation (12).

The standard ink used, designated as ink A, was made of carbon black dispersed in a mineral oil of 27 poise in the ratio 1:4 by weight. Three other carbon black inks were also used to show the effect of change of ink. Ink B was similar to ink A but its vehicle was a litho varnish of viscosity 24 poise. Ink C was obtained by reducing the pigment concentration of ink A to 10 per cent by weight. Ink D had a low pigment concentration of 9 per cent, but a viscous litho varnish of 140 poise. All viscosities mentioned refer to 20°C. To determine R_f, ink films of various thicknesses were laid on sheets of smooth Astrafoil, and their reflectances measured against a white backing.

Samples taken at random from the papers were also measured for roughness by other methods, which included the Bendtsen tester, Chapman tester, Talysurf instrument and the oil track method. For each paper 18 readings were taken on the Bendtsen tester, which measures the rate of air leak in cm^3 per min. Five samples were tested on the Chapman tester, which observes an area of about 5 cm^2 and gives the percentage area F of the surface in optical contact with a glass prism under a known pressure, 19 kg/cm^2 in this experiment. The Talysurf instrument, made by Taylor–Hobson, traces the profile of a sample 2.5 mm long and indicates the results in *CLA*. Thirty such readings were taken for each paper. In the oil track method[11] the volume of oil received by the paper is calculated from the length of track left by a given quantity of oil from a slot, which slides over the surface at known velocity. A range of some ten different velocities were employed, and by extrapolation to infinite velocity the volume of oil in the surface of the paper, *R*, equivalent to *m*, could be found.

TABLE 1. PAPER SPECIFICATIONS

Paper	Class	Furnishes	Substance (g/m²)	Thickness (μ)
A1	Art	50% esparto 50% sulphite	93	94
A2	Art	50% esparto, 10% hardwood, 20% each of sulphite and kraft	118	100
A3	Art	45% esparto, 40% sulphite, 15% hardwood	117	85
P1	Process coated	60% sulphite, 30% mechanical 10% hardwood	68	74
P2	Process coated	50% mechanical 25% each of sulphite and kraft	84	65
P3	Process coated	85% sulphite, 15% hardwood	87	84
SC	Super-calendered printing	90% sulphite, 5% each of kraft and esparto	87	82
NP	Newsprint	65% mechanical, 30% sulphite, 5% kraft	62	72
OC	Offset cartridge	50% sulphite, 35% esparto, 10% hardwood, 5% straw	112	120
MF	Machine-finished litho	80% esparto, 20% sulphite	71	84
AB	Antique book	90% esparto, 10% hardwood	85	150

Sulphite: Coniferous bleached sulphite
Kraft: Coniferous bleached kraft

In trying to establish if the reflectance R_1 of a given surface is affected by its opacity, an experiment involving plastic films was performed. Transparent nitrocellulose films 50 to 60 μ thick and somewhat similar to paper in their surface topology were coated with ink in the same way as described for paper. The film was then measured for reflectance, when pressed against the backing of a machine finished paper and also against that of a matt aluminium surface. In each case the backing surface covered with clear nitrocellulose film was taken as having 100 per cent reflectance. The matt aluminium surface was obtained by dipping an aluminium litho plate in a hot solution of sodium hydroxide.

All experiments were carried out in a room maintained at 20 ± 0.5°C and 65 ± 2 per cent relative humidity.

RESULTS AND DISCUSSION

General

Results are plotted as A on the probability scale versus the logarithm of l. U is also given in the same graph. Figure 1 shows the results of the coated

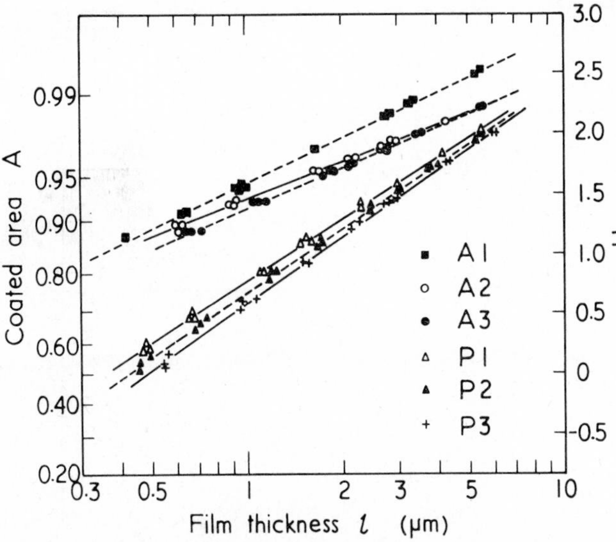

Fig. 1. Relation between area A (probability scale) or u and ink film thickness l (logarithmic scale) for six coated papers.

papers and Fig. 2 those of both felt and wire sides of the uncoated papers. It is obvious that in all cases straight lines can be drawn, and this fact confirms that the roughness distribution in paper is generally of the normal

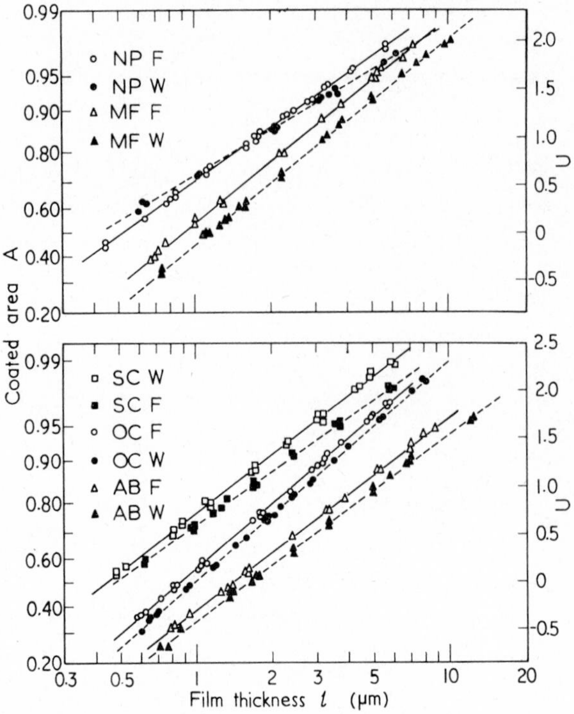

Fig. 2. Relation between area A (probability scale) or U and ink film thickness l (logarithmic scale) for five uncoated papers.

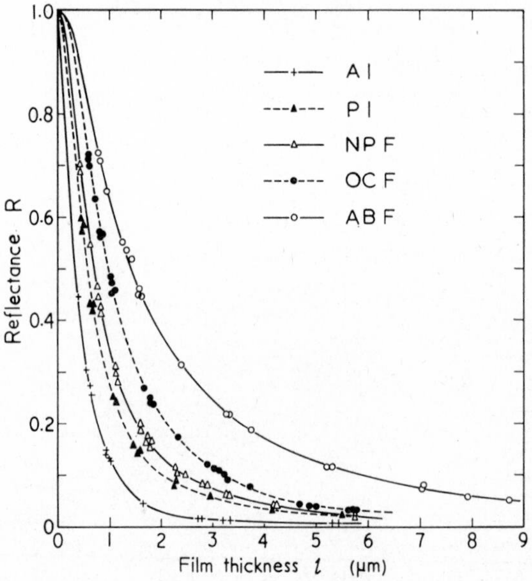

Fig. 3. Agreement between experimental points and calculated curve.

logarithmic type. Illustrated in Fig. 3 on linear scales are some of the satisfactory agreements between observed points and calculated curves according to equations (4) and (12). The standard deviation s of U upon ln l is given in Table 2, together with the ratio (C.E.) of s to the difference in U (calculated from the regression line) between the observed limits of ln l. The parameters M and σ were determined, whence the roughness indices m, r and CLA were calculated and are also listed in Table 2.

TABLE 2. ROUGHNESS RESULTS BY THE INK COATING METHOD

Paper	s	C.E. (%)	M (μ)	σ	m (μ)	r (μ)	CLA (μ)
A1	0.026	2.0	0.058	1.83	0.31	0.002	0.40
A2	0.023	1.8	0.062	2.01	0.47	0.0011	0.64
A3	0.025	2.8	0.045	2.16	0.47	0.0004	0.67
P1	0.030	1.6	0.36	1.34	0.88	0.060	0.88
P2	0.044	2.3	0.42	1.29	0.96	0.080	0.93
P3	0.035	1.8	0.48	1.25	1.05	0.101	0.98
SC F	0.033	1.8	0.49	1.22	1.03	0.110	0.95
W	0.037	1.6	0.45	1.12	0.84	0.128	0.72
NP F	0.025	1.2	0.52	1.22	1.10	0.117	1.00
W	0.020	1.2	0.43	1.43	1.20	0.055	1.28
OC F	0.049	1.7	0.87	1.03	1.48	0.30	1.16
W	0.035	1.4	0.97	1.01	1.62	0.35	1.25
MF F	0.054	2.4	0.89	1.08	1.60	0.28	1.31
W	0.051	2.1	1.12	1.10	2.05	0.335	1.71
AB F	0.044	1.9	1.37	1.15	2.65	0.365	2.3
W	0.028	1.3	1.58	1.18	3.15	0.39	2.8

F = Felt side W = Wire side

The scattering of results is very small, as shown by the standard deviation s, which means that the method is capable of resolving differences between similar surfaces. Thus Fig. 1 shows different lines for similar art papers and for similar process coated papers. The difference between two sides of a paper can also be easily detected, as in Fig. 2. Furthermore, the results so obtained are reproducible; tests carried out on different samples of the same paper with an interval of one–three months gave results in good agreement.

The various roughness indices lead however to different rankings of the papers. CLA and m are of somewhat similar sensitivity over the entire range, but r is not sufficiently sensitive for rough papers. On the whole, m is preferable since it is the minimum volume of ink required for complete coverage.

The frequency distribution of roughness has been calculated according to equation (3), and some typical distributions are shown in Fig. 4 for five different types of paper. It is obvious that the rougher the surface, the flatter is the distribution. The mode of the distribution, i.e. the maximum frequency, is almost at zero for coated papers, and moves away from zero as the surface becomes rougher. But for printing papers under impression it is very rarely beyond 0.5 μ, which is about the lower limit of film thickness that can be satisfactorily achieved in practice.

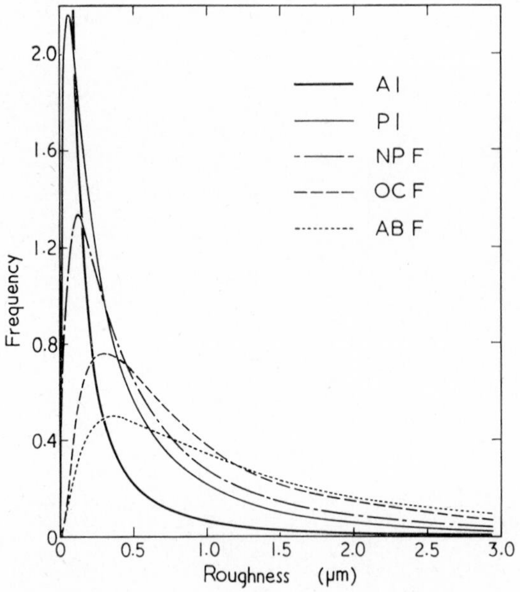

Fig. 4. Frequency distribution of roughness for various papers.

Correlation between different methods

Results obtained with Bendtsen, Chapman, Talysurf, and oil track methods are tabulated in Table 3. The mean and the coefficient of variation (C.V.) are given where appropriate. The Bendtsen tester gives rather large coefficients of variation, whereas the Chapman tester gives low coefficients. The Talysurf and the oil track method show similar variations intermediate between those of Bendtsen and Chapman.

The figures obtained on the Bendtsen and Chapman testers are not really suitable for direct comparison with the other three methods, which measure linear depression. For comparison the Bendtsen data are better expressed in the form of quadric root, as one would expect something like a fourth power relation between volume rate of flow and linear gap. Its coefficient of variation given in Table 3 should therefore be divided by a factor of about 4, when it then approaches the Talysurf figure. The Chapman F appears to be least sensitive for uncoated papers but becomes very sensitive for art papers.

TABLE 3. ROUGHNESS EVALUATED BY CONVENTIONAL METHODS

Paper	Bendtsen		Chapman		Talysurf		Oil track	
	B(cm^3/min)	C.V.(%)	F(%)	C.V.(%)	$CLA(\mu)$	C.V.(%)	$R(\mu)$	C.E.(%)
A1	11	21	80	3.8	0.55	18	1.1	6.1
A2	13	26	40	3.2	0.73	12.1	1.5	5.7
A3	13	24	33	4.5	0.80	12.8	1.6	7.9
P1	48	25	24	2.4	1.55	10.8	3.1	5.4
P2	66	18	23	4.5	1.65	7.8	3.6	13.3
P3	78	13	21.5	2.5	1.5	12.5	3.1	9.9
SC F	39	12	20.5	2.4	1.2	8.9	4.1	5.7
W	41	20	19.5	2.3	1.35	5.1	3.3	4.8
NP F	45	20	21	2.4	1.7	7.8	3.4	3.4
W	56	15	21	3.0	1.8	10	3.3	5.9
OC F	93	9	15.5	2.3	2.05	7.3	4.7	5.8
W	96	10	15	2.6	2.2	6.1	5.1	4.0
MF F	63	22	16.2	4.6	2.0	6.5	4.4	6.8
W	78	20	13.8	2.8	2.15	6.0	5.7	12.1
AB F	580	10	12.4	1.9	3.2	6.1	7.9	5.9
W	685	9	12.1	1.3	3.4	6.1	9.1	2.3

This is what might be expected. As the distance involved in optical contact is only a small fraction of the wavelength of light, a slight improvement in smoothness which cannot otherwise be detected could greatly affect the optical contact. On the other hand, increase in depth of surface recesses can have little effect on the optical contact, which could therefore be similar for two surfaces of quite different depths. However, if F^{-2} rather than F is taken as the Chapman roughness, it will become reasonably comparable with other methods. The coefficient of variation of F^{-2} is about the same as those of the other roughness indices.

The Bendtsen $B^{\frac{1}{4}}$, Chapman F^{-2}, Talysurf *CLA*, and oil track R are compared with m of the proposed ink coating method in Fig. 5. There is very good correlation over the entire range of papers, but if the range is limited to those similar in roughness, for example Pl to MF, correlation is less satisfactory. If extrapolated, the regression lines do not pass through the origin. This shows that the regression may not be strictly linear near the origin. On the other hand, the positive intercept is possibly due to the effect of applied stress, which was higher in the ink coating method; a paper surface which is otherwise rough could become perfectly smooth under high impression pressure. The best correlation is between R of the oil track and m of the present ink coating method. This is expected since R and m are essentially the same in nature. The main difference is in the applied pressure,

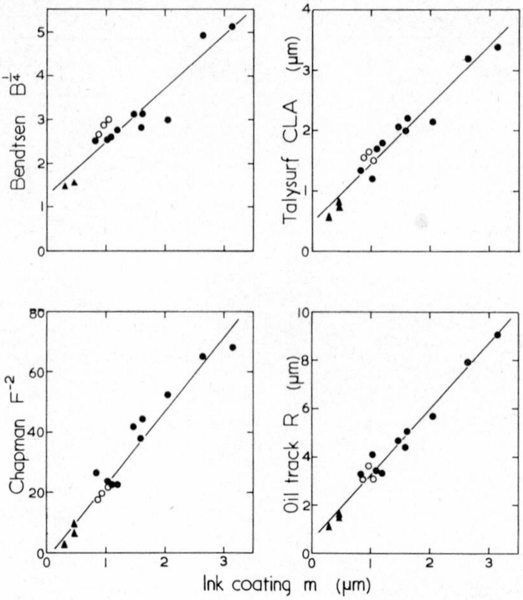

Fig. 5. Correlation between ink coating method and other methods of roughness evaluation. ▲—art; ○—process coated; ●—uncoated.

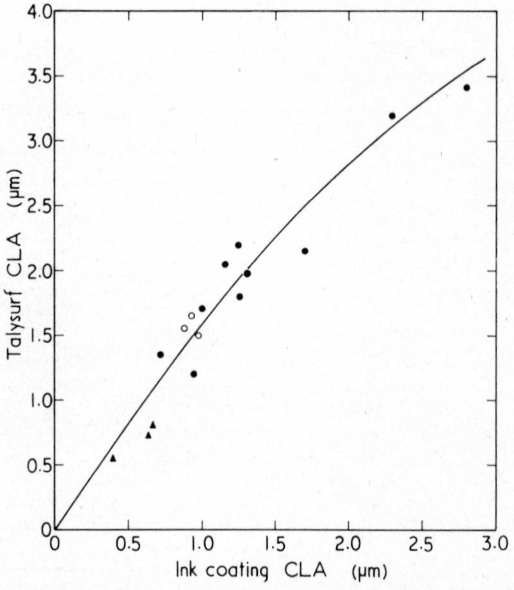

Fig. 6. Correlation in *CLA* values between ink coating method and Talysurf instrument. ▲—art; ○—process coated; ●—uncoated.

which is very small in the oil track method. This accounts for the observation that, on the average, the results differ by a factor of about three between the two methods. The positive intercept in this case could be taken to mean that in the oil track method the slot might not be completely emptied in a run.

The ink coating results can also be expressed in *CLA*, but there is a non-linear relation between this *CLA* and the Talysurf *CLA* values (Fig. 6),

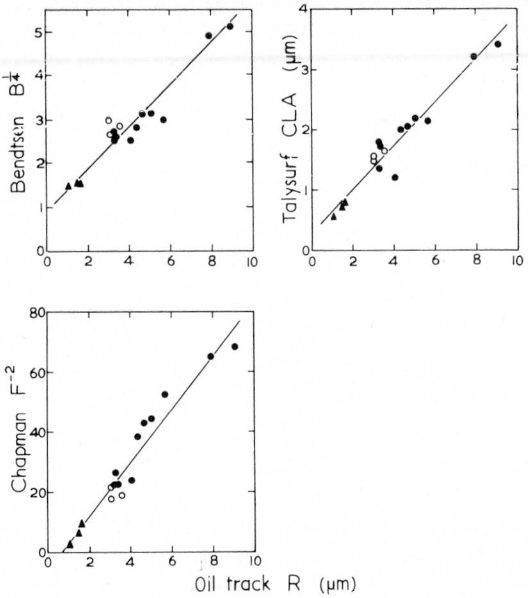

Fig. 7. Correlation between oil track method and other methods of roughness evaluation. ▲—art; ○—process coated; ●—uncoated.

which is not surprising in view of the different types of stress in a roller impression and a stylus tracing.

As a matter of general interest, the correlation of the oil track method with the Bendtsen ($B^{\frac{1}{4}}$), Chapman (F^{-2}) and Talysurf instruments is shown in Fig. 7, and that of the Talysurf instrument with the Bendtsen and Chapman testers as well as that between the Bendtsen and the Chapman in Fig. 8. All the correlation coefficients are listed in Table 4.

It may be concluded that there is generally very good correlation among all five methods, which are based on quite different principles. What must be emphasized, however, is that with the all important problem of comparing or ranking individual papers, especially similar papers, different methods give different answers (Table 5). Insofar as printing roughness is concerned, the proposed ink coating method would be the preferred choice since it is based on printing and offers several advantages.

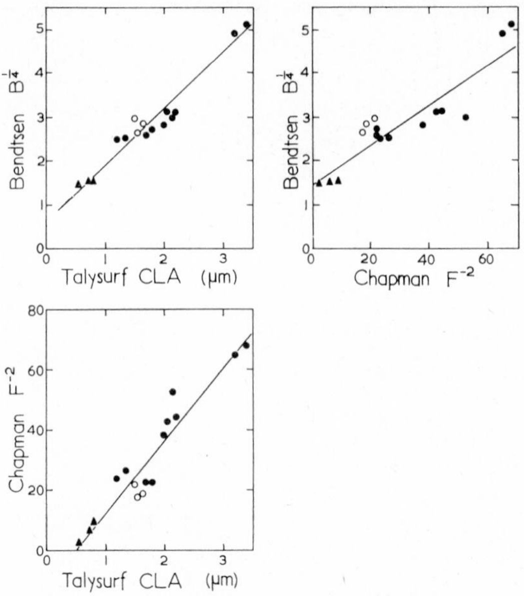

Fig. 8. Correlation between conventional methods of roughness evaluation. ▲—art; ○—process coated; ●—uncoated.

TABLE 4. CORRELATION COEFFICIENTS

x \ y	Oil track R	Talysurf CLA	Chapman F^{-2}	Bendtsen $B^{\frac{1}{4}}$
Ink coating m	0.98	0.97	0.97	0.94
Oil track R	—	0.965	0.97	0.945
Talysurf CLA	—	—	0.95	0.965
Chapman F^{-2}	—	—	—	0.91

Effect of impression on roughness

One of the main features of the proposed new method is that roughness is measured under impression. This makes possible the study of the effect of impression on roughness distribution. Measurements have been obtained under various impression loads, and some typical results are shown in Fig. 9 for the Pl and AB papers. They all obey equation (4), whence the parameters M and σ can be determined and the frequency distribution of roughness calculated. Figure 10 illustrates the distributions of the AB paper under various impression loads. With decreased load, the mode increases and the distribution curve becomes flatter.

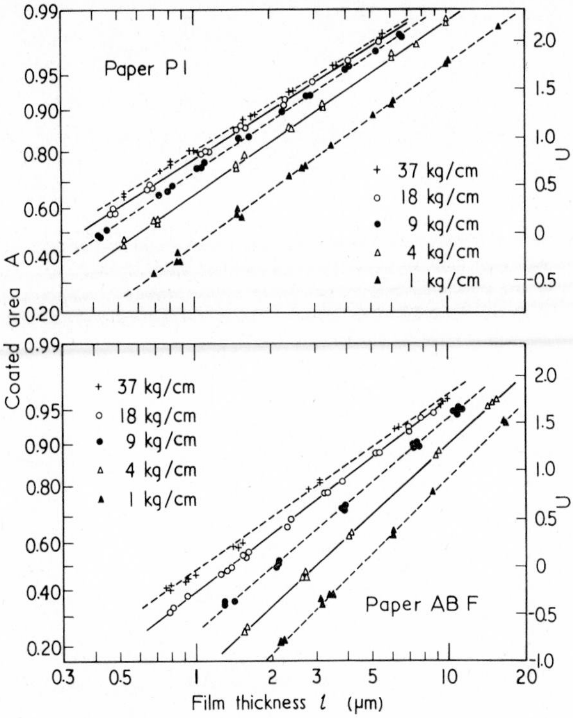

Fig. 9. Effect of impression load on the relation between area *A* (probability scale) or *U* and ink film thickness *l*.

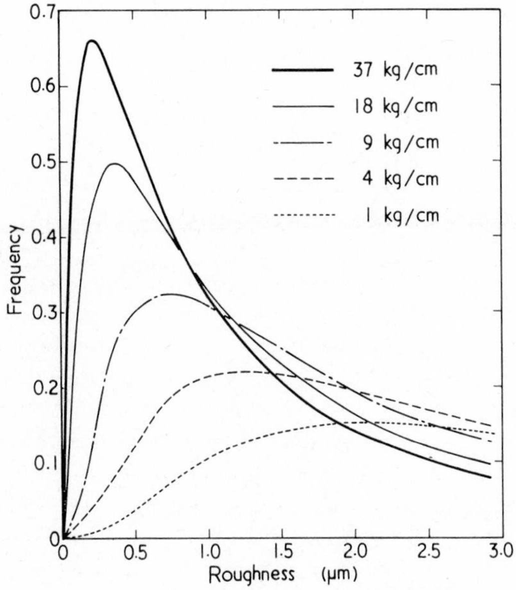

Fig. 10. Effect of impression load on the frequency distribution of roughness in paper AB F.

The effect of impression load can perhaps be better seen by plotting roughness index *m* against impression load, as in Fig. 11 for Al, Pl, MF and AB papers. For comparison, the results by the oil track method have also been included in the figure, the impression load being taken as zero. Impression load is seen to have a very large initial influence on roughness. As load increases, however, improvement in smoothness becomes progressively

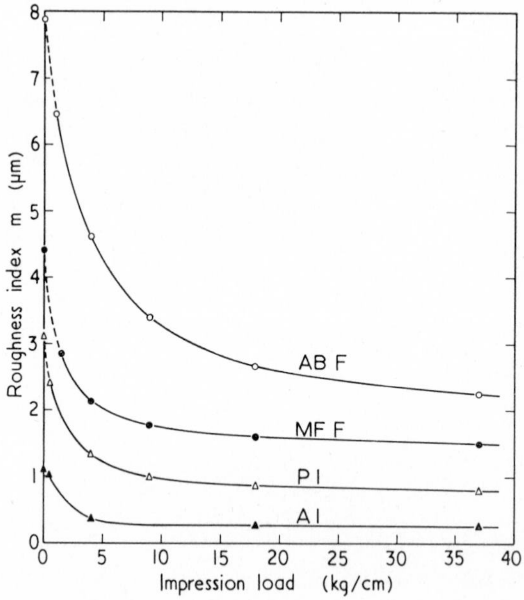

Fig. 11. Effect of impression load on roughness index *m*.

smaller, and the trend indicates the existence of a limiting smoothness for each paper.

The pronounced non-linear effect of load has been attributed[(8)] to three factors: (1) the distribution of pressure in the nip, (2) the number of stress-bearing sites in the surface, and (3) the interaction between these sites and their neighbours. It is the maximum pressure in the pressure distribution which really affects the roughness, yet the maximum pressure is non-linearly related to load. Moreover, the actual stress in the surface is also non-linearly related to the maximum pressure, for the number of stress-bearing sites rises with increasing pressure. Finally, when the pressure is low there is the interaction between a few widely dispersed stress-bearing sites and their neighbouring elements. This interaction lessens as the sites become more numerous with increase in pressure.

It may be added that printing velocity also affects the roughness measured: the higher the velocity, the rougher becomes the paper. This is due to the visco-elastic nature of a porous material like paper. At higher velocity the surface has less time to deform under impression, and thus appears rougher.

TABLE 5. SMOOTHNESS RANKING

	Ink coating *m*	Oil track *R*	Talysurf *CLA*	Bendtsen *B*	Chapman *F*
A1	1	1	1	1	1
A2	2	2	2	3	2
A3	3	3	3	2	3
P1	5	4	7	7	4
P2	6	9	8	10	5
P3	8	5	6	11	6
SC F	7	10	4	4	9
W	4	6	5	5	10
NP F	9	8	9	6	7
W	10	7	10	8	8
OC F	11	12	12	13	12
W	13	13	14	14	13
MF F	12	11	11	9	11
W	14	14	13	12	14
AB F	15	15	15	15	15
W	16	16	16	16	16

Effect of ink

Results obtained with inks A, B, C and D on the Pl paper are shown in Fig. 12. These are in agreement with the earlier findings(8) that, up to about 95 per cent coverage, ink does not appear to have any marked effect on the results. This means that absorption in the nip and in the few seconds afterwards is very small, since any absorption cannot be independent of flow properties, which are different for the four inks. In this connection it may perhaps be helpful to look further into details of the absorption by pores and the filling-in of surface recesses. Strictly speaking, both will depend on the properties of the liquid, applied pressure and time. But if pressure is very low, time short and the liquid viscous, some difference in flow properties would not be expected to have a noticeable effect on the filling-in of recesses, as distinct from absorption by pores. When the ink film is so thin that it does not completely fill all recesses, the paper surface is in direct contact with the impression roller, and it is the surface and not the ink which has to bear the applied load. Thus, the surface is under great stress but the liquid pressure is very small. Liquid flow is then largely caused by the capillary effect, which is small, and in the few seconds interval between coating and reflectance measurement its extent is likely to be so limited that its variation with ink will not be apparent. Any flow of this kind may be classified as contributing to surface roughness and not absorption. Of course, if the difference in viscosity is very great, say by a factor of 1000, then the results can no longer be expected to be independent of the liquid.

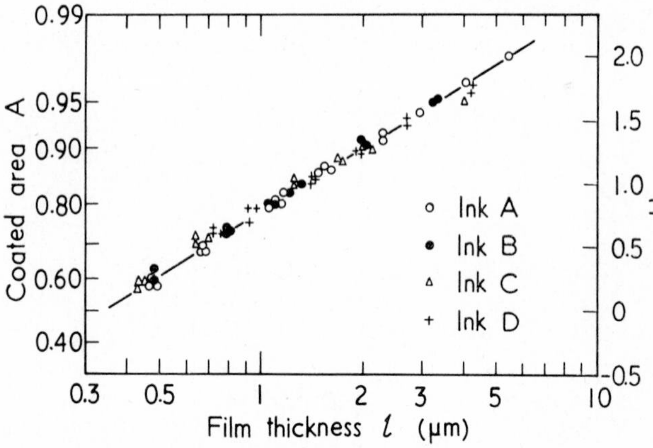

Fig. 12. Independence of coated area *A* on ink.

Relation between reflectance and area

In the theoretical treatment above, the amount of light reflected from the speckles has been taken as proportional to their area. This is, of course, the starting point from which the Murray–Davies equation was obtained for the relationship between dot size and halftone optical density. It is, however, well known that because of the effect of multiple internal reflections in paper, the reflectance of a halftone print is not linearly related to dot size, particularly with fine screen rulings.(12–14) To account for the observed difference Yule and Neilsen(12) introduced a factor *n*, which has to be found empirically. Selivanov and Sinjakov(15) derived an equation involving a constant *K*, which can be determined independently, and claimed good agreement between theory and experiments. The question naturally arises whether the penetration of light introduces a similar complication into the relation between reflectance and the speckle area of a solid print. Tollenaar(16) assumed such a solid print to be the same as a halftone print made with a very fine screen, and further assumed the optical density to be additive. There is, however, room for discussion.

The individual speckles in a solid print are irregular in shape and different in size, and their number varies with the ink film thickness applied. Their distribution in size and their number depend on the particular surface texture of the paper, and this fact makes a detailed theoretical treatment remote. Experimental observation is also difficult, since by the time the area can be actually measured (on a photomicrograph), ink may have penetrated and the portion that does remain on the surface will vary in thickness from one point to another. Then the reflectance will depend partly on this variation and partly on the speckle area. Here, a different experiment was tried in which ink was coated on to a rough, transparent nitrocellulose film and its reflectance with paper backing compared with that with aluminium backing. The results are given in Table 6. It is seen that over a wide range there is no difference in reflectance between the two backings. If there were obvious differences, the problem would be settled. As it is, no definite conclusion can be reached because of uncertainties introduced by a layer of plastic film between the ink and the paper surfaces.

TABLE 6. REFLECTANCES OF NITROCELLULOSE FILMS WITH DIFFERENT BACKINGS

Paper (%) ..	81	57	36	18	8.8	4.4	2.3	1.03
Aluminium (%)	80	56	36	18	8.9	4.4	2.3	1.07

Although a mathematical analysis is not simple, it is possible to look qualitatively into the effect of light penetration on reflectance. This effect depends on the length of boundary between the coated and clear speckles, which in turn depends on the number and size of these speckles. In the case of a halftone print the boundary is greatest at 50 per cent dot size and grows with increasing fineness of screen ruling. In a solid print, however, at 50 per cent coverage the speckles are generally large. If comparable at all, they are nearer to coarse screen than to fine screen dots, the former being known to be little affected by light penetration. Thus, the boundary is limited and the effect of light penetration is unlikely to be large. Furthermore, the normal distribution function is such that U is least sensitive to changes in A at 50 per cent A, which means any error in A due to light penetration will become negligible in the final results based on U. The function becomes increasingly sensitive to changes in A as A approaches 100 per cent, but then the speckles are not only small in size but also diminishing in number. So, as in a halftone shadow region, the effect of light penetration is again likely to be small. Therefore, reflectance from a solid print may be expected to be additive.

Indirect support for the argument is provided by the satisfactory correlation in results between this method and many other methods of roughness determination. The curves in Fig. 11 when extrapolated give intercepts in reasonable agreement with the oil track results.

CONCLUSIONS

A new method of evaluating roughness has been proposed which has three distinct features:

(1) Ink is used as the medium of evaluation.

(2) The surface is measured under specific conditions of load and velocity, so that the roughness obtained is that under impression.

(3) The frequency distribution of roughness and a number of standard roughness indices are obtained as required.

The method gives reproducible results and is capable of resolving differences between similar surfaces.

Over a wide range of papers there is satisfactory correlation among various methods of roughness measurement, which include, in addition to the new method, the Bendtsen, Chapman, Talysurf, and oil track methods. However, within a limited range of papers, especially those having similar surface textures, the ranking is different by different methods.

The frequency distribution of roughness in paper is generally of the normal logarithmic type. Surface roughness under impression is affected by impression load as well as by velocity, but there appears to be some kind of limiting smoothness for each paper. Within the normal range ink does not show any apparent effect on the roughness determined.

ACKNOWLEDGEMENTS

Thanks are due to the Wiggins Teape Research and Development Limited for making the Talysurf measurements, to Mr. C. V. Hawkes for applying the oil track method, and to Mr. K. Fellows for most of the arithmetical computations.

REFERENCES

1. J. F. Monroy, *Intern. Bull. Print. All. Tra.*, No. 61, 60 (1952).
2. S. D. Winn and L. E. Boxall, PATRA Printing Laboratory Report No. 19 (1958).
3. G. E. Carlsson, *Intern Bull. Print. All. Tra.*, No. 61, 63 discussion (1952).
4. Baysung Hsu, *Patra J.* **2,** No. 3, 5 (1961).
5. Baysung Hsu, *Brit. J. Appl. Phys.* **13,** 155 (1962).
6. Baysung Hsu, *Print. Tech.* **6,** No. 2, 89 (1962).
7. Baysung Hsu, *J. Oil Col. Chem. Ass.* **46,** 263 (1963).
8. Baysung Hsu, *Brit. J. Appl. Phys.* **14,** 301 (1963).
9. D.I.N. 4762.
10. British Standard 1134:1961.
11. C. V. Hawkes and T. Bedford, PATRA Printing Laboratory Report No. 51 (1963).
12. J. A. C. Yule and W. J. Neilsen, *TAGA Proc.* **3,** 65 (1951).
13. F. P. Callahan, *J. Opt. Soc. Amer.* **42,** 104 (1952).
14. F. R. Clapper and J. A. C. Yule, *J. Opt. Soc. Amer.* **43,** 600 (1953).
15. Ju. P. Selivanov and N. Y. Sinjakov, *Polgraficeskoe Proizvodstvo, U.S.S.R.*, No. 9, 11 (1962).
16. D. Tollenaar, *Problems in High Speed Printing*, ed. W. H. Banks, Pergamon Press, Oxford, 1962, p. 214.

DISCUSSION

TOLLENAAR: Do you get the same value for the printed area from reflectance measurements and by direct evaluation?

HSU: The direct measurement of printed area has not been carried out for the practical reason given in this paper that such a measurement cannot be completed within a few seconds after printing. Owing to the flow of ink, the area measured some time after printing will not be the same as the initial area.

TOLLENAAR: In your paper you refer to a published statement of mine in which I said that optical densities were additive. This statement was made with certain reservations. The first case is trivial; if the densities of the specks deviate only slightly from the mean it does not matter whether we make our calculations with aid of densities or with reflectances.

The second case deals with the optical density within one speck, that is, within a small area of relatively constant density. Within such a speck the reflectances may vary greatly from point to point. Nevertheless the halftone effect will alter the overall reflectance of the speck in such a way that an additivity of densities will be obtained. This additivity does not apply to the overall density of prints with large differences between the densities of the specks.

HSU: I am glad you agree with me that in general the reflectance is additive.

YULE: In connection with Dr. Tollenaar's question, could the method of measuring reflectance with a coloured ink at two wavelengths described in the paper given by Calabro *et al.* in this conference be used to check the area?

HSU: I am not sure if such a technique could be used but I shall look into this. I have found that when the reflectance is measured with a suitable colour filter, the area calculated according to equation (12) is the same whether a black or a coloured ink is used.

GINMAN: I notice that you have found that the viscosity of the ink does not influence the distribution curve. Our experience is different. I doubt whether the length of time between printing and reflectance measurement would have any influence on this because we have printed the same paper twice and measured reflectance after 30 sec and again after 24 hr, and we got almost identical distribution curves.

HSU: The reflectance tends to change with time, especially in the 30 sec after printing. The absolute change may be only a few per cent, but it will affect the results in the relatively thick film region. Another reason for the discrepancy in our results is that the printed region area is given in my paper whereas reflectance is used in your paper. If one ink is optically less dense than the other, the reflectance will be different in the thin film region even if the area printed is the same for both inks.

VAN DER VLOODT: I should like to know what sort of packing was used on the IGT Printability Tester, because it has been found to influence the measurement of the roughness. I think that with different packings you could get quite different distribution of curves.

HSU: The standard paper packing of the IGT Tester was used. I would expect to get different results with different packings.

EVALUATION OF THE SMOOTHNESS OF COATED PAPERS

by R. GINMAN, P. PANIGRAHI, and L. NORDMAN
The Finnish Pulp and Paper Research Institute

Abstract—The Bendtsen, Bekk, Talysurf, and micro-contour smoothness of 12 machine-coated papers have been determined, and these results correlated with the depression at maximum frequency, calculated from the curve of distribution of depression in the paper surface as described by Hsu. Micro-contour smoothness displays the best relationship to this property. A definite relationship has been found between Bekk, Talysurf, and micro-contour smoothness. A study has also been made of the influence of pressure, ink viscosity and printing velocity on the depression distribution curve.

INTRODUCTION

As smoothness is one of the most important properties of printing papers, particularly when printing halftones, many methods of measuring smoothness have been developed over the years. Nevertheless, there is still no single method which can be used on all kinds of paper, neither is there one which can even for one type of paper give a value which completely describes the smoothness at the moment of impression. New smoothness-testing methods are still required.

As machine-coated papers are a rather new type of paper, which is of increasing importance, it was decided to study the suitability of different testing methods. The smoothness of 12 machine-coated papers was measured employing five different testing methods. These were Bendtsen and Bekk smoothness, Talysurf centre-line average, the micro-contour test, and the method developed by Hsu for determination of the distribution of depression in the paper surface. Hsu's method[1] is of very great interest, as it provides the whole distribution curve, and not a single number. In the Bendtsen or the Bekk tester, for example, a paper with many small cavities will give the same reading as a paper with few deep cavities, even if the effect upon the resultant print is quite different. Hsu's method cannot be used as a quality control method as it is too slow, but it could be valuable in the evaluation of simpler and faster smoothness tests. Another new tester which also gives the distribution curve, but which unfortunately was not available, has been described by Brecht and Geenen[2].

MEASUREMENTS

Bendtsen smoothness, Bekk smoothness

The Bendtsen smoothness was measured with a Bendtsen tester Model 5, using an air pressure of 150 mm (water gauge). The Bekk tester was the new Korput model. Both testers are well known and need no further description.

Talysurf centre line average

Hendry[3] has described how the Talysurf tester can be used to measure paper smoothness; he reported good correlation between centre line average values and print quality for coated art papers.

The instrument used in this investigation was the Model 100, surface texture meter. A stylus with a diameter of 0.0036–0.0051 mm is drawn over the sample surface with a load of 0.2–0.4 g. The operative length of traverse is 3.0 mm, and the maximum wavelength cut-off 0.76 mm. The centre line average value measured by the instrument is defined as the average value of the departures of the profile from its centre line throughout the sampling length.

The paper sample was set on the front table of the tester, and a smooth glass slide bearing a 50 g weight was placed on top of the sample. On each side, 15 measurements were made in the cross direction. The average coefficient of variation was 7.7 per cent.

Micro-contour test

In this test, developed by Bowles and Richardson[4], the surface of the paper sample is covered with an excess of a special blue ink of the type used for copperplate printing which only fills the valleys and irregularities of the surface but is not absorbed into the paper. The surplus of ink is then removed by wiping with a soft cloth. The amount of ink which remains on the surface is a measure of the overall smoothness. The deeper the colour, the lower is the smoothness. The depth of colour has been reported as the difference in reflection measured in the Elrepho instrument, using filter FMX/C (amber), before and after the application.

Distribution of depression in the paper surface

In Hsu's method[1] for measuring the distribution of depression, the paper is printed with ink films of different thicknesses on the plate. The area covered with ink at each film thickness is calculated from reflection measurements. Knowing the areas covered with ink and the corresponding ink film thickness values two parameters k and n, which are constants for a given paper and a given set of printing variables, are determined graphically. From these constants the depression and its frequency can be calculated when the corresponding thickness of the ink film on the plate is known, and the distribution curve can be plotted. Hsu has suggested that the depression r at which the maximum frequency occurs should be taken as a surface roughness index. Statistical terminology is employed in what follows, by reference to "r" as the mode depression. The value of r can be calculated directly from k and n.

This method was developed for ink transfer between two flat surfaces. In the paper Dr Hsu is giving at this conference[(5)] he describes how the distribution curve can be calculated when the ink transfer occurs between

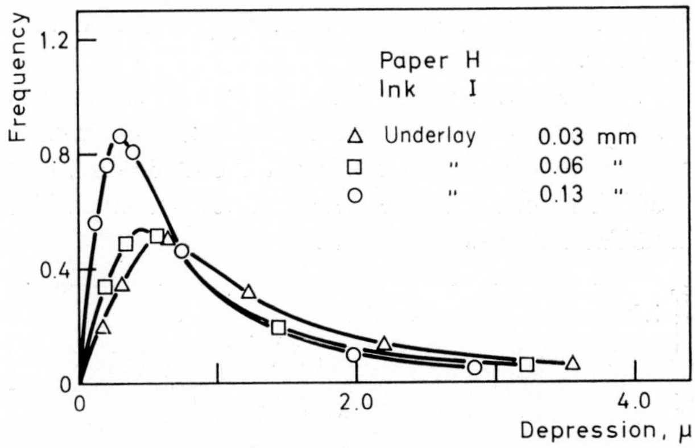

Fig. 1. Influence of underlay on the distribution curve.

two cylinders of small diameter. In the present investigation the printing was performed in a Vandercook No. 4 proof press using a solid plate 10 × 10 cm. These conditions are closer to platen printing than to rotary printing considering the possibilities of sideways flow of ink out of the nip.

The reflection of the printed surface was measured 24 hr after printing in a Zeiss Elrepho instrument with filter R 46 T (blue), employing a thick pad of the same paper as backing.

Before the samples were printed, some preliminary investigations were made on the influence of pressure, ink and printing velocity on the distribution curve.

The impression was regulated by changing the thickness of the packing according to the relation:

$$d = 1.010 - p + i$$

where d is the thickness of packing in mm, p that of the paper in mm, i the thickness of the underlay.

The quantity 1.010 is the distance between printing cylinder and printing forme. Paper *H* was printed at three different impressions, 0.03, 0.06, and 0.13 mm with ink *I*. The curves are plotted in Fig. 1, and Table 1 gives the values of *k*, *n*, and mode depression *r*.

TABLE 1. INFLUENCE OF PRESSURE ON DISTRIBUTION CURVE

mm	*k*	*n*	*r*, (μ)
Underlay 0.03	0.87	2.3	0.60
0.06	1.0	2.0	0.47
0.13	2.8	2.0	0.28

The mode depression *r* decreases with increasing pressure, and the maximum frequency increases.

Paper *F* was printed at 0.03 mm impression with three inks of which I and II were newsprint inks, and ink III a gloss letterpress ink. The viscosity of ink I was about 16 poise and that of ink II about 28 poise. Unfortunately, the viscosity of ink III could not be measured but was much higher.

Figure 2 and Table 2 show the results.

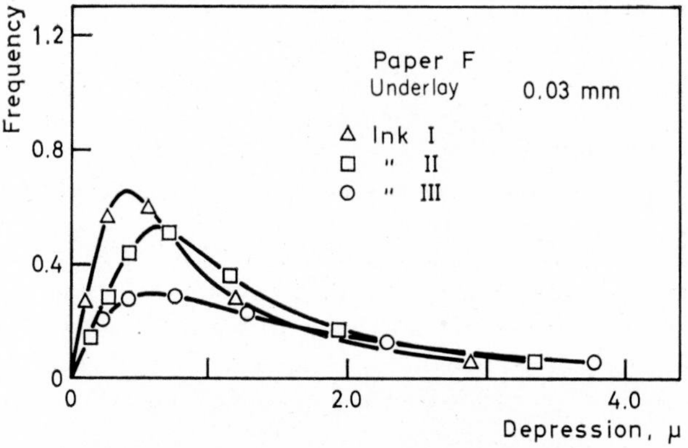

Fig. 2. Influence of ink on the distribution curve.

TABLE 2. INFLUENCE OF INK ON DISTRIBUTION CURVE

	k	*n*	*r*, (μ)
Ink I	1.5	2.1	0.41
II	0.87	2.5	0.65
III	0.40	1.7	0.62

The shape of the curve is as expected influenced by the ink viscosity. The maximum frequency decreases with increasing viscosity. For inks I and II higher viscosity gives a higher *r*-value, as one would expect, but ink III, with a flatter curve than the others, gives a *r*-value of about the same magnitude as ink II.

The influence of printing velocity is shown in Fig. 3 and Table 3. Paper G was printed at 0.03 mm impression with ink I at three different velocities.

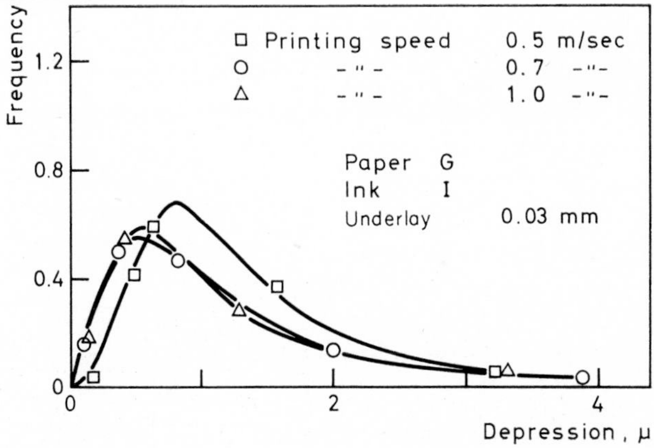

Fig. 3. Influence of printing velocity on the distribution curve.

TABLE 3. INFLUENCE OF PRINTING VELOCITY ON DISTRIBUTION CURVE

Printing velocity m/sec	k	n	r (μ)
0.47	0.95	3.6	0.79
0.74	1.1	2.2	0.53
1.04	1.2	2.4	0.55

With increasing velocity the value of *r* first decreases and then becomes constant or increases a little. As Dr Hsu points out in his second paper[(5)] one would expect the mode to increase with increasing velocity.

The effect of the velocity was also studied in a higher velocity range by printing in the GFL press. Paper *E* was printed with ink I at a linear pressure of 5 kg/cm at two speeds, 1.8 and 4.6 m/sec (Fig. 4, Table 4). In Fig. 4 there is also drawn the distribution curve for the same paper printed in the Vandercook press with 1.0 m/sec at 0.03 mm impression. When the speed in the GFL press is increased the mode increases somewhat, but not much considering the big increase in speed.

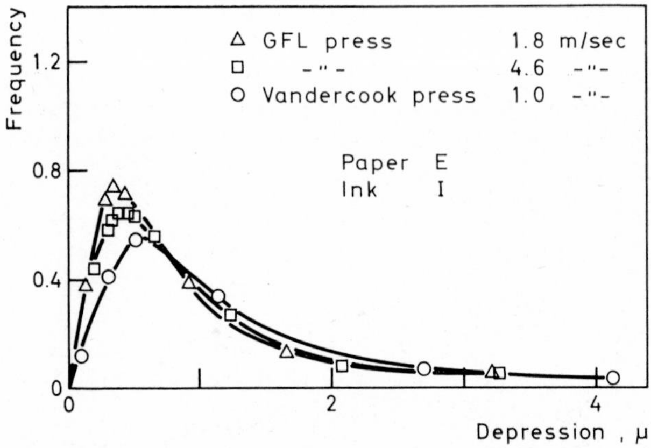

Fig. 4. Influence of printing velocity and press on the distribution curve. Impression in Vandercook press 0.03 mm, linear pressure in GFL press 5 kg/cm.

TABLE 4. INFLUENCE OF PRINTING VELOCITY IN GFL PRESS ON DISTRIBUTION CURVE

Press	Printing velocity m/sec	k	n	r (μ)
GFL	1.8	2.0	2.1	0.37
5 kg/cm pressure ..	4.6	1.6	2.2	0.44
Vandercook (0.03 mm underlay)	1.0	2.7	2.6	0.40

On the basis of the preliminary investigation, it was decided to print the samples with ink I, at a velocity of 0.5 m/sec, and 0.03 mm impression. This rather low impression was chosen to facilitate a comparison of mode depression with Talysurf and micro-contour smoothness, which are measured at low pressure.

The values of mode depression, k, and n for each sample are listed in Table 5.

TABLE 5. SMOOTHNESS MEASURED BY THE DIFFERENT METHODS
(Wire side—ws, topside—ts.)

Sample	Substance g/m²	Bendtsen smoothness 150 mm(w.g.) ml/min		Bekk smoothness sec		Talysurf smoothness μ		Micro-contour test %		Distribution of depression: Mode depression μ	Constants of curve k	Constants of curve n
		ws	ts	ws	ts	ws	ts	ws	ts	ts	ts	ts
A	117	10	10	831	838	0.80	0.79	9.9	10.1	0.34	1.7	2.0
B	170	12	13	665	737	0.72	0.80	14.3	14.2	0.50	1.5	2.4
C	85	50	38	254	256	1.24	1.25	21.6	22.3	0.70	0.81	2.5
D	160	89	82	264	267	1.26	1.28	19.2	19.7	0.72	0.89	2.9
E	110	27	26	567	567	1.16	1.21	22.9	22.6	0.40	2.7	2.6
F	100	37	33	916	918	1.21	1.23	30.7	31.3	0.41	1.5	2.1
G	110	35	29	187	195	1.27	1.29	28.3	29.0	0.77	0.82	3.1
H	95	31	42	227	208	1.31	1.29	29.0	29.2	0.60	0.87	2.3
I	95	48	43	474	465	1.42	1.35	34.6	35.3	0.61	1.1	2.6
K	80	30	29	225	347	1.33	1.33	34.5	34.7	0.79	0.58	2.6
L	85	40	43	239	256	1.87	1.89	36.3	48.8	0.75	0.62	2.5
M	200	—	97	—	132	—	1.64	—	43.8	0.90	0.48	3.0

The distribution curves for paper *A*, which had the smallest, and for paper *M*, with the greatest mode depression, are plotted in Fig. 5. Figure 6 shows that curves with about the same mode depression can be of quite a different

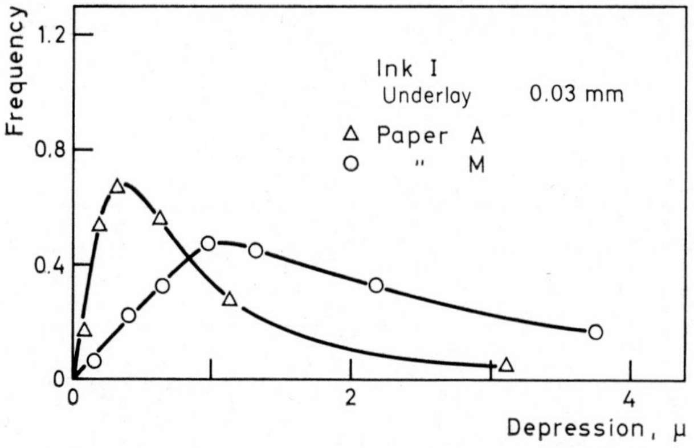

Fig. 5. The distribution curves giving the lowest and the highest mode depression values.

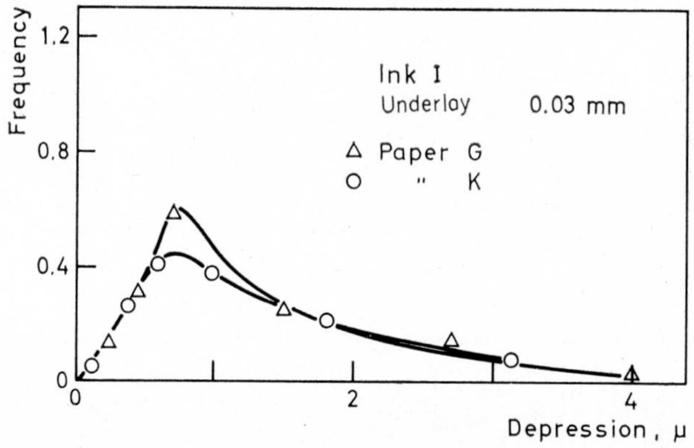

Fig. 6. Distribution curves with the same mode depression but different maximum frequency.

shape, which was also demonstrated in Fig. 1. Perhaps one or two parameters in addition to mode depression would more fully define the distribution curve and give more information about the surface smoothness. This requires further study.

COMPARISON OF SMOOTHNESS VALUES MEASURED BY THE DIFFERENT METHODS

All the smoothness values are summarized in Table 5. The extent of a relationship between two variables is usually defined by calculating the correlation coefficient, but in this investigation, comprising only 12 samples,

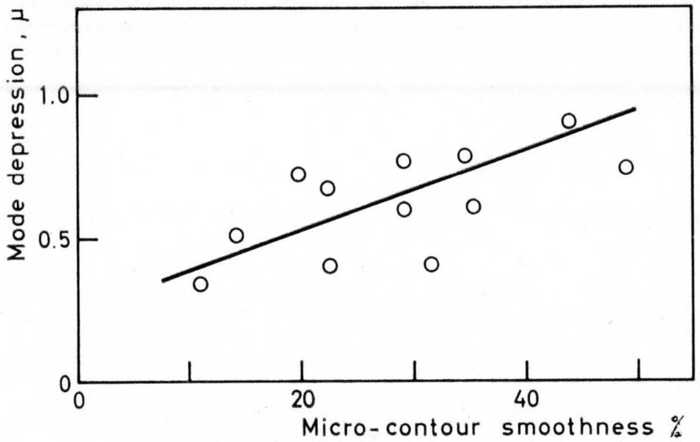

Fig. 7. The relationship between micro-contour smoothness and mode depression.

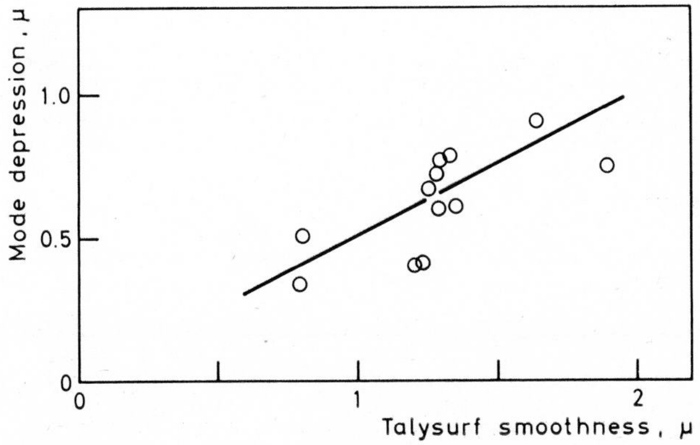

Fig. 8. The relationship between Talysurf smoothness and mode depression.

it was thought that the correlation coefficient could give no more information than a visual study of the scatter diagram.

Figures 7–10 show plots of the scatter diagrams for the relationships between smoothness measured according to the method of distribution of depression and the values of the four simple smoothness tests, Bendtsen, Bekk, Talysurf, and micro-contour. The best correlation exists between mode depression and micro-contour smoothness (Fig. 7). Talysurf smoothness

(Fig. 8) and Bekk smoothness (Fig. 9) both give about the same degree of relationship. The poorest relationship is the one between mode depression and Bendtsen smoothness (Fig. 10). As Dr. Hsu points out the fourth root of the Bendtsen values would give better correlation.[5] The scatter diagrams which illustrate the mutual relationships between the four simple smoothness

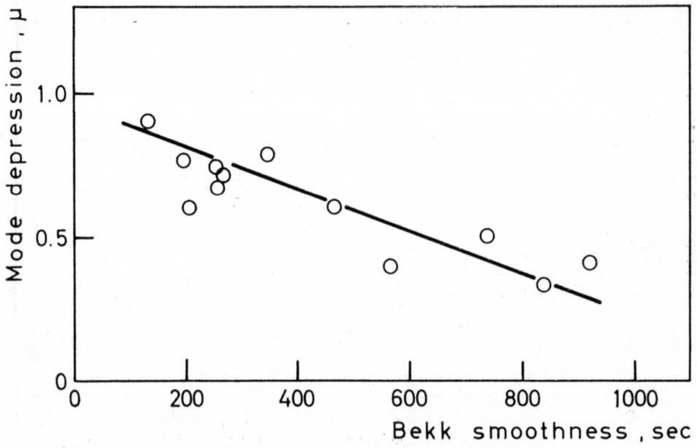

Fig. 9. The relationship between Bekk smoothness and mode depression.

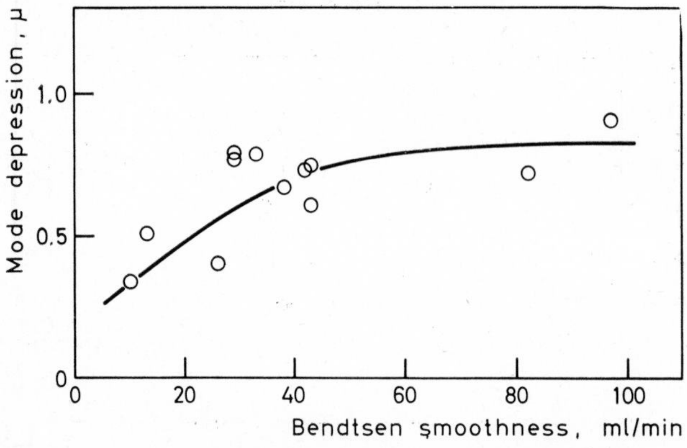

Fig. 10. The relationship between Bendtsen smoothness and mode depression.

tests are plotted in Figs. 11–16. Quite a good relationship is established between Talysurf and micro-contour smoothness (Fig. 11); this could be expected, as both these properties gave good relationships with mode depression. The relationship is also good between Talysurf and Bekk smoothness (Fig. 12). A somewhat lower degree of correlation exists between micro-contour and Bekk smoothness (Fig. 13), while the three remaining relationships, Bekk–Bendtsen, Talysurf–Bendtsen, and micro-contour-Bendtsen, are more indefinite, at least if they are presumed to be linear.

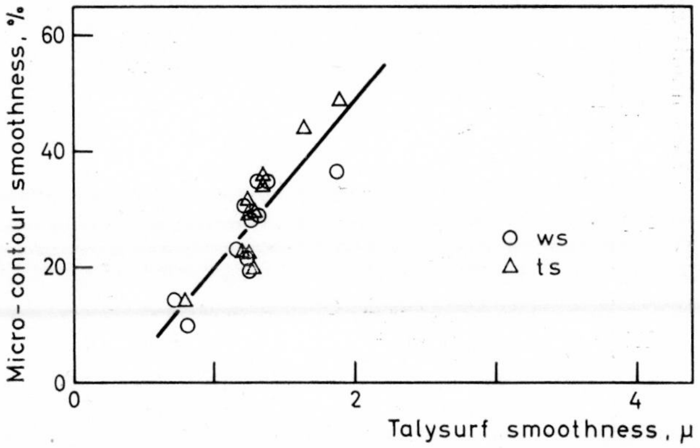

Fig. 11. The relationship between Talysurf and micro-contour smoothness.

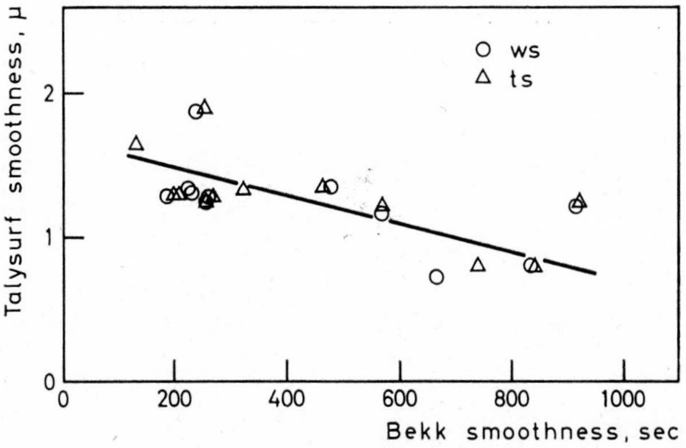

Fig. 12. The relationship between Bekk and Talysurf smoothness.

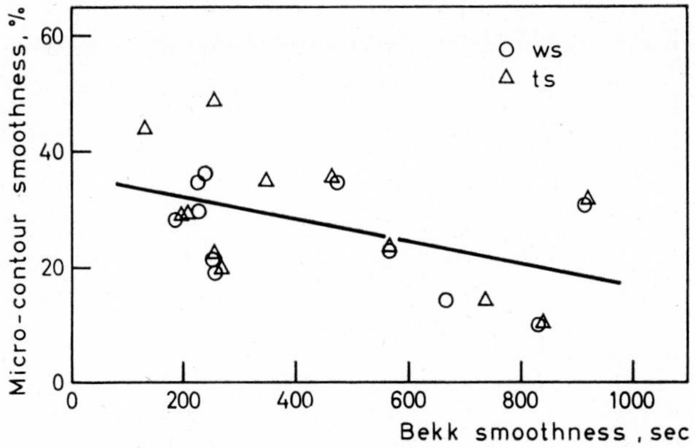

Fig. 13. The relationship between Bekk and micro-contour smoothness.

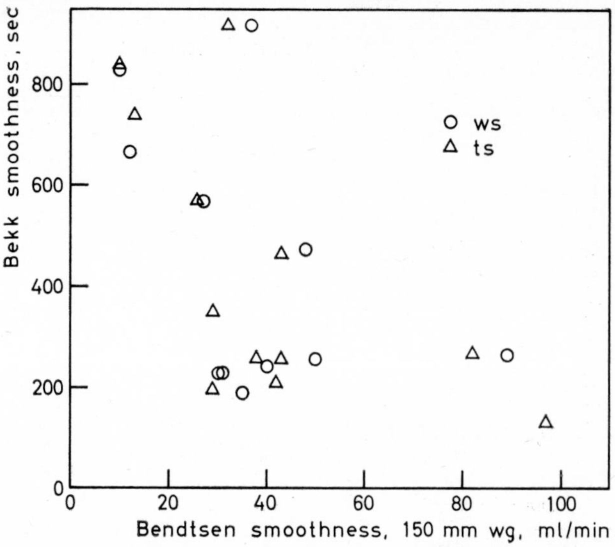

Fig. 14. The relationship between Bendtsen and Bekk smoothness.

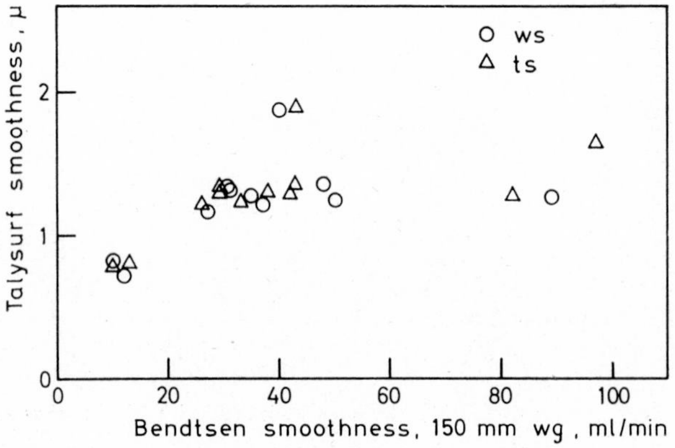

Fig. 15. The relationship between Bendtsen and Talysurf smoothness.

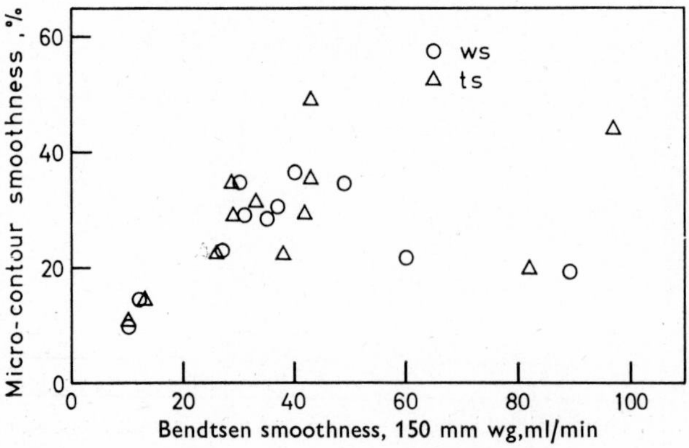

Fig. 16. The relationship between Bendtsen and micro-contour smoothness.

CONCLUSIONS

The sequence of the four simple smoothness tests arranged in order of decreasing degree of relationship with mode depression (depression when maximum frequency occurs) is as follows: Micro-contour, Talysurf, Bekk, and Bendtsen smoothness.

Distinct linear relationships were found between Talysurf and micro-contour smoothness, between Talysurf and Bekk smoothness, and between micro-contour and Bekk smoothness, while the correlation between Bendtsen smoothness and the three other simple smoothness tests was poorer.

The study of the influence of pressure on the curve of distribution of depression shows that the value of mode depression decreases, or in other words the paper becomes smoother, and the maximum frequency increases with increasing pressure. When printing with newsprint inks, the mode depression value increases and the maximum frequency decreases with increasing ink viscosity. When the printing velocity increases, the mode depression first decreases and then becomes almost constant.

Further study is needed to determine if some parameter should be used in addition to mode depression for characterization of the distribution curve, as it has been shown that two papers can have distribution curves with the same mode depression but of different shape, and with different values of maximum frequency.

REFERENCES

1. B. Hsu, *Brit. J. Appl. Phys.* **13,** 4, 155, 1962.
2. W. Brecht, H. Geenen, *Das Papier* **13,** 21/22, 519, 1959.
3. I. F. Hendry, *Tappi* **44,** 10, 725, 1961.
4. R. F. Bowles, P. G. Richardson, *Print in Britain* **6,** 3, 145, 1958.
5. B. Hsu, *Advances in Printing Science and Technology*, Pergamon Vol. 3. (Note this last reference is to paper 20 of this conference.)

DISCUSSION

Reimann: According to Table 5 papers F and H are almost equally smooth, as judged by the Bendtsen and micro-contour tests, whereas the Bekk instrument gives a marked difference. Do you think this can be ascribed to differences in porosity between the papers, the Bekk results being more influenced by such differences than the Bendtsen?

Ginman: The porosity was not measured. As you say the Bekk method is sensitive to porosity effects and that could explain the differences.

Christensen: The mechanism of the micro-contour ink test does not apply to paper with an open structure because the blue pigment will be forced into the pores of the paper. Because of this, the results are a combined effect of porosity and surface smoothness.

Ginman: I have no experience of the use of the micro-contour test on other qualities than coated papers. In this connection it would be interesting to get a definition of "cavity" and of "pore." If we look at cavities of increasing depth, when do they become pores and what is the difference in their effect on printing smoothness?

MME BENEDITE: Was there any special reason why a Blue filter (R 46) was used when making reflectance measurements with the Elrepho?

GINMAN: There are now reasons for preferring the use of the green filter and we would certainly do so in any repetition of the work. However, this would in no way change the results we have obtained.

YULE: Using a stylus instrument such as the Talysurf, could an analysis similar to that used for measuring the granularity of photographic materials be used?

GINMAN: I am not familiar with frequency analysing instruments but I would guess that it would be possible to analyse the output from the Talysurf in this way.

INK TRANSFER IN GRAVURE PRINTING AND ITS EFFECT ON HALFTONE REPRODUCTION

by EVELYN J. PRITCHARD and W. FINKLE

The Printing, Packaging & Allied Trades Research Association, Leatherhead, Surrey, England

Abstract—Studies of ink transfer in the gravure process have been made on a Vandercook proof-press with a doctor blade attachment, using a gravure-type ink in a slow-drying solvent, printing from plates of different depth of etch. This ink permits the use of the weighed-shell technique.

Transfer curves have been produced on a variety of papers and on rough and smooth plastic sheets with variations in pressure and ink viscosity. The effects of absorbency and roughness on transfer and tone reproduction have been noted, with particular reference to speckle and the production of hollow rings instead of complete squares.

INTRODUCTION

THE mechanism of ink transfer to paper has been the subject of research for many years, the weighed-shell technique for the production of ink transfer curves being used since 1939.

All these investigations have been made on the letterpress process, most of them on solid prints. There appears to have been little or no attempt to study transfer on tone reproduction or, except for the work of Hyvarinen, Manner and Aaltio,[1] by the gravure process, owing most probably to the fact that the use of a volatile ink precludes the use of the weighed-shell technique.

There are several other possible methods of studying transfer, such as the use of radioactive tracers in the ink, or the extraction of the ink from the papers after printing. Since, however, there are various objections to all these methods, it was decided to use the direct approach of the weighed-shell technique, circumventing the difficulty of solvent evaporation during the experiments by the use of an essentially gravure-type ink, but based on a non-volatile solvent.

EXPERIMENTAL

The weighed-shell technique was used with an ink based on a non-volatile solvent, printing from nine gravure plates of different depths of etch on the Vandercook proof-press fitted with a doctor blade.

Ink

The two ink properties that would be expected to have the greatest effect on transfer are viscosity and surface tension. An ink was formulated on normal gravure ink pigment and resin, replacing the solvent by one of very slow evaporation rate. Apart from evaporation rate, the physical properties of the ink were very similar to those of a normal gravure ink.

The ink formula was as follows:

Phthalocyanine Blue	9.7%
Zinc Calcium Resinate	31.2%
High Boiling Petroleum Fraction 290/320	59.1%

The viscosity of the ink was 180 centipoises at 25°C. The surface tension of the H.B.P.F. 290/320 at 20°C was 25.7 dynes/cm, compared with 22.2 dynes/cm for a normal solvent. Whereas the standard gravure ink took 15 sec to become touch-dry, this ink took 100 hr. Thus no trouble was encountered from evaporation losses during the experiments.

Plates

Nine copper plates were cut to 3.5 × 5.5 in. from standard 0.020 in. gravure plate, leaving a 0.25 in. unetched margin all round, eight of them were etched to various depths covering the range normally encountered in gravure printing, the ninth plate being a much deeper etch. Table 1 below shows the depths of etch, as measured on the Vickers projection microscope, together with the average optical density relative to the paper of tones printed on newsprint.

TABLE 1

Plate	A	B	C	D	E	F	G	H	I
Depth μ	2.0	2.5	4.2	5.6	8.4	11.5	12.8	16.4	36.3
Optical density of print (Newsprint). .	0.13	0.23	0.44	0.52	0.66	0.80	0.82	0.89	1.04

Proof-press

A spring-loaded doctor blade in a holder was made to fit on the Vandercook proof-press, in the position normally occupied by an inking roller.

The printing plate was held by vacuum to a Huck pressure-sensitive base, so that the pressure could be measured.

The impression cylinder was covered with a 0.065 in. lithographic blanket and one sheet of 0.008 in. manilla.

Inking

Initially, the leading edge of the plate was smeared with ink, and attempts made to spread and doctor in one operation. This was unsatisfactory, as was application by roller and by silk-screen squeegee. The best method was found to be to brush the ink over the plate with a $\frac{1}{2}$ in. paint brush, followed by doctoring. This gave excellent results, the angle of the doctor blade being kept constant at 45°.

Procedure

Printing pressure was varied by means of the packing beneath the Huck base.

The doctor blade was tested to ensure a clean wipe. A gravure plate was cleaned in carbon tetrachloride, dried and weighed. It was placed on the Huck base, the vacuum pump switched on, and ink brushed into the cells. The impression cylinder was tripped (out of impression) and moved forward until the doctor blade was over the leading edge of the plate, the blade being then lowered on to the plate. By moving the cylinder smoothly forward the doctor blade was carried across the plate, lifted and cleaned, and the cylinder, carrying the blade clear of the plate, then returned to the head of the press. The plate was released from the base, any surplus ink wiped carefully from the edges, and the plate re-weighed. After returning plate to base, a print was taken in the normal way, and the plate again weighed, in order to calculate the percentage of ink transferred from it.

All the experiments were carried out at 65% r.h., 68°F.

The weight of ink on a given plate after doctoring was found to be extremely reproducible. Hence, once this weight had been obtained, doctoring and printing could be carried out in one operation, weight being checked only occasionally to guard against any drift.

Ink transfer on various materials

With conditions as specified above, prints were made from each plate at a pressure of 40 lb/linear inch on newsprint, process coated, art paper, and on rough and smooth sides of an Astrafoil sheet. Widely divergent materials were used initially to obtain the greatest differences. The results are shown in Table 2, together with optical density readings on the prints.

TABLE 2

Plates	A	B	C	D	E	F	G	H	I
Ink on plate after doctoring (mg)	8.5	15.3	27.5	36.1	52.4	73.4	77.5	95.2	194.0
Newsprint									
% Transfer ..	28.6	35.4	43.9	46.1	50.6	50.2	48.8	50.2	46.0
Optical density ..	0.11	0.19	0.35	0.41	0.56	0.67	0.73	0.79	1.03
Process coated									
% Transfer ..	20.3	33.3	40.0	47.6	49.4	48.7	50.1	50.3	44.2
Optical density ..	0.10	0.22	0.40	0.51	0.67	0.86	0.89	0.97	1.15
Art paper									
% Transfer	23.2	34.6	43.6	50.5	51.4	52.1	51.3	50.0	45.5
Optical density ..	0.09	0.19	0.42	0.58	0.82	1.08	1.05	1.20	1.25
Astrafoil smooth									
% Transfer	30.4	41.2	45.7	47.7	50.3	47.5	47.3	47.1	41.4
Optical density ..	0.18	0.35	0.67	0.96	—	—	1.52	—	1.93
Astrafoil rough									
% Transfer ..	5.0	11.2	10.0	32.0	30.0	44.5	47.0	46.5	44.0
Optical density ..	0.02	0.06	0.09	0.39	0.43	—	1.15	—	1.93

Figure 1 shows the percentage of ink transferred plotted against the amount of ink on the plate.

The most striking point is the close similarity of the transfer curves on four very different materials. The Bendtsen smoothness and PATRA surface oil absorption figures on these materials are shown below:

	Bendtsen smoothness (ml/min)	S.O.A.T. sec
Newsprint	150	5
Process coated ..	30	50
Art paper	20	25
Astrafoil smooth ..	0	∞
Astrafoil rough ..	75	∞

Initially the curves rise steeply; after the fourth plate a maximum is reached at about 50 per cent transfer, this value being maintained as far as the deepest plate, which shows a small decrease in transfer in all cases. This drop is to be expected, as it is obviously impossible for 50 per cent transfer to be maintained from all depths of cell. The only curve that differs considerably from the others is that for rough Astrafoil, which has a much lower and variable transfer, particularly from the shallow cells.

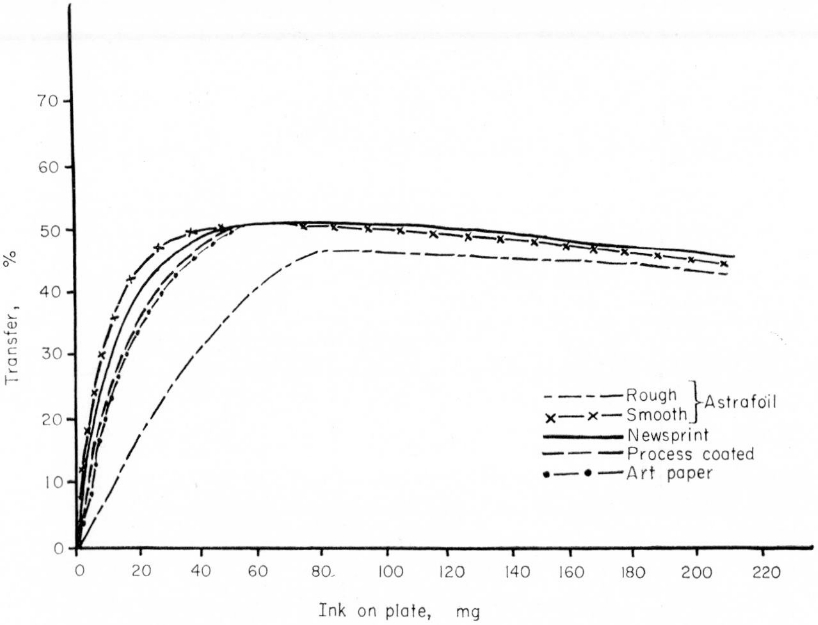

Fig. 1. Ink transfer curves on various materials 40 lb/min in pressure.

The curves on the rough and smooth Astrafoils show the marked influence of surface roughness, for here we have the same material, identical in all respects except surface contour. The roughness is not extreme, the newsprint being rougher as judged by the Bendtsen tester, yet the transfer curve on newsprint is closest to that on smooth Astrafoil.

At first sight, the absorbency of the material appears to be playing little part in transfer. It is possible, however, that the absorbency of the newsprint is acting in an opposing direction to the roughness, so producing better transfer than would be expected. It is also likely that the newsprint is more compressible than the rough Astrafoil, and is therefore smoother under pressure.

Figure 2 shows the curves obtained by plotting optical density of the prints against weight of ink transferred to the paper. Clearly a given quantity of ink produces very different optical densities on the various surfaces. These optical densities are in the same order as the oil absorption values, i.e. the non-absorbent Astrafoil produces the highest density and the absorbent newsprint the lowest, suggesting that a higher optical density results

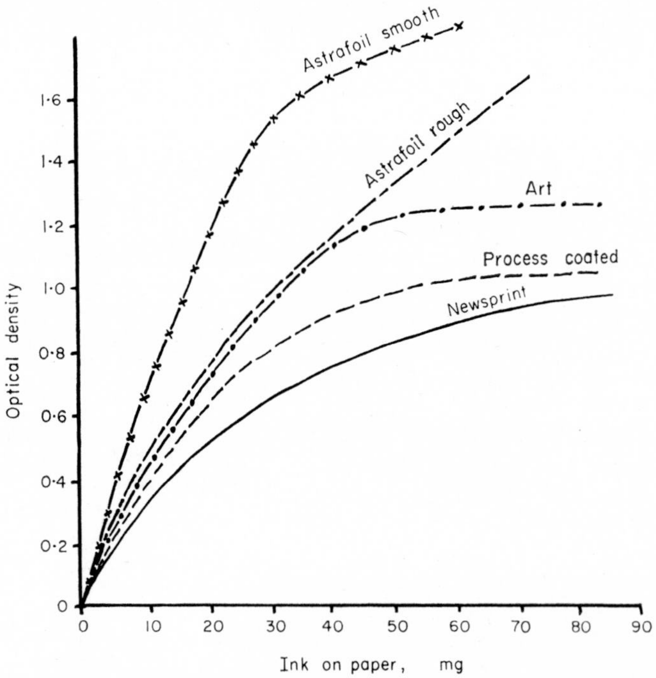

Fig. 2. The optical density versus amount of ink on paper.

when the ink lies on the surface than when a proportion has sunk into the underlying layers.

A further point of interest is the difference between the rough and smooth Astrafoils. With the same quantity of ink on the two surfaces, the optical density is lower on the rough side, and must therefore also be affected by the way in which the ink lies on the surface of the material.

Thus, although absorbency does not appear to be influencing transfer to a marked extent, it does affect the appearance of the final print, as more ink must be transferred to produce a given optical density on an absorbent material.

Influence of pressure

To determine the effect of pressure on transfer, the experiments were repeated at 120 and 200 lb/linear in. using the same materials as before.

The results obtained are shown in Table 3.

TABLE 3
% Transfer

Plates	A	B	C	D	E	F	G	H	I
120 lb/linear in.									
Newsprint	43.3	52.7	55.6	56.6	59.0	60.3	59.3	58.3	51.0
Process coated ..	27.9	46.7	52.1	56.9	53.8	52.9	52.5	52.8	45.2
Art paper	34.3	46.0	51.3	54.5	51.0	51.3	51.2	49.0	45.6
Astrafoil smooth ..	37.5	44.1	50.8	46.9	46.7	47.9	47.8	46.8	44.3
Astrafoil rough ..	13.9	27.8	40.6	43.9	49.1	47.3	50.0	49.1	45.6
200 lb/linear in.									
Newsprint	46.0	55.4	58.5	59.6	58.0	58.3	57.0	55.4	50.1
Process coated ..	35.2	49.8	50.4	52.2	52.8	52.2	51.4	50.1	45.3
Art paper	47.6	52.9	53.0	54.5	51.0	52.3	51.6	49.0	46.1
Astrafoil smooth ..	46.2	46.5	46.6	47.5	46.4	47.4	47.5	46.8	44.9
Astrafoil rough ..	16.3	33.1	44.8	47.4	50.5	50.4	49.6	49.8	46.3

The effect of pressure on each material separately is shown in Figs. 3–7.

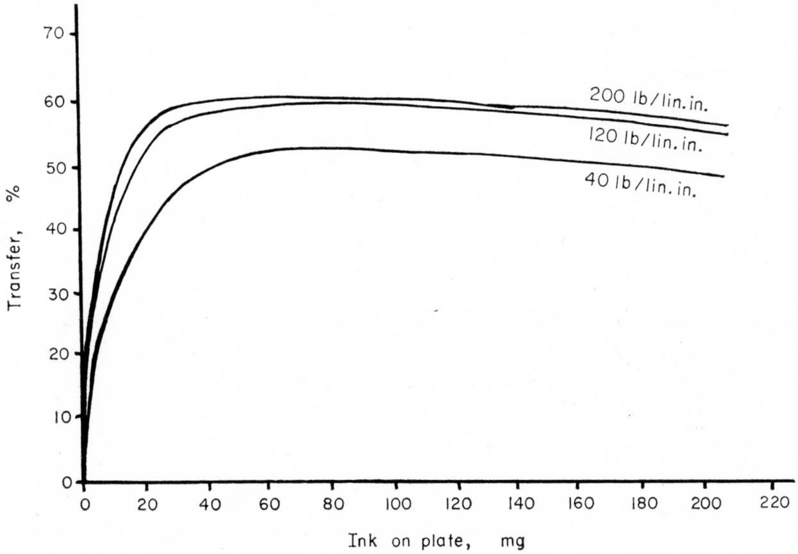

Fig. 3. The effect of pressure on transfer to newsprint.

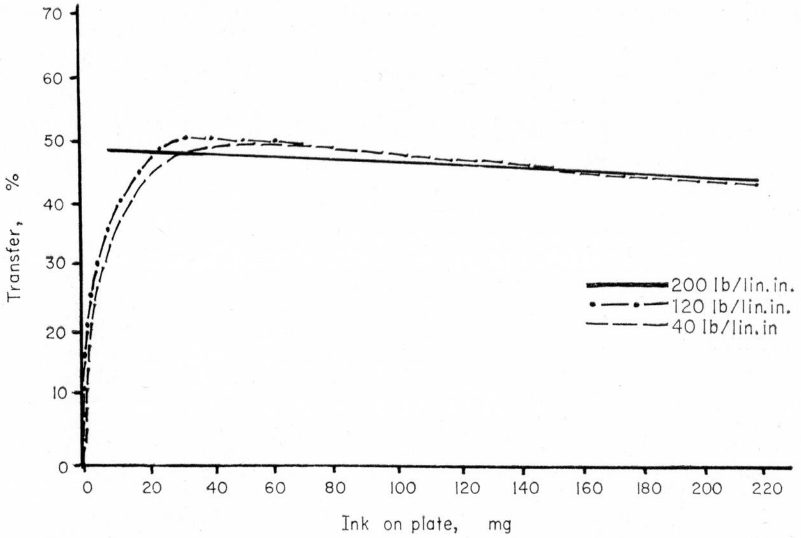

Fig. 4. Effect of pressure on transfer to smooth Astrafoil.

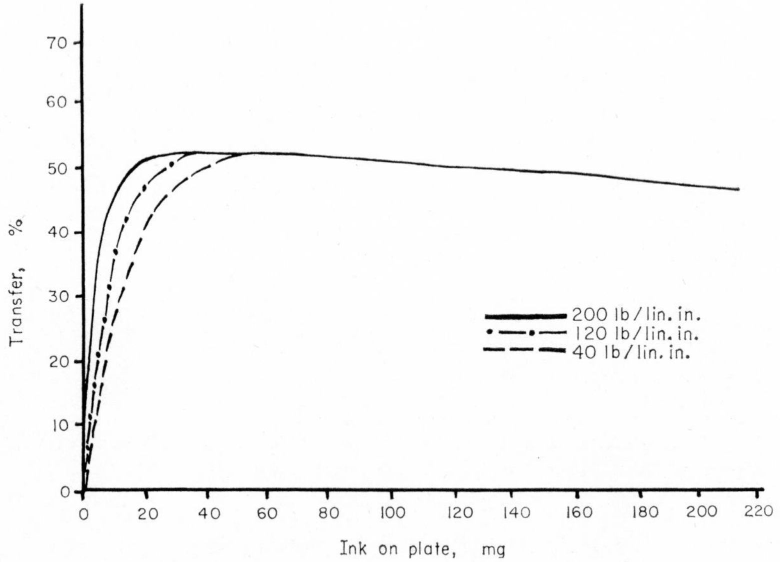

Fig. 5. Effect of pressure on transfer to art paper.

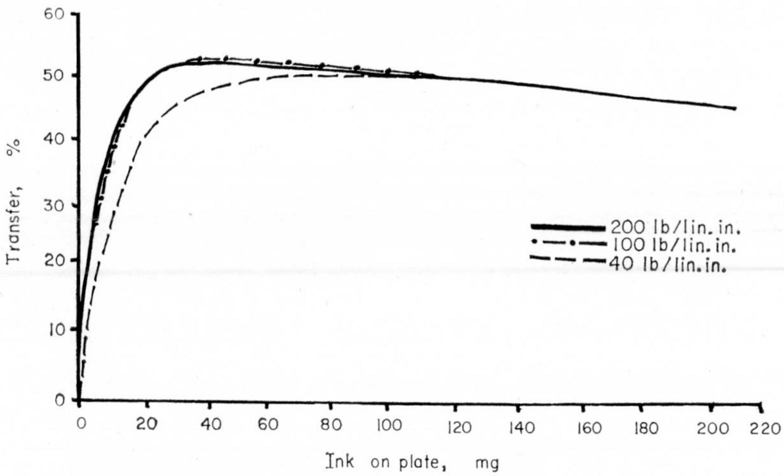

Fig. 6. Effect of pressure on transfer to process coated paper.

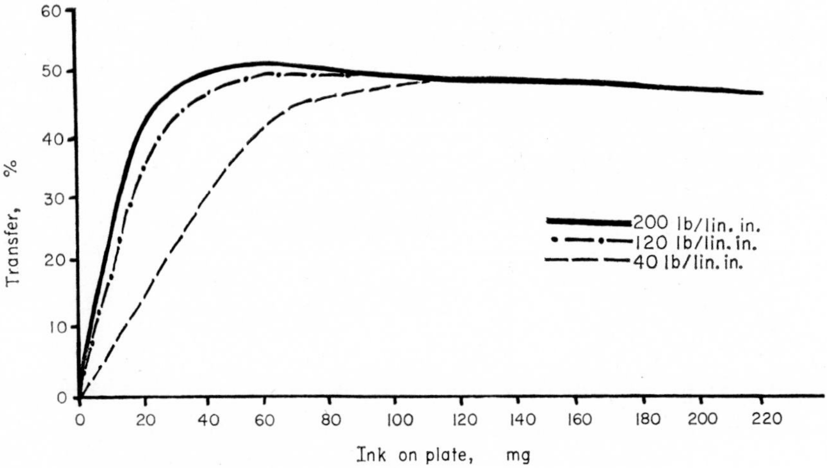

Fig. 7. Effect of pressure on transfer to rough Astrafoil.

The main pressure effects can be summarized as follows:

1. Pressure has no influence on transfer from the deeper plates, i.e. in the dark tones of the prints, except on newsprint.
2. The effect of increased pressure on transfer is greatest on the shallow plates, i.e. the highlight areas of the prints, the greatest increase in transfer occurring on those materials having the lowest transfer initially.

3. With sufficient pressure, the transfer curve on smooth Astrafoil is a straight line. A transfer of 47–50 per cent is occurring from all the plates.
4. Increased pressure has opened out the curves, so there is now a clearer differentiation between the various materials.

It appears from these experiments that, with the ink used, 47–50 per cent is the maximum transfer that can be obtained on a smooth, non-absorbent material. With the coated papers, the maximum transfer is still in this region. The newsprint, however, now shows a figure of up to 60 per cent. It seems likely that the increased transfer possible with this material is due to absorbency.

Effect of speckle

It had been noted that a high percentage of speckle occurred on the light tones on the various papers, owing to some cells failing to transfer any ink at all. If this happens, the average transfer from the other cells will be higher than is shown by the weighings. The transfer curves should therefore be corrected to take this effect into account.

The prints were viewed at × 25 magnification under a binocular microscope and the number of missing cells in a given area were counted. Five areas were viewed, each containing five hundred cells, counts of missing cells being expressed as a percentage. The percentage transfer was then corrected for this effect.

The results obtained are shown in Table 4.

TABLE 4

Plate	Art paper			Process coated			Newsprint		
	% Transfer	% Speckle	Corrected transfer	% Transfer	% Speckle	Corrected transfer	% Transfer	% Speckle	Corrected transfer
A	23.2	28	32.2	20.3	30	29	28.6	40	48
B	34.6	16	41.5	33.3	20	41	35.4	30	51
C	43.6	4	45.0	40.0	14	46	43.9	20	55
D	50.5	—	50.5	47.6	5	50	46.1	20	57
E	51.4	—	51.4	49.4	—	49.4	50.6	15	59
F	52.1	—	52.1	48.7	—	48.7	50.2	10	55

The corrected curves are shown in Fig. 8 together with the curve for smooth Astrafoil. The latter needed no correction as there was no speckle. It can be seen that the transfer curves for the two coated papers are now identical with the smooth Astrafoil, whereas the newsprint transfer is now well above it. The curves obtained for smooth Astrafoil can be taken as the basic transfer curves for a smooth, non-absorbent material. Transfer is not affected by absorbency, unless the latter is excessive, as shown by the fact that the transfer

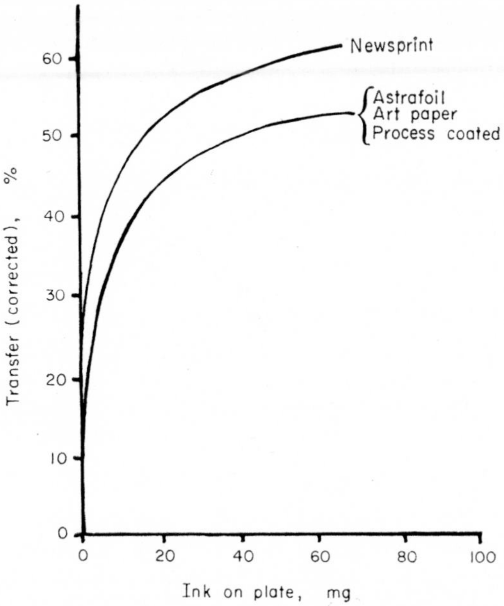

Fig. 8. Transfer curves corrected for percentage of cells that fail to print.

on coated papers has not risen above that for Astrafoil, though the S.O.A.T. time in one case was down to 25 sec, indicating a fair degree of absorbency. On materials such as newsprint, absorbency increases transfer while roughness reduces it, since some cells fail to transfer. When the coated paper curves are corrected for this failure they then become the same as those for a smooth, non-absorbent material. When the newsprint curves are similarly corrected, the transfer rises above that for smooth Astrafoil. This increase is therefore a measure of the absorbency effect.

Thus, on non-absorbent materials, or materials of absorbency not greater than that shown by the coated papers, the deviation of the transfer curve from that of smooth Astrafoil provides a measure of the degree of speckle likely to occur in the light tones.

Speckle is one of the major defects in the light tones of gravure prints. Previous work[(2)] has shown that smoothness as measured by conventional methods does not give a correct indication of the likely amount of speckle. Present work suggests that, on coated papers, the percentage transfer compared with that on smooth Astrafoil may give a measurement of the tendency of the paper to cause speckle. On more absorbent materials the effect of absorbency has to be taken into account. The work also shows that speckle can be much reduced by increased pressure.

The previous work on speckle suggested that conventional smoothness tests failed to predict the printability of gravure papers since they produced only an average figure, whereas some sizes and depths of pit in the paper surface were more likely than others to cause failure of cells to transfer. Some justification for this view regarding the effect of surface depression size is given by the transfer curves and prints on two grades of Astrafoil, differing in surface roughness. Table 5 shows the percentage transfer figures obtained on two sheets of Astrafoil on the rough side, the Bendtsen figures on these samples being 75 ml/min and 25 ml/min.

TABLE 5

	A	B	C	D	E	F	G	H	I
Astrafoil 75 ml/min	5.0	11.2	10.0	32.0	30.0	44.5	47.0	46.5	44.0
Astrafoil 25 ml/min	25.0	40.0	47.0	48.0	48.0	48.0	49.0	49.0	43.0

The transfer has increased considerably on the smoother material. Even more interesting is the appearance of the prints. On the first sample of Astrafoil, the print was so speckled and broken in appearance that it was difficult to detect the cell structure at all. On the second sample, there are no missing cells, and the cells have printed as complete squares, with a slightly jagged outline due to the roughness. This material is still rough, with a noticeably rough feel, but because the roughness is on a much smaller scale it has not caused cells to fail to print.

Effect of viscosity

The experiments were repeated at 40 lb/linear in. with two other inks of viscosity 60 cp and 230 cp respectively. The percentage transfers obtained are shown in Table 6, together with results from the 180 cp ink as used in the previous experiments.

The influence of viscosity on ink transfer is shown graphically in Figs. 9–11. The use of the 60 cp ink has increased the percentage transfer compared with that from the original 180 cp ink. The effect is greatest on the newsprint, as would be expected as this is an absorbent material. There is an overall increase on the Art paper, but to a lesser degree. On smooth Astrafoil the

TABLE 6. PERCENTAGE TRANSFER

		A	B	C	D	E	F	G	H	I
Newsprint	60 cp ink	38	49	56	54	56	56	—	55	47
	180 cp	25	35	42	45	46	47	46	51	43
	230 cp	34	43	47	47	48	47	—	47	45
Art paper	60 cp ink	34	45.5	53.5	53.5	51.5	51.5	51	53	45
	180 cp	26	40	49	49	48	47	48	48	42
	230 cp	36	39	48	48	46	45	—	46	42
Astrafoil	60 cp	48	48.5	49	49	47.5	47.5	48.5	48.5	44
Smooth	180 cp	30	41	46	47	47	47	—	47	43
	230 cp	40	45	46	46	45	47	—	47	41
Astrafoil	180 cp	25	40	47	48	48	48	49	49	43
Rough	230 cp	20	39	45	49	48	48	—	47	43
(25 ml/min)										

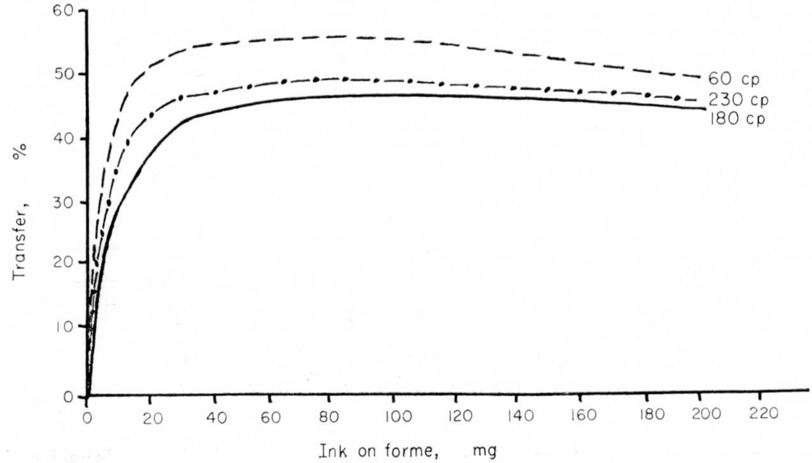

Fig. 9. Effect of ink viscosity on transfer. Newsprint.

increased transfer has occurred only on the first four plates, so that the transfer curve is now a straight line, giving 48 per cent transfer from all plates, with the usual slight decrease on the deepest plate.

In fact, comparing Figs. 9–11 with Figs. 3–5, it can be seen that decreasing the ink viscosity has had exactly the same effect on ink transfer as that produced by increasing the pressure. On an absorbent material, both these

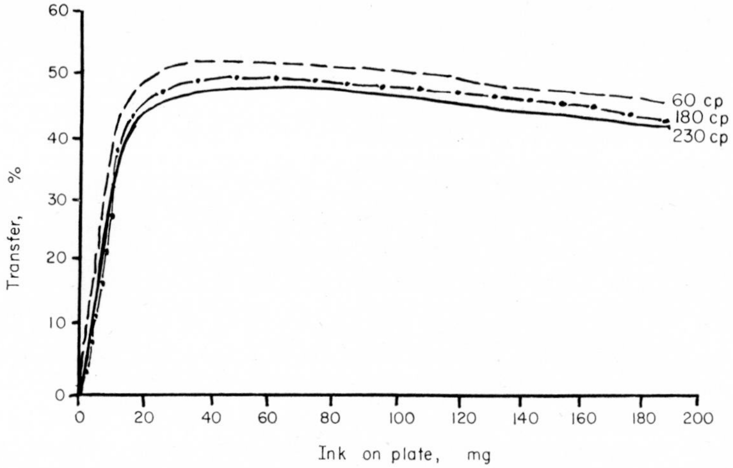

Fig. 10. Effect of viscosity on transfer. Art paper.

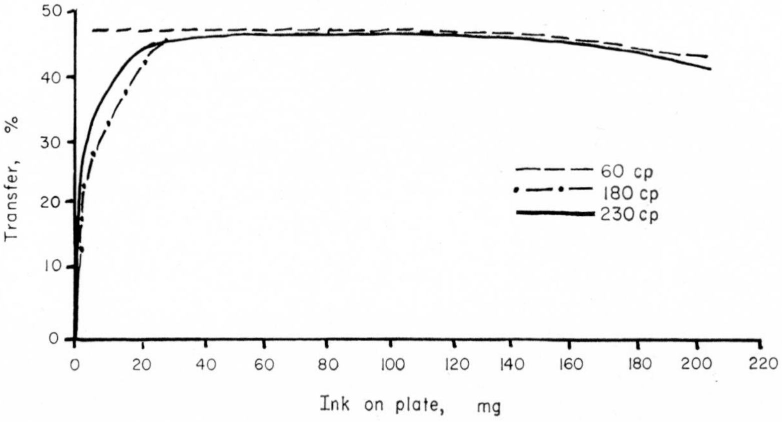

Fig. 11. Effect of viscosity on transfer. Smooth Astrafoil.

effects are easy to understand, and would be expected. An explanation in the case of smooth Astrafoil is not so obvious.

Raising the viscosity to 230 cp has produced unexpected results. In general transfer from the deeper plates has either been unchanged or slightly reduced, but transfer from the shallow plates is above that produced from 180 cp ink.

At present these results cannot be explained, and much further work is necessary on viscosity effects. It can be stated, however, that the results are due to conditions during transfer, and not as at first thought to differing amounts of ink on the plates after doctoring. Table 7 gives, for all three inks,

TABLE 7

Wts. of ink on plate after doctoring (mg)	A	B	C	D	E	F	G	H	I
60 cp ink	8.6	15.3	27.8	36.1	52.6	73.2	77.5	95.6	196.2
180 cp ink	8.5	15.3	27.5	36.1	52.4	73.4	77.5	95.1	194.0
230 cp ink	8.7	15.1	27.5	36.0	52.4	73.6	77.5	96.0	194.2

the weights of ink left on the plates after doctoring. These figures are averages from all the experiments made on all the materials and, as stated earlier, such results have been found to be extremely reproducible over long periods.

The specific gravities were 0.9436, 0.9569 and 0.9627 for the 60 cp, 180 cp and 230 cp inks respectively. Correcting for specific gravity will only alter the results by an extremely small fraction, so the figures can be taken as representative of volumes. Thus with all three inks the quantity of ink presented for transfer is the same from any given plate.

Examination of the prints

The appearance of the ink film laid down is markedly different on the various materials printed, particularly on the prints from the shallow cells.

On Astrafoil the cell structure is clearly defined, but the cells print in outline only, with hollow centres. As the tone value increases the rim of ink becomes larger until the cells eventually join, but the hollow centre is still maintained. There are no missing cells.

Both the coated papers give similar cells with hollow centres, but the light tones show only partial outlines. Speckle is very apparent, owing to many cells failing to transfer at all. Cells fail to transfer in lines in the machine direction of the paper, often three or four contiguous cells being missing. Under glancing illumination the paper shows a micro-corrugated effect in the surface, missing cells corresponding to the valleys of the corrugations. It is suggested that this effect has been caused by expansion of the base paper on one side during the coating application, with consequent shrinkage during drying under tension, rather than by any patterning of the coating during application.

The light tones on the newsprint show a high percentage of speckle and an overall broken appearance of the cells. Here the speckle takes a different form, as it is rare to find more than one cell missing at a time; and in each case the missing cell can be seen to be due to a pit in the paper surface, usually where two fibres cross. Where complete cells are able to print, they do so as complete squares, and show no sign of hollow centres.

The very rough Astrafoil gave a similar print, with a higher degree of speckle and broken cells, such that the cell structure was barely visible. On the less rough Astrafoil there was no speckle, the cells printing as complete squares with a slightly ragged edge.

Whereas it is generally agreed that a good gravure print can be obtained from a printed cell structure of full squares, hollow rings or even inverse printing from the bridges, it will be difficult to predict the likely total values if the type of transfer on a material is unknown.

The main effects of increased pressure appear to be to reduce considerably the incidence of speckle and to join the cells across the bridges rather earlier in the plate sequence. Increased pressure does not seem to minimize the production of hollow rings from smooth materials.

Decreased viscosity of the ink blurs the formation of the cells, and prints enlarged cells, so that they join across the bridges much earlier in the plate sequence. For example, with the 180 cp ink on Art paper, the cells print in outline, clearly defined. They begin to join on the fourth plate, but the bridges remain open in random lines on all but the last plate. With the 60 cp ink, on the first plate the cells are printing in outline, but are already so enlarged that the bridges have almost gone. On the second plate the cells are touching, and have joined on the third plate.

Speckle appears to die out more rapidly with the low viscosity ink, and the middle tones are much smoother in appearance, but the print from the deep plate shows a much greater mottle.

It is also clear from this work that, under these conditions, "doughnuts"—i.e. printing from the walls of the cells only, so that the ink transfers as a hollow ring—are associated with smooth surfaces. The smooth Astrafoil and the coated papers all gave this type of printing from the shallow plates. The only materials on which the ink has attempted to transfer as a complete square, where gross roughness has not interfered, are newsprint and rough Astrafoil, one absorbent and the other non-absorbent material. It has often been argued that to print a complete square the paper must dip down into the cell to contact the surface of the ink, and that failure to do this resulted in "doughnut" printing. Since "doughnuts" have occurred on smooth materials and complete squares on rough ones, and that increased pressure has not changed this effect, the explanation given above does not appear to be correct. Possibly the hollow rings are caused by air bubbles trapped between ink and paper when the paper is smooth, whilst the air can escape when the printed surface is rough.

SUMMARY

On a non-absorbent material 48 per cent appears to be the maximum ink transfer attainable. This can be obtained from all depths of cell (provided the depth is not excessive) with sufficient pressure and a low viscosity ink.

Under low pressure and with higher ink viscosity, the transfer from the shallow cells drops, even on a smooth material. Transfer is further decreased from the shallow cells by surface roughness, since some cells fail to transfer at all where they coincide with surface pits. A smooth material attains 48 per cent transfer throughout more rapidly than a rough one.

Absorbency does not appear to influence transfer to any extent unless the absorbency is very high, as with newsprint. Highly absorbent materials can raise the transfer to 60 per cent or above, this effect growing with increased pressure and low ink viscosity. A smooth, absorbent material may be capable of even higher transfer, as a rough surface acts in opposition to absorbency, and decreases transfer.

Absorbency has a marked effect on the appearance of the print, as the optical density produced by a given weight of ink is higher on a non-absorbent material where the ink is wholly retained on the surface.

On materials in which the absorbency is not excessive, such as the coated papers tested, it seems possible that the deviation of the transfer curve from that of smooth Astrafoil will give a measure of the tendency of a paper to cause speckle.

The pattern in which the ink is put down on the paper will affect the tone value produced. The cell pattern printed differs markedly from one material to another. It appears that, apart from the partial printing, or completely missing cells on rough surfaces, fully covered squares are printed wherever possible. Outlined rings, with hollow centres, seem to be associated particularly with smooth surfaces. Changes of pressure or ink have not affected these basic patterns.

With lower viscosity ink the cells spread and join more readily across the bridges. This seems to minimize the appearance of speckle, and give a smoother print in the mid-tones.

Speckle is also considerably reduced by raising the pressure.

The results from a very viscous ink appear anomalous at present. Transfer seems to be somewhat increased from the shallow plates, and little affected or reduced from the deeper plates. The volume of ink left on the plates after doctoring is the same for all three inks.

It is emphasized that this work is only in the initial stages, and that the conclusions are based on the use of comparatively few materials. The results, however, appear of sufficient interest to warrant further work by this method.

ACKNOWLEDGEMENT

We wish to record our appreciation of the assistance given by Sun Printers Ltd., in etching the plates and making up the inks used in this work.

REFERENCES

1. P. Hyvarinen, P. Manner, and E. Aaltio, *Papeir Ja. Puu.* **40,** 10, 509–16, 15 Oct., 1958.
2. E. J. Pritchard and R. A. Desmond, PATRA Printing Laboratory Report, No. 50, December 1962.

DISCUSSION

Tollenaar: I am not quite convinced that your experiments prove conclusively that absorption does not play a part in the transfer of gravure inks to coated papers, but increases the transfer on newsprint. It seems to me that roughness is the most important property. The difference in transfer between coated papers and newsprint could be explained by the increased specific contact area on the rougher papers.

Miss Pritchard: On the contrary, I think the experiments have shown that roughness decreases transfer, due to decreased contact. Rough Astrafoil, for instance, gave much lower transfer figures than smooth Astrafoil.

I have assumed that absorbency was responsible for the increased transfer above 50 per cent, as this was only attainable on newsprint, the most absorbent material.

Christensen: In the slides that you have shown, the pattern of ink distribution in the cells is quite unusual, proving that the ink surface produced in the cells after doctoring has a different configuration from that obtaining in practical printing. Commercial prints are always heavier in the back corners of the cells than in the front.

The shape of the ink surface is important in transfer, and will vary from highlight to shadows, and with printing speed.

We have a gravure test press, and are aware of the difficulties of interpreting the phenomena occurring when printing under different conditions, such as pressure, speed, angle of doctor blade, especially on process coated papers. Special problems occur when printing at very high speeds, such as 4–6 m/sec.

Miss Pritchard: I agree that it is usual to see a heavier deposit of ink from the back of the cells in gravure printing, but this is not always so. I have examples of commercial printing showing the same patterns as those in our slides.

When we dispensed with the waiting period between doctoring and printing, while the plate was weighed, we did obtain prints showing this effect of apparently more ink in the back of the cells. However, we were not able to detect any difference in the amount transferred between prints made with and without this waiting period.

Jansen: We are also working on experimental gravure printing, using magazine papers and normal gravure inks. This work is not yet complete, but the results to date confirm those of Miss Pritchard, particularly with regard to the effect of ink viscosity on transfer.

We have also found that speckle, or the number of missing dots is reduced by printing on papers of higher moisture content, presumably due to the increased softness. Greater differentiation between papers may therefore be found if they are tested at lower humidities than 65 per cent. Have you tested in different atmospheric conditions?

Miss Pritchard: All our experiments have been carried out at 65 per cent r.h., 68°F. I would expect that at lower r.h. we would obtain a greater degree of speckle, but this would not necessarily give a greater differentiation between papers. If the degree of speckle is very high, the counting is more laborious.

Larsson: When you studied the effect of varying the viscosity, how was the variation produced? Was the temperature constant?

MISS PRITCHARD: All the experiments were done at 68°F. Different viscosities were produced by varying the formulation of the ink, particularly the resin content.

HULL (Communicated) This work is a good example of the adaptation of a small laboratory operation to imitate a larger scale printing process. In general the results appear reasonable, and approximate to those I would expect from my knowledge of paper and gravure printing.

(1) The angle of the doctor blade was 45°. I am familiar with doctor blades closer to the vertical, although I am aware that an angle of 45° is used. Does doctor blade angle affect the results either by changing the shape of the printed dot or altering the transfer?

(2) Halftone apparently refers here to printing from a conventional gravure screen. I am used to this term being used for letterpress and offset litho screens, but not for gravure.

(3) The speckle problem in gravure is known to be related to paper smoothness, and your work has confirmed this. Presumably, however, the type of paper smoothness desired for gravure has a different criterion than for letterpress or offset.

MISS PRITCHARD: (1) The effect of the doctor blade angle on transfer is next on our programme of transfer studies. We have no data on this as yet.

(2) I have used "halftone" to describe the tonal range. Perhaps I should have used the word "tone" alone.

(3) Surface smoothness requirements for gravure may differ from those for letterpress and litho. Pits of certain sizes and depths appear to be particularly objectionable in gravure. On the other hand, so far as I am aware, no one has approached the smoothness requirements of the other processes in terms of the effects of pit-size distributions.

FRØSLEV-NIELSEN: (1) You have related the hollow rings mainly to the smoothness of the material, suggesting that they may be caused by air trapped between the paper and the ink. Is it not possible that as the newsprint is more compressible than Astrafoil, the newsprint may dip down into the cells to contact the ink, whereas, the Astrafoil will not, and that the hollow rings could be explained in this way?

(2) What method will you use to determine transfer on the gravure machine?

MISS PRITCHARD: (1) I agree that there is a greater likelihood of the newsprint being pressed down into the cells to contact the ink, but this will not explain the difference in transfer pattern between rough and smooth Astrafoil.

(2) Initially we intend to try out a fluorimetric technique for measuring transfer on the experimental press.

A PHOTOGRAPHIC TECHNIQUE FOR DETERMINING THE NUMBER OF DISCRETE TONES REQUIRED FOR DIGITAL REPRESENTATION OF PICTURES

by ERWIN JAFFE, HAROLD C. DURBIN and R. W. PRINCE
ANPA Research Institute, Inc.
Easton, Pennsylvania, U.S.A.

Abstract—In considering the use of facsimile transmission by newspapers, digital transmission of pictures has been proposed. This paper describes a photographic method of simulating the picture quality obtainable from variable numbers of discrete tone steps which could be transmitted by digital techniques. This method is used prior to electronic "breadboarding" and defines the design parameters of the digital scanning and transmission units; reducing the amount of circuit trial and error building required.

FACSIMILE transmission of information has been in use in newspapers for many years. In addition, recent months have seen the growth of the use of computers and computer technology in newspaper applications. From this mixture of techniques has sprung the approach that will permit the transmission of images by digital methods.

Digital facsimile transmission amounts to electronically screening a picture prior to wire or radio transmission. This technique, therefore permits sending both photographic and text matter in the same form. Type matter that is digitally coded can be sent much faster than facsimile type. It has the added advantage of being received in a manner capable of being converted into any desired type face and size. This permits a much wider style variation than that of regular facsimile which is integrally linked to the font and size of the original type matter.

The picture being sent by digital transmission is already screened, thus saving a later screening operation. An additional advantage is being able to store the picture information in any digital memory (core, magnetic tape, magnetic drum, paper tape), and in a form capable of being processed by a computer. The information can be coded for security. Digital transmission can offer greater speed for a given bandwidth and is less subject to the effects of noise and fading signal. All of these items offer distinct advantages to this method of transmission.

By comparison, the disadvantages of limited picture size, no enlargement or reduction, and the inability to use finer halftone screen patterns without rescreening are more than outweighed by the advantages of the technique.

The development path that leads from an initial concept to a working reality is normally long, tedious, and costly. The development of a digital picture transmission system is no exception to this general pattern and, it was in the hopes of shortening the work involved and reducing its cost, that the photographic technique to be described was proposed.

The problem was a relatively simple one. We wished to know how few distinct tone steps would be required in a digital facsimile system to convert a continuous-tone original photograph to a halftone image. Although done via a digital method, we still wished to retain an image that was visually "photographic" in appearance.

If the electronic system of a digital facsimile transmitter and receiver were used, we could have performed experiments that would have produced an end product in a wide variety of tone step responses. However, no such equipment was available to us. Yet, this information was still needed to determine the number of electronic channels (corresponding to tone steps) required to accomplish the necessary transfer of information.

Verbal and written contact with various electronic firms working in similar areas showed that their "educated guesses" indicated the need of from 7 to 20 distinct tone steps to produce a visually acceptable reproduction of a continuous-tone picture as a halftone image. This lack of definite and reliable information prompted us to find a way to determine the minimum number of tone steps needed to make the required image.

An initial approach to obtain the needed number of distinct steps was suggested by Mr. Austin Cooley of Westrex Division of Litton Industries and was as follows:

> Place a preselected perforated metal mask (having the required number of holes to the inch) over the continuous-tone print. Through each opening in the metal mask measure and record the density and location of the tone that appeared. Then, divide a gray scale of density range suitable for the printing process into the number of tone steps desired. The average density value of each tone step could be computed and could be represented by a single dot area size. A simulated reproduction could then be made by pasting a black dot of the required size in its proper position on a

grid pattern. These dots would agree in position and equivalent tone value with the original picture as seen through the perforated metal mask. The picture could then be compared with a normal camera-made halftone image for quality.

We started with this proposed technique and had reached the stage of making an oversize print and metal mask for ease of handling and densitometer measurement. These were made at $6\frac{1}{2}$ times size. The metal mask had 10 dots to the inch. We planned on reducing the final image so that we would end up with a 65-line screen image.

This oversize image technique meant that we were only intending to reproduce a final print size of about 2 in.^{2} and that we had to make 8000 density readings through the metal mask to get our figures. At even 5 sec per reading, we calculated this would take a minimum of 11 hr of actual work. This represented too great a time investment for the small picture area involved; and we, therefore, decided to search for a new approach to aid in solving the problem.

A photographic technique was conceived that for want of a better name was called "zone masking." In general, it can be described as a technique utilizing partial exposure to limited tone area (zone) negatives and positives to produce an image. The selected zones cover the desired tone range, and break this range into whatever number of steps is required.

Our procedure was as follows:

1. Test exposures were made to determine the minimum exposure (base exposure) necessary to produce a solid black image on the film, without anything blocking the light path. This was determined to be 4 sec. To make this method more convenient to use, a 0.6 neutral density filter was put in the light path bringing the base exposure to 16 sec.
2. The shadow density of the original continuous-tone negative was read on a densitometer. This was 0.140 and therefore required a 22.1 sec exposure to produce a solid black.
3. Highlight density of original was read as 1.596 and the density range of the original was determined as $1.596 - 0.140 = 1.456$.
4. To permit a procedure that would let us divide the original tone scale into a wide variety of steps, we decided first to divide the original tone scale into 20 steps. We would then use these steps in single or multiple form to develop any amount of steps from 1 through 20 (which had been previously suggested to us as a maximum). The original negative and all films made afterward were punched in register with a Kodak Register punch.

5. Table 1 lists the exposure times for the series of 19 exposures that were made on separate films. This permitted us to divide the original density into equal increments. All exposures were made on Kodalith Type 3 Film and developed in Kodalith Ready-Mix developer for 3 min at 68°F.

TABLE 1. FIRST GENERATION FILMS

Step*	Original density range covered	Exposure (sec)
19	0.0–0.084	26.8*
18	0.0–0.168	32.5*
17	0.0–0.252	39.5*
16	0.0–0.336	48.0*
15	0.0–0.420	58.0*
14	0.0–0.504	17.6
13	0.0–0.588	21.3
12	0.0–0.672	25.8
11	0.0–0.756	31.4
10	0.0–0.840	38.0
9	0.0–0.924	46.0
8	0.0–1.008	56.0
7	0.0–1.092	68.0
6	0.0–1.176	82.5
5	0.0–1.260	100.0
4	0.0–1.344	122.0
3	0.0–1.428	147.0
2	0.0–1.512	179.0
1	0.0–1.596	217.0

* With 0.6 neutral density filter

6. Because the visual appearance of films in the same set often looked like mixed negatives and positives, we determined to use the phrases, "first generation film," and "second generation film," rather than the terms "negative" or "positive" which later become confusing.
7. These images contained a great deal of "soft image" area which is common when continuous-tone images are exposed on lith-type emulsions. To eliminate this "soft, fuzzy" edge effect, the first generation prints were contact printed to make a second generation set.
8. The second generation set had the high contrast necessary for our needs. However, the tone areas were reversed. A black area existed where we needed clear film and vice versa. For this reason, a third generation set was made by contact printing. Later experience showed us that the third generation set—and possibly the second generation set also—was not necessary.

9. Our third generation set gave us records of an original image broken into 19 steps, each step recording the areas of the original from the lowest shadow density to a different maximum density. These were ready to create the zone masks which would produce records that would isolate various limited segments of the total density range (Fig. 1).

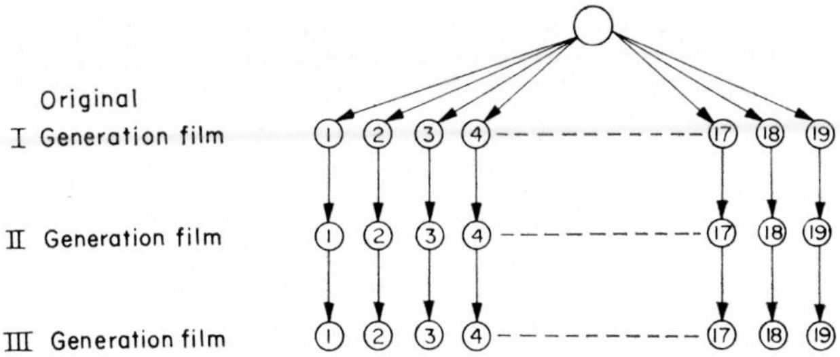

Fig. 1. Procedural steps to third generation films.

10. The zone masks which were actually a fourth generation film, were made on Kodak Autopositive film exposed 3 min to yellow light (image covered with Kodapak yellow sheeting and exposed by 2 Ascorlux PXA lamps at 3 ft), and a white light clearing exposure (no yellow sheeting) of 5 sec. The film was developed in Kodalith Ready-Mix developer for 2 min at 68°F.

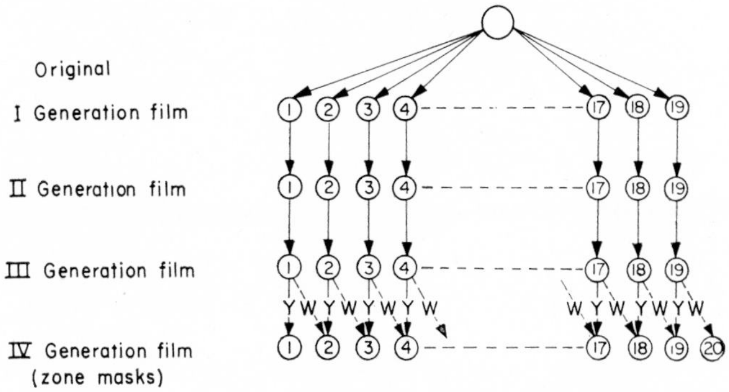

Fig. 2. Procedural steps to create zone masks.

11. The arrangement of all steps to this point is summarized in Fig. 2. The zone masks represent a density area of the original in increments of 0.084 and have separated the original tone range into 20 distinct steps.

12. The exposure for each step was selected to give a dot size that is in a reasonable visual progression throughout the tone range. The final image is made by a composite exposure on a single piece of film through a magenta contact screen (Fig. 3).

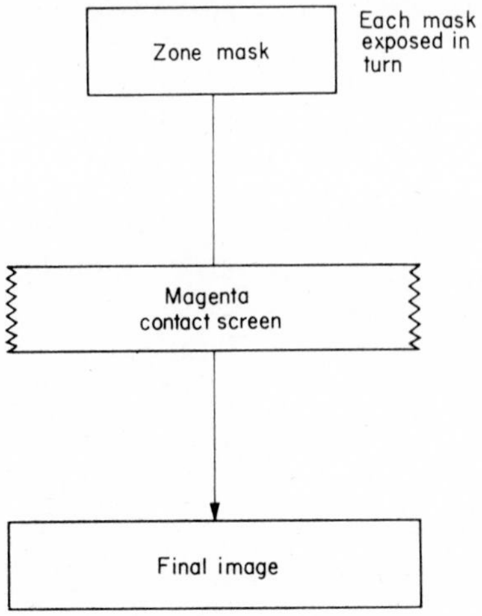

Fig. 3.

TABLE 2. ZONE MASK EXPOSURES FOR HALFTONE IMAGES

Zone mask	Exposure seconds	Lens aperture
1	11	*f* 32
2	14	↑
3	18	
4	23	
5	29	
6	38	
7	46	↓
8	55	*f* 32
9	32	*f* 22
10	37	↕
11	49	*f* 22
12	32	*f* 16
13	40	↑
14	50	↓
15	60	*f* 16
16	33	*f* 11
17	37	↑
18	42	
19	48	↓
20	55	*f* 11

13. The following exposures and apertures (Table 2) were used to make the 20-step final image. It was produced on a DURST G 139 enlarger having a 500 W lamp and a vacuum baseboard with Kodak register pins. The enlarger head was set at 39 in. above the baseboard, and

TABLE 3. EXPOSURE TIMES FOR 8 STEP IMAGE

Tone	Zone masks used	Aperture	Exposure (sec)
1	1 + 2 + 3 + 4	*f* 32	14
2	5 + 6	*f* 32	22
3	7 + 8	*f* 32	36
4	9 + 10	*f* 32	59
5	11 + 12	*f* 22	47.5
6	13 + 14	*f* 16	35.25
7	15 + 16	*f* 11	31
8	17 + 18 + 19 + 20	*f* 11	50

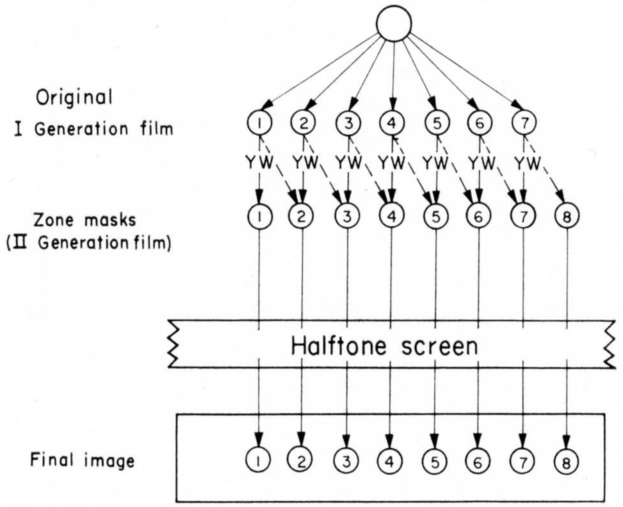

Fig. 4.

the lens to board distance was 26 in. A 65-line Kodak Magenta Screen was used.

14. This procedure produced a final image having 20 distinct steps of a single dot size within each step and having distinct maximum and

minimum density cutoff values as would be generated by electronic equipment designed for digital transmission.

15. Utilizing this technique, other final images were made breaking the continuous-tone image into 12, 10, and 8 steps. These were produced by making equal exposures through a few zone masks on a single piece of film (Table 3).
16. In later use of this system, we believe the procedure outlined can be shortened by the elimination of the second and third generation steps. This would permit a final procedure as in Fig. 4.

The trial and error determination of the necessary exposure for proper dot size when utilizing a combination of zone masks on a single film was time consuming. To determine correctly these values, a test was made to permit the production of a minimum 5 per cent, and a maximum 95 per cent dot. The exposures for these values turned out to be 14 and 400 sec respectively.

DISCUSSION

YULE: Dr. Levine of Fairchild Graphic Equipment Inc., Long Island, N.Y. recently showed me how he had used the Fairchild Variable Response Unit with the Scan-a-graver to determine the number of discrete tones required. This provides a very simple method. Unfortunately I do not remember how many tones he found to be necessary.

REPLY: A Fairchild Variable Response Unit and Scan-a-graver combination was also used at the ANPA Research Institute Research Center to determine the minimum number of distinct tone steps required to give a photographic quality of representation. By custom tailoring masks, a minimum number of 8 steps proved to be marginally satisfactory for most copy. However, this technique gave harsh breaks in tonal value where extremely gradual tone changes existed in the original photograph. Twelve tone steps seemed more suitable than the minimum 8 tone steps. When it is noted that in binary counting and coding $2^3 = 8$ and $2^4 = 16$, it is obvious that any number of tonal steps from 9 to 16 inclusive will require 4 binary bits. Since 8 tonal steps (3 binary bits) were considered to be barely minimal and 16 tonal steps can be sent as quickly as the 12 tonal steps deemed normally suitable, 16 tonal steps were determined to be the most desirable for digital facsimile photograph transmission.

HALFTONE REPRODUCTION ON NEWSPRINT

by G. Calabrò, I. Fabbri, and A. Quattrucci
The Graphic Laboratory of Ente Nazionale per la Cellulosa e per la Carta, Roma, Italia

In the Graphic Laboratory of the Ente Nazionale per la Cellulosa e per la Carta, a detailed study of the influence of printing conditions on halftone rendering on newsprint paper under closely controlled conditions was made.

Two new methods, especially developed, have proved to be of particular interest: the first one to evaluate the inking of the block and consequently the ink transfer; the second one to determine printed areas by means of densitometric measurements, which also allow the determination of ink film thickness in the case of coloured prints. A suitable plotting of experimental data was adopted to correlate printing conditions with printed results.

MATERIALS AND METHODS

The printing was done on the felt side of a machine finished newsprint, particularly soft, and with a smoothness value of 55 Bekk. The inks were the commercially available ones for flat-bed letterpress machines: a black ink with a viscosity of 35 poises and a yield value of 44.500 dyne/cm^2, and a cyan ink with a viscosity of 32 poises and a yield value of 25.500 dyne/cm^2, at 20°C.

A set of eight zinc blocks with a screen ruling of 28 lines/cm and percentage dot areas of about 1, 9, 16, 27, 46, 69, 93, 100 were used.

The printing was done on a Vandercook proof press: the printing speed was kept constant at a value of about 0.4 m/s while the linear pressure was varied in the range between 10 and 80 kg/cm. Pressures were measured by means of a load cell connected with a galvanometric recorder.

On the prints we determined the absorption factors and the optical densities, deduced from measurements obtained with an Elrepho reflectometer, using a blue, a green and a red filter, which respectively have their peak transmission at wave-lengths of 457-540-620 mμ; the reflectometer was calibrated using a strip of the same paper utilized for the printing.

Dot area measurements on the blocks were made by means of a microscope; by the same method, the area actually printed (per cent) was determined on the prints. On each block, the perimeter of the dots was measured and is

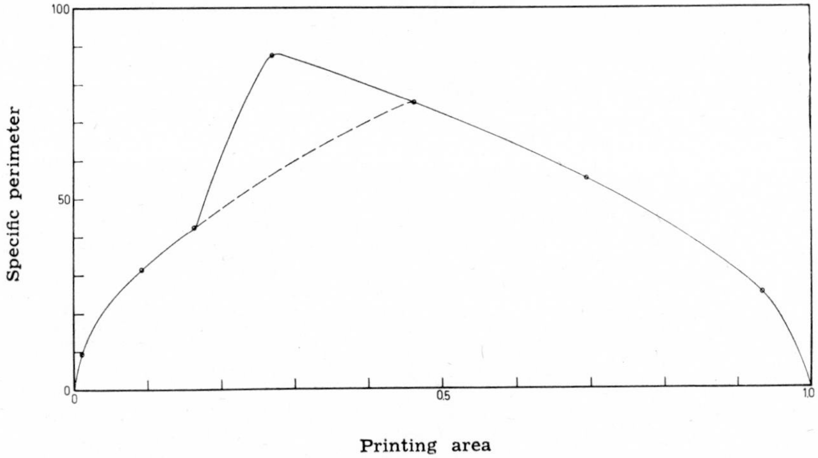

Fig. 1. Relationship between dot perimeter (in cm) per 1 cm² of block area and printing area.

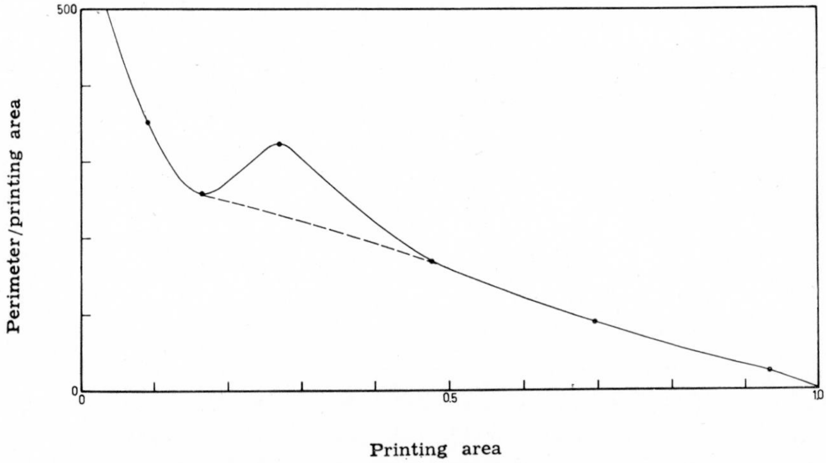

Fig. 2. Relationship between dot perimeter (in cm) per 1 cm² of effectively printing area and printing area.

represented in Figs. 1 and 2 as a function of the dot area; in Fig. 1, the ordinate represents the perimeter (in cm) corresponding to 1 cm² of block area (specific perimeter); and, in Fig. 2, the perimeter (in cm) corresponding to 1 cm² of actual printing area. It appears from the graphs that the curves show a maximum corresponding to a dot area of 27 per cent, while the expected shape of the curves should have been that shown by the dashed ones[(1)]: this disagreement is to be attributed to the fact that the block with a dot area of 27 per cent shows the dots connected by thin bridges causing an enlarged increase of the perimeter. It is advisable to take into account this curve shape when examining the phenomena connected with the lengths of the perimeter as, for example, the per cent transfer and the relationship between printing and printed areas.

During printing, the amount of ink on the block and that transferred to the paper have been determined by weighing the block. Naturally, the determination of the weight of ink as a whole is, for the halftone blocks, of little practical value since it expresses nothing about the distribution of this ink, which, particularly for the higher inkings, will run considerably over the dot shoulders, thus giving too low transfer values. Furthermore the weighing of the forme, which can be used only as a laboratory method, becomes absolutely useless when the dot area is not constant over the whole surface of the forme as is always so in practice. In order to overcome such difficulties and to devise a method of measuring ink transfer, which could be utilized in industrial practice as well, the following method was used. A small roller, a few centimeters wide, was added to the inking system and driven by friction. This subsidiary roller could readily be removed and its size and shape made possible its weighing with an analytical balance. A series of measurements made with a solid block established the existence of an exact proportionality between the amount of ink (expressed in g/m^2) present on the subsidiary roller and the amount transferred to the forme. Thus knowing the proportionality factor, the weighing of the forme was circumvented.

In the case of the halftone blocks, it has been arbitrarily assumed that the inking rollers would lay down on the dot faces an ink film of exactly the same thickness as that laid on a solid block; this extrapolation, in our opinion, represents a convenient assumption: we do not pretend that it gives the exact value of the amount of ink actually present on the top of the dots, but it gives a good approximation to the truth for the largest dot areas and an approximation, perhaps less accurate, but still usable in practice, for the smallest areas. The inking of the forme, thus "calculated" as above mentioned, represents, then, the amount of ink that the rollers would transfer to the forme if this ink could be laid only on the dot faces and was uniform over their whole surface. Naturally, these two ideal conditions cannot be realized in practice: some ink will, in fact, be deposited also on the dot walls near the top, and for this reason the total amount of ink on the plate will tend to be greater than calculated; on the other hand, the ink thickness over the whole dot surface will not be even but will tend to decrease towards the dot periphery, giving, in this way, a decrease of the ink present on the tops of the dots, as compared with the "calculated" one. It is evident that the two phenomena have contrary effects and both increase gradually the more the dot perimeter increases in relation to its surface and the more the ink amount increases.

Figure 3 represents the ink amount determined by direct weighing of the forme, in relation to the "calculated" quantity determined as mentioned

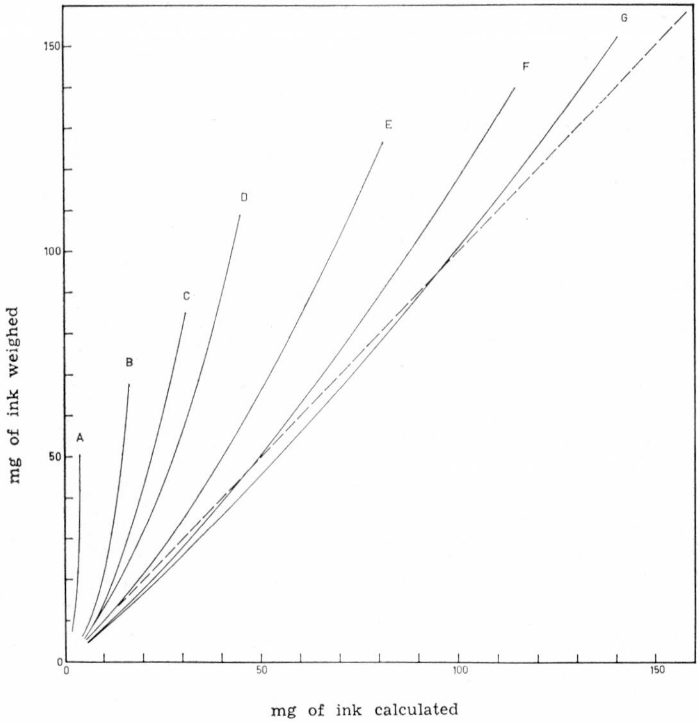

Fig. 3. Relationship between mg of ink determined by direct weighing of the forme and the "calculated" values for the following printing areas: $A = 0.1$; $B = 0.2$; $C = 0.3$; $D = 0.5$; $E = 0.7$; $F = 0.8$; $G = 0.9$.

above for each block; it can be remarked that either phenomenon is liable to outweigh the other one according to the printing area and the inking level but, as was to be expected, the weighed amount is almost constantly greater than the "calculated" one. In conclusion, it is thought that the "calculated" inking can give a fairly realistic picture of the ink fraction which, in effect, takes part in the printing process, the amount which obviously will not be involved in the process (because of its distance from the dot surface) being rightfully neglected.

The assessment of the proportionality coefficient—relating the amount of ink on the plate to the inking of the subsidiary roller—which was absolutely necessary for our work, would hardly be of any use in practice. However, the method itself, i.e. the use of a light and removable subsidiary roller, the inking of which can be accurately determined and used as reference point, might be of general interest.

EXPERIMENTAL RESULTS

Indirect method for measurement of printed area and ink thickness on paper

Figure 4 for the cyan ink shows the variation of the absorption factors measured with the aid of three filters, as a function of the printed area and of the ink amount on the paper, expressed in grams per square metre of actually covered area. From a close examination of these graphs it is possible to deduce that a variation of the inked area for a same ink thickness, results, for each of the various filters, in absorption factor values quite distinct from those which can be observed when the inked area is kept constant and only the ink thickness is varied, since the chromaticity change is remarkably different in either case. Consequently, the measurement of the absorption factors, using at least two adequate filters, makes possible the simultaneous evaluation of both the ink thickness and the inked area, having once established a suitable graph for a particular combination of ink and paper. Because of the great interest of such a determination and of the difficulty or impossibility of performing it directly in practice, we tried to prepare a nomogram. Among all different possible plottings, the one reproduced in Fig. 5 was chosen. From the two families of curves here reproduced it is possible to deduce—by interpolation—what ink thickness and printed area correspond to a given set of absorption factors measured on a given print, or vice-versa. The expected sensitivity of such a method, which appeared to be quite good in our case, is obviously related to the choice of the filters, through which the measurements are taken, and to the particular chromaticity changes exhibited by the ink.

Figure 5 shows, in the upper part, another curve having as abscissa the same ratio B/R as the main graph, and as ordinate the ratio of the absorption factors for the blue filter to the factors for the green filter B/G; utilizing these ratios between the absorption factors on both axes, it has been found that the representative points of every possible area and thickness fall upon a unique curve. This curve introduces a third absorption factor, which makes it possible to ensure that the ink–paper combination is exactly the one for which the graph has been plotted and that its colorimetric characteristics have not been changed by any eventual addition of ink thinner or by any

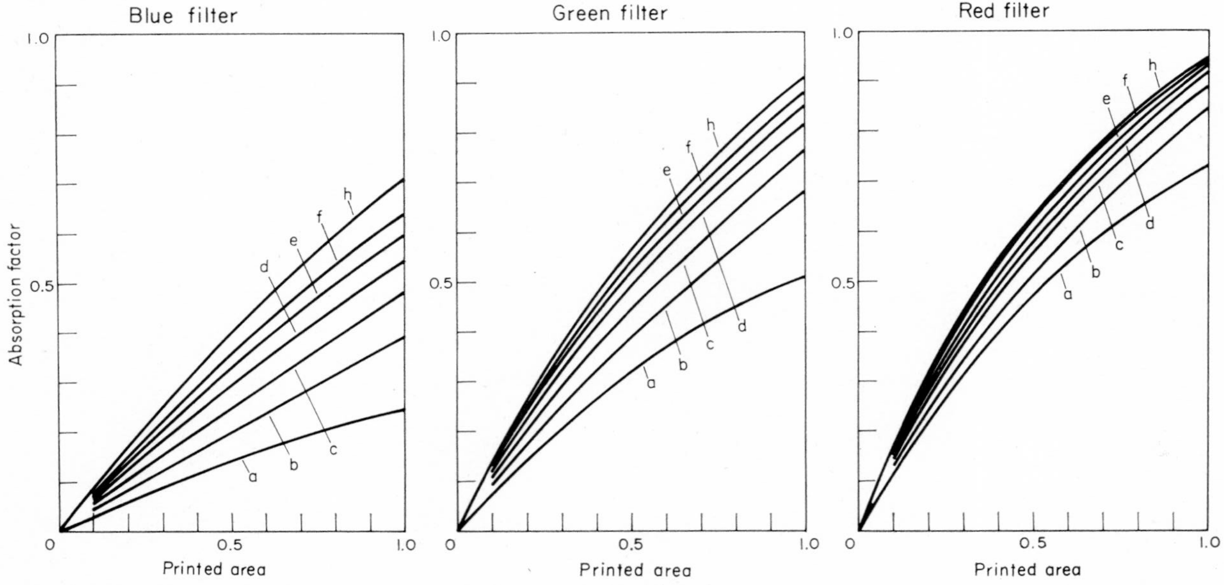

Fig. 4. Absorption factors as a function of printed area for some thicknesses of cyan ink on paper: a = thickness corresponding to 1 g of ink/m² of area actually inked; $b = 2$ g/m²; $c = 3$ g/m²; $d = 4$ g/m²; e = 5 g/m²; $f = 6$ g/m²; $h = 8$ g/m².

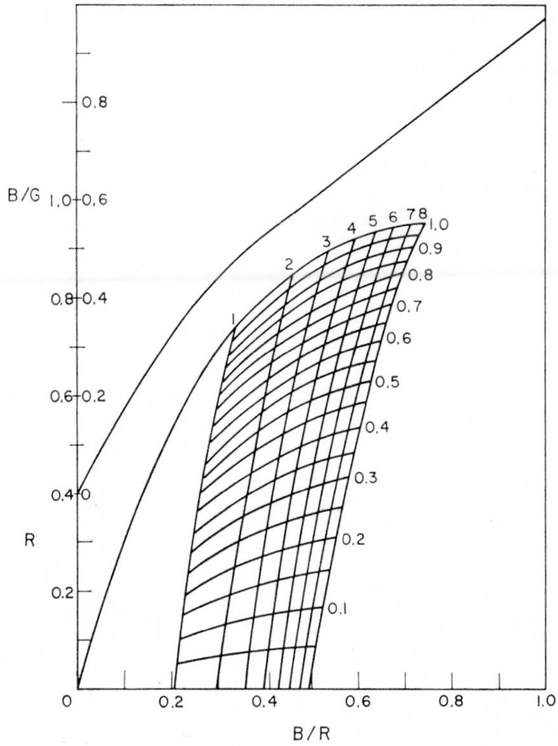

Fig. 5. Absorption factors for the red filter (*R*) as a function of the ratios of the absorption factors for the blue filter (*B*) to the ones for the red filter for several printed areas and for the thicknesses corresponding to: 1; 2; 3; 4; 5; 6; 7; 8 g/m^2 of cyan ink. The upper curve, suitable for all the areas and thicknesses, was plotted by means of the ratios of the absorption factors for the blue filter (*B*) to the ones for the green filter (*G*).

other cause: if such had been the case, the representative points would not have lain on the upper curve.

As to the black ink, the absorption factor measurements have been made through the same above mentioned filters. In Fig. 6, only the curves relative to the measurements through the green filter are reported, since the measurements performed through the other filters do not display noticeable differences. In this case, as was to be expected, the chromaticity changes exhibited by the print when varying either the ink thickness or the inked area, were too close to enable the use of the above method. However, since black ink is, in practice, the most commonly used one, measurements of ink film thickness or at least the printed areas were attempted by making use of measurements of absorption factors. To this end some formulas mentioned in the literature(2,3,4) have been used. A good correspondence has been found between the experimental curves (showing the variation of the absorption factor as a function of the inked area, for a constant ink thickness on the paper) and the values deduced from the following formula:

$$R = [1 - a(1 - R_s^{1/n})]^n$$

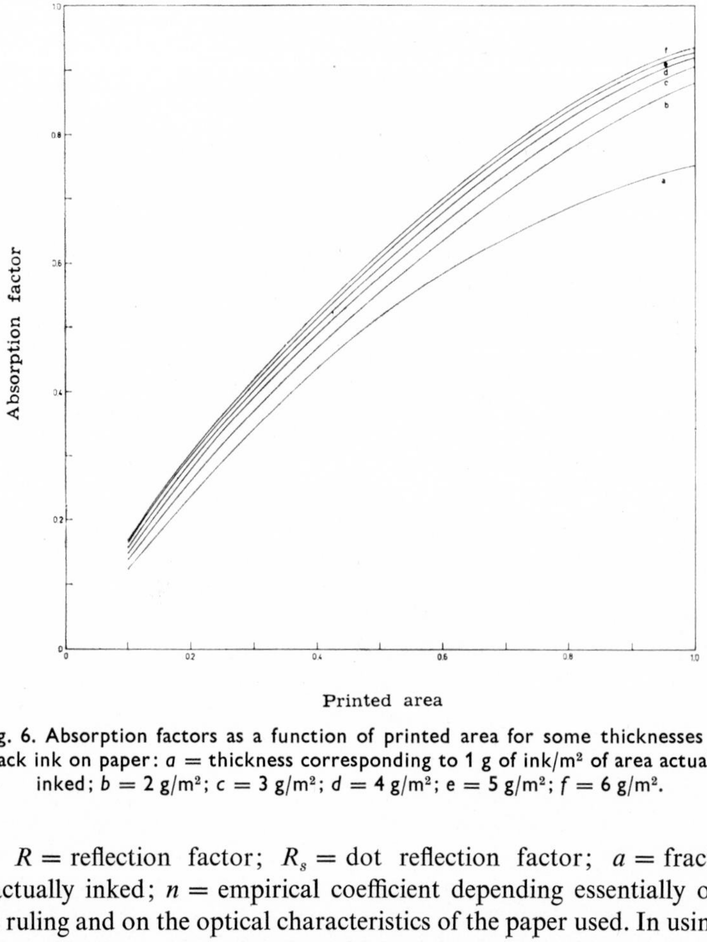

Fig. 6. Absorption factors as a function of printed area for some thicknesses of black ink on paper: a = thickness corresponding to 1 g of ink/m² of area actually inked; $b = 2$ g/m²; $c = 3$ g/m²; $d = 4$ g/m²; e = 5 g/m²; $f = 6$ g/m².

where R = reflection factor; R_s = dot reflection factor; a = fractional area actually inked; n = empirical coefficient depending essentially on the screen ruling and on the optical characteristics of the paper used. In using this formula, n has been given the value of 2.3 while the dot reflection factor has been given the value measured on the solid print having the same ink thickness. It is necessary, of course, to consider that the ink thickness is not even over the whole area of each dot, nor generally will the average ink thickness be constant when the printing area varies on the block; consequently, the assumption that the absorption factor for a dot can be derived from the measurement performed on a solid area of the same print introduces a certain error. It has been found, however, that this inexactness did not invalidate the results to a great extent.

Transfer phenomena in the case of halftones

As for the evaluation of the transfer and of the other printing characteristics, the two inks employed, having similar rheological properties, behaved in the same way; therefore what will be said about one of them is to be considered qualitatively valid for the other too. The method above illustrated

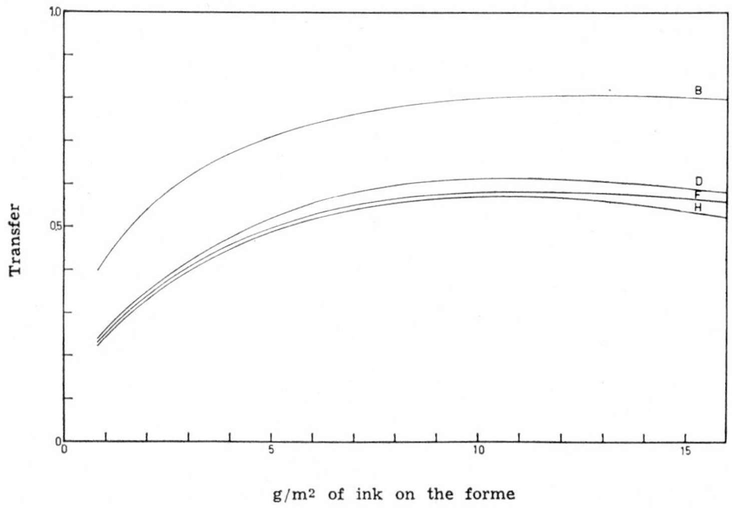

Fig. 7. Fraction of ink transferred on the paper as a function of ink amount on the forme, for the following printing areas: $B = 0.2$; $D = 0.5$; $F = 0.8$; $H = 1.0$.

for the determination of the block inking (in grams of ink/m² of actually printed area) allowed a conventional evaluation of the transfer (ratio of the amount of ink on paper to the "calculated" amount of ink on the forme). Figures 7 and 8 show, for a linear pressure of 30 kg/cm, the variation of the transfer as a function of the inking of the block for various printing areas, and as a function of the printing area for various inkings on the block.

Figure 8 shows that the transfer increases when the printing areas decreases with a maximum for an area of about 10 per cent and, below this value, a drop. This behaviour could be explained as follows. During printing, around each dot of the forme pressed on the paper a fringe of ink is formed, partially due to the ink spread from the dot surface because of the pressure and, mainly from the ink previously laid on the upper part of the dot walls; when the paper is lifted from the plate, while the ink between the dot surface and the paper splits, as in the case of a solid print, the ink constituting the fringe around the dot, being anchored on one side to the paper and on the other side to the sloping wall of the dot, will tend to transfer prevailingly on the paper, giving therefore a higher average transfer and, the more so the higher the dot perimeter relative to the dot area. On the other hand it must be remembered that the transfer is measured on the basis of the "calculated" inkings of the forme: but when the dot surface becomes particularly small, it may happen that the ink distribution between the dot top

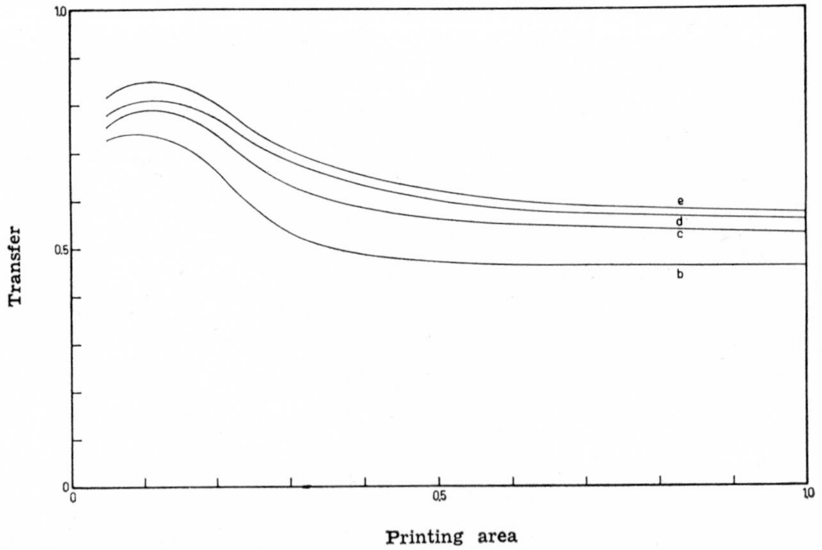

Fig. 8. Fraction of ink transferred on paper as a function of printing area, for the following amounts of ink on the forme: $b = 4\ g/m^2$; $c = 6\ g/m^2$; $d = 8\ g/m^2$; $e = 10\ g/m^2$.

and walls will be greatly out of balance, so that the ink remaining on the dot will be only a very small fraction of the "calculated" amount, leading to apparently low transfer values. This could explain the transfer drop for the areas below 10 per cent.

When the pressure varies, the transfer curves are slightly displaced, with their shape almost unchanged. Figures 9 and 10 just show the variation of the transfer as a function of pressure for some areas and inkings.

The influence on transfer variation of pressure changes as well as variable printing areas is felt, in practical printing, when a composite forme is printed, consisting of full tone areas (solids) next to halftones of various tonal values. It is a well known fact that in such a case, the printer has to set the solid area slightly higher (this being equivalent to a pressure raise) in order to compensate for the transfer variations in the various zones.

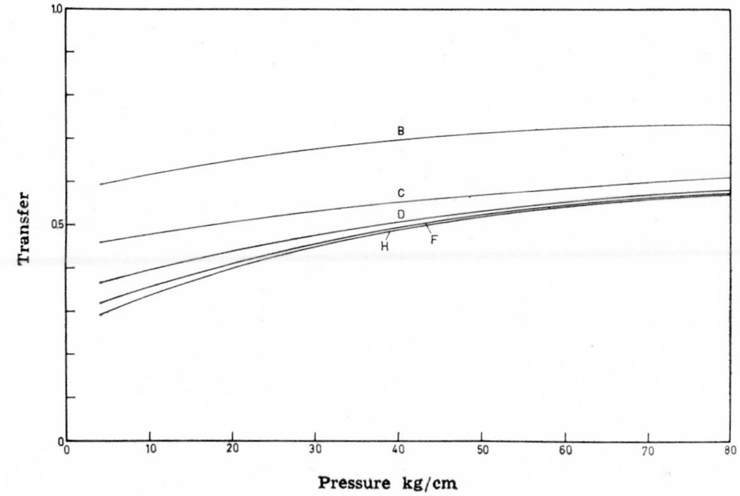

Fig. 9. Transfer variation as a function of pressure for an inking on the forme of 4 g/m² and for the following printing areas: $B = 0.2$; $C = 0.3$; $D = 0.5$; $F = 0.8$; $H = 1.0$.

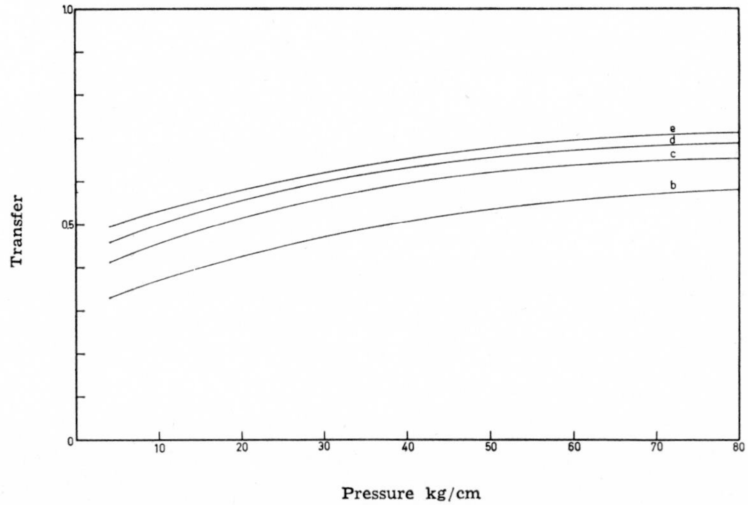

Fig. 10. Transfer variation as a function of the pressure for a printing area of 0.5 and for the following amounts of ink on the forme: $b = 4$ g/m²; $c = 6$ g/m²; $d = 8$ g/m²; $e = 10$ g/m².

Relationships between experimental conditions and printing results

Figure 11 gives the printed area variation as a function of the inking of the block for several printing areas and pressures: these illustrate some characteristics of the prints as a function of experimental conditions. Beside this overall representation, the effects of some particular parameters are

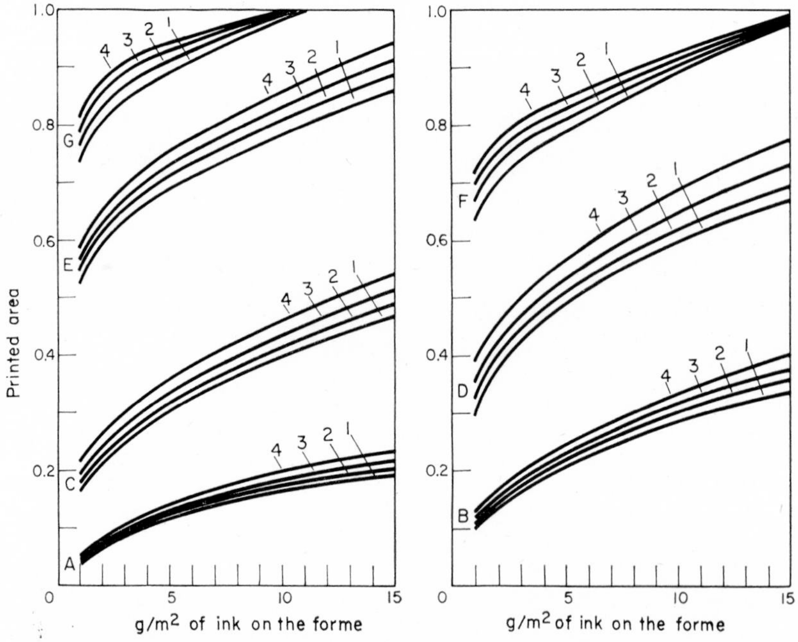

Fig. 11. Printed area variation as a function of the ink amounts on the forme for the following printed areas: $A = 0.1$; $B = 0.2$; $C = 0.3$; $D = 0.5$; $E = 0.7$; $F = 0.8$; $G = 0.9$; and for the following printing pressures: 1 = 10 kg/cm; 2 = 30 kg/cm; 3 = 50 kg/cm; 4 = 80 kg/cm.

shown in more detail in Figs. 12 and 13. The comparison of these graphs shows that the influences of the various variables are not equivalent and it explains why, in industrial practice, a defective composite block (where for instance, all dots would be too small to render the exact tonal values) cannot be corrected either by an increase of inking or by an overall increase of pressure, since both procedures would inevitably lead to strong distortions in the tonal balance. Moreover, considering the optical densities, another variable not mentioned in the above graphs comes into the picture, i.e. the average ink thickness *on the paper*. In fact, the ink thickness has a very marked effect on the density of the prints and, mainly, on their chromaticity

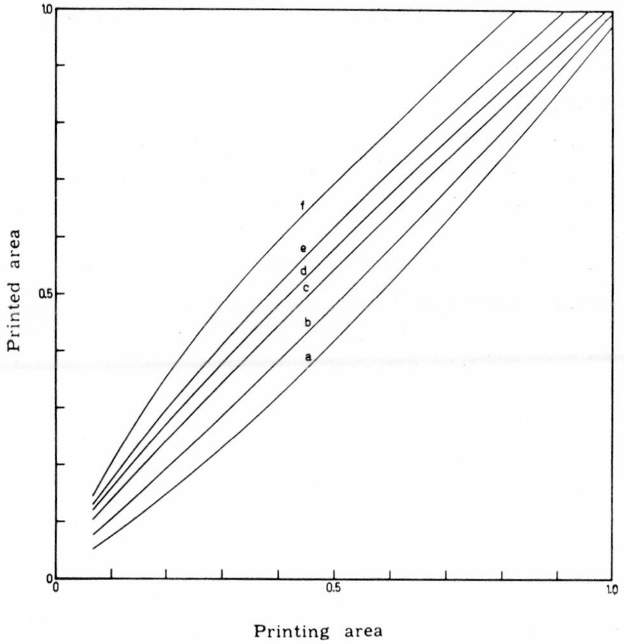

Fig. 12. Relationship between printed area and printing area for the pressure of 30 kg/cm and for the following ink amounts on the forme: $a = 2\ g/m^2$; $b = 4\ g/m^2$; $c = 6\ g/m^2$; $d = 8\ g/m^2$; $e = 10\ g/m^2$; $f = 15\ g/m^2$.

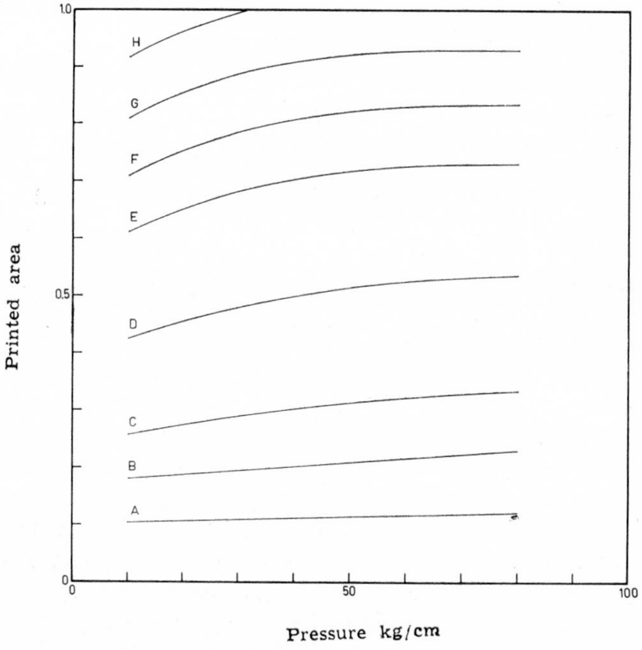

Fig. 13. Printed area variation as a function of pressure for the inking on the forme of $4\ g/m^2$ and for the following printing areas: $A = 0.1$; $B = 0.2$; $C = 0.3$; $D = 0.5$; $E = 0.7$; $F = 0.8$; $G = 0.9$; $H = 1.0$.

in the case of coloured inks. From Fig. 14 it can be seen that the prints obtained with a constant inking of the block, for different printing areas, do not have, in general, the same ink thicknesses on the paper, because of the complexity of the phenomena involved in the transfer and, more precisely, because of the general shape of the transfer curve and of the printed area/printing area curves. These variations of the ink film thickness on the paper become more pronounced at higher inkings.

As already mentioned, the reproduction of a printing area may lead, according to pressure and inking conditions, to an increase (as generally

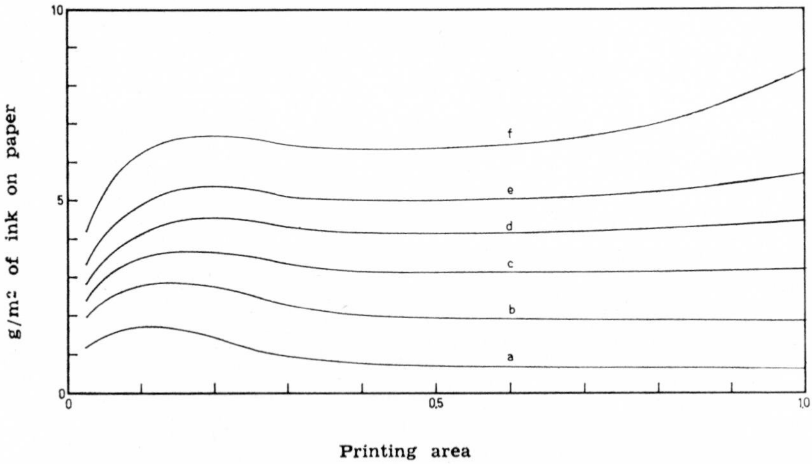

Fig. 14. Variation of the ink amount on paper as a function of printing area for the pressure of 30 kg/cm and for the following ink amounts on the forme: $a = 2$ g/m²; $b = 4$ g/m²; $c = 6$ g/m²; $d = 8$ g/m²; $e = 10$ g/m²; $f = 15$ g/m².

happens in practice) or to a reduction of the dot areas: owing to the importance of such a phenomenon in practice, we thought it useful to introduce a "variation index of the area" defined as ratio of printed area to printing area, and to observe its behaviour under a given pressure and for each printing area, as a function of the inking on the block. The resulting graphs (only the one corresponding to the pressure of 30 kg/cm is represented, Fig. 15) show a very interesting behaviour: in fact the curves representing the different printing areas cross one another within a rather limited zone, thus revealing, for each given pressure, the existence of a specific inking at which all the printing areas have a variation index fairly close to 1, i.e. they are reproduced without modifications. Figure 16 shows the variation of this specific inking as a function of the pressure. Of course, considering the optical density instead of the printing area only, the thicknesses of ink transferred to the

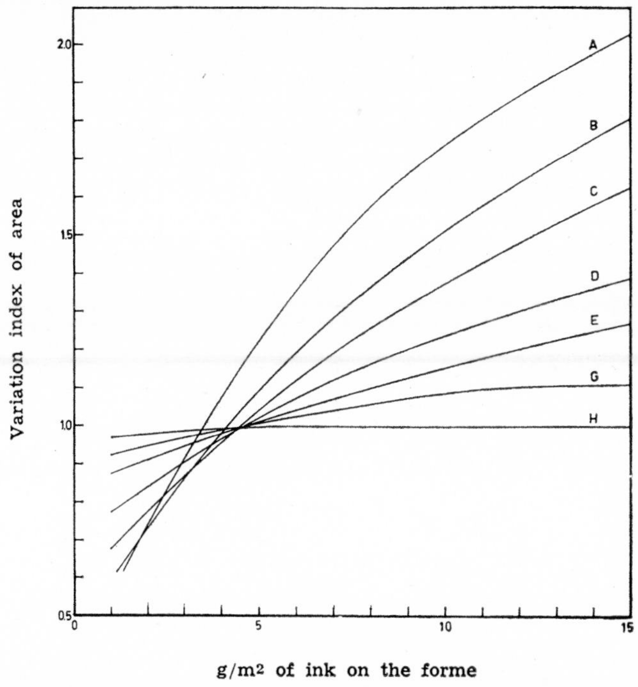

Fig. 15. Variation of the ratio printed area/printing area as a function of ink amount on the forme, for the pressure of 30 kg/cm and for the following printing areas: $A = 0.1$; $B = 0.2$; $C = 0.3$; $D = 0.5$; $E = 0.7$; $G = 0.9$; $H = 1.0$.

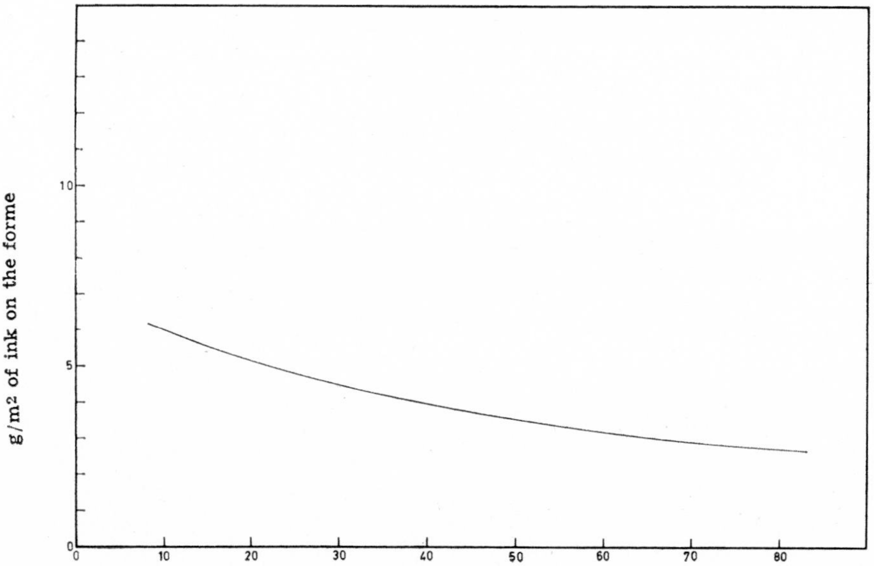

Fig. 16. Ink on the forme, corresponding to a *variation index of area* = *1*, as a function of pressure.

paper, as already stated, will not be constant over the various areas and will, in turn, affect the density values. For what concerns the variation of printed density for variable printing areas it is possible, also, to find a specific inking value exhibiting a very particular behaviour. If, for a given pressure and for each printing area, we plot the ratio of the print density to the corresponding printing area as a function of the inking of the forme, graph 17 (at a pressure

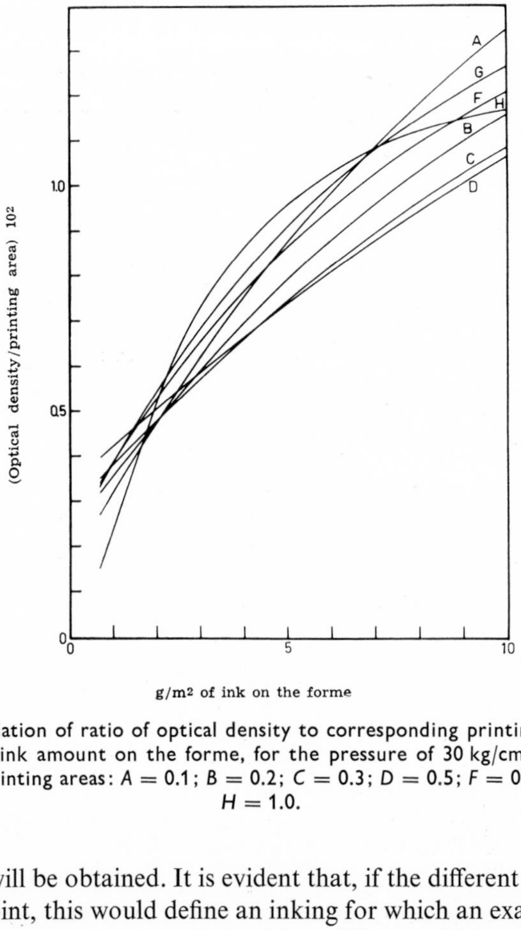

Fig. 17. Variation of ratio of optical density to corresponding printing area, as a function of ink amount on the forme, for the pressure of 30 kg/cm and for the following printing areas: $A = 0.1$; $B = 0.2$; $C = 0.3$; $D = 0.5$; $F = 0.8$; $G = 0.9$; $H = 1.0$.

of 30 kg/cm) will be obtained. It is evident that, if the different curves crossed at the same point, this would define an inking for which an exact proportionality between printing areas and densities of the resulting prints would be obtained. Although these curves do not meet just in one point, it is possible to determine an inking value for which the spread has a minimum dispersion: graph 18 gives, for this inking value, the density variation as related to the printing area which, as can be seen, is not far from proportionality. In this particular case, because of the low inking value and of the kind of paper on which the prints have been made, the maximum density appears, in fact, too low to be acceptable in practice. In the above exposition, however, we thought it useful to report the procedures applied for the determination of some inking values of particular interest with the purpose of pointing out that the proper interpretation of such graphs is not only of academic interest, but may also lead to the solution of specific practical problems on a

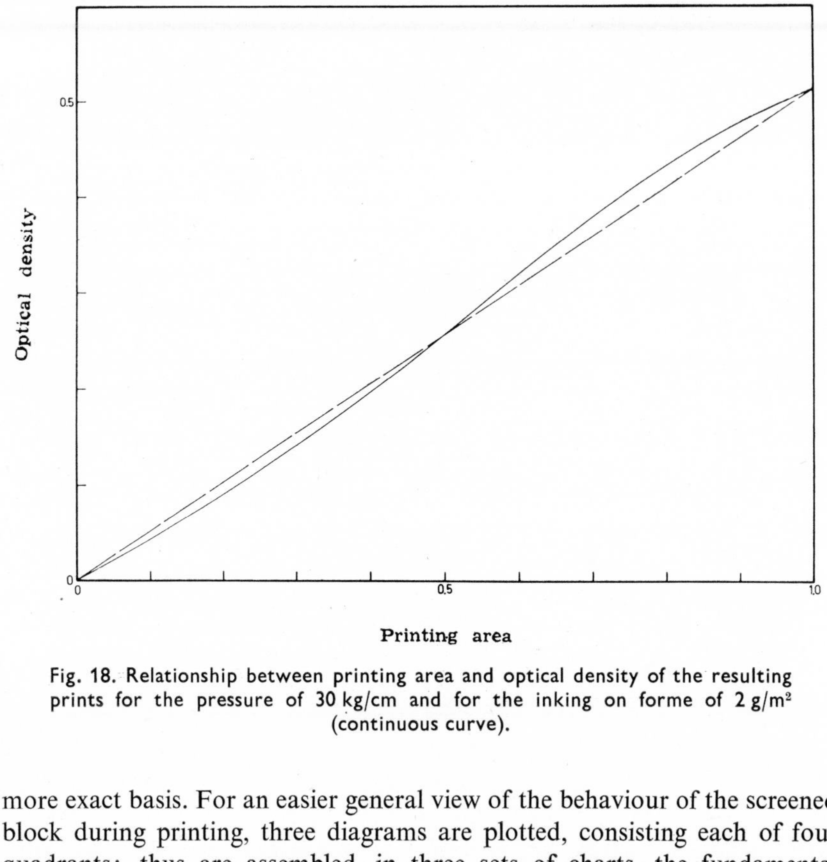

Fig. 18. Relationship between printing area and optical density of the resulting prints for the pressure of 30 kg/cm and for the inking on forme of 2 g/m^2 (continuous curve).

more exact basis. For an easier general view of the behaviour of the screened block during printing, three diagrams are plotted, consisting each of four quadrants: thus are assembled, in three sets of charts, the fundamental variables related respectively to prints performed either under constant pressure (Fig. 19) or at constant inking (Fig. 20) or for a "variation index of area" equal to 1 (Fig. 21). In the case of the last graph, it should be pointed out that, as seen in Fig. 16, each pressure corresponds to a well defined inking value for which the printed area exactly equals the printing area; therefore, in graph 21, each pressure at the same time defines this corresponding inking.

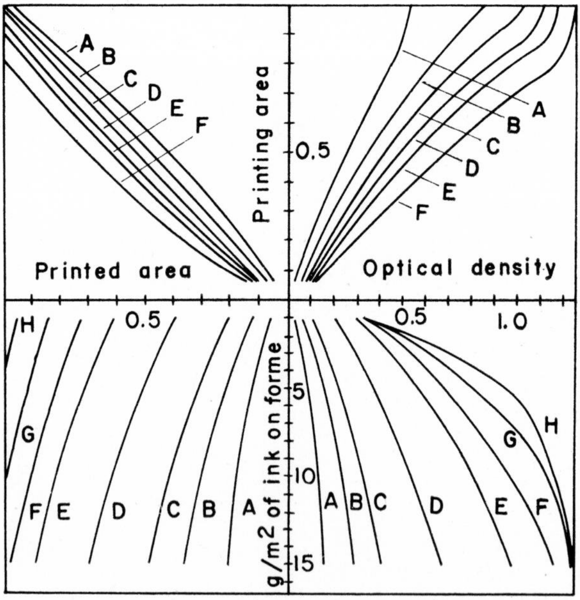

Fig. 19. Relationships between printing area, optical density, inking on forme and printed area for the pressure of 30 kg/cm, for the following printing areas: $A = 0.1$; $B = 0.2$; $C = 0.3$; $D = 0.5$; $E = 0.7$; $F = 0.8$; $G = 0.9$; $H = 1.0$ and for the following amounts of ink on the forme: $a = 2$ g/m²; $b = 4$ g/m²; $d = 8$ g/m²; e = 10 g/m²; $f = 15$ g/m².

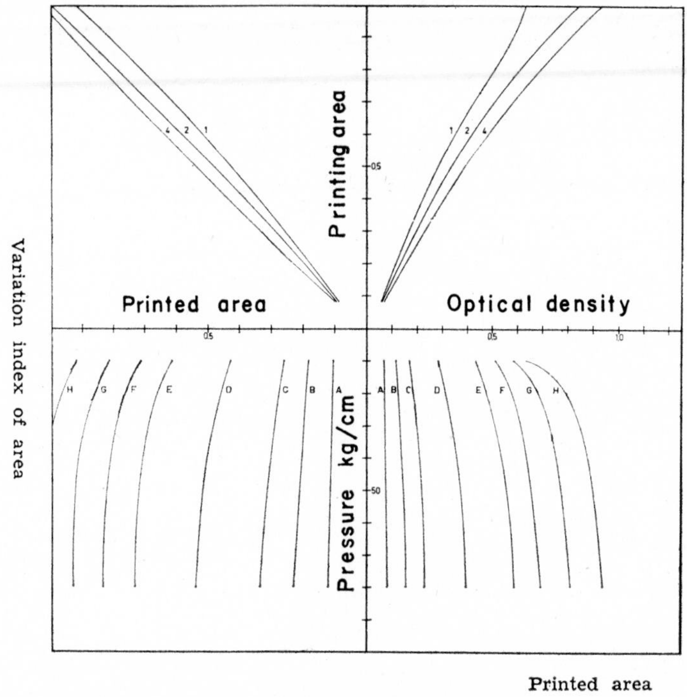

Fig. 20. Relationships between printing area, optical density, pressure and printed area for the inking on forme of 4 g/m^2, for the following printing areas: $A = 0.1$; $B = 0.2$; $C = 0.3$; $D = 0.5$; $E = 0.7$; $F = 0.8$; $G = 0.9$; $H = 1.0$ and for the following pressures: 1 = 10 kg/cm; 2 = 30 kg/cm; 4 = 80 kg/cm.

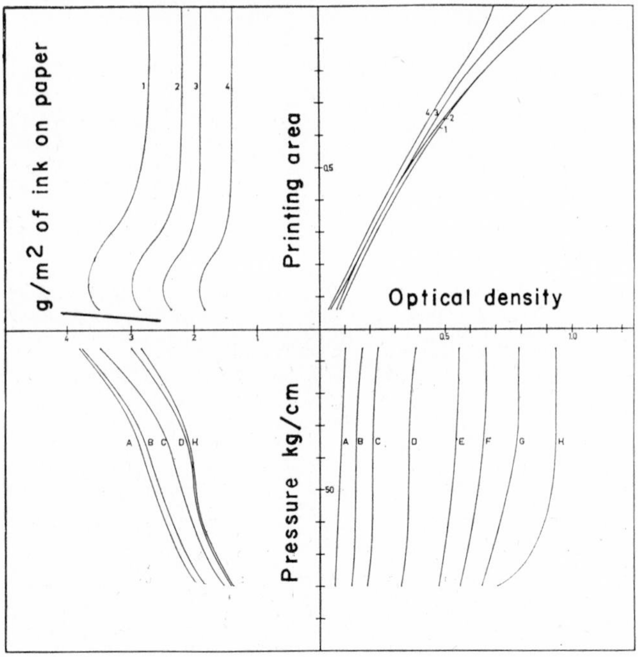

Fig. 21. Relationships between printing area (equal to the printed area), optical density, pressure and ink on paper, for a *variation index of area* = *1*, for the following printing areas: $A = 0.1$; $B = 0.2$; $C = 0.3$; $D = 0.5$; $E = 0.7$; $F = 0.8$; $G = 0.9$; $H = 1.0$ and for the following pressures: 1 = 10 kg/cm; 2 = 30 kg/cm; 3 = 60 kg/cm; 4 = 80 kg/cm.

CONCLUSIONS

It may be concluded from the study of a large set of prints, performed under controlled experimental conditions, that it is possible to devise some working methods which may prove useful also in practice; a deeper knowledge of the mechanism of halftone block reproduction has been gained and relationships between results and printing conditions have been established. The methods described result essentially in the use of a small subsidiary roller added to the inking system (whose weighing makes possible the easy evaluation of the inking on the forme) and of a pre-established chart, by means of which, in the case of coloured inks, the printing area and the thickness of the film deposited on paper can be deduced, from reflection factor measurements performed on the prints through two suitably chosen filters.

The screened block reproduction has been investigated and it has been shown that the mechanism of transfer is, in this case, very different from what was known of the transfer of solids, this difference being essentially due to the importance of the edge-effects which appear to prevail in the case of small areas.

Several sets of graphs show the relationships between the fundamental variables: transfer, inking, area, density, etc., allowing one to forecast the results of prints performed under determined experimental conditions, or, even better, to predetermine the best printing conditions for a particular result. For example, once having established the printing pressure and inking liable to give the density desired for the solid area, it should be possible to determine the printing areas necessary to obtain on the print a predetermined scale of densities, thus enabling a fair reproduction of the various tonal values of the original copy.

Finally we describe the possibility of defining some particular inking values which, under a certain pressure, will give either an exact reproduction of the printing area without distortion (variation index of the area = 1) or density increases directly proportional to the increase of printing area.

REFERENCES

1. G. M. W. LASEUR, Ink transfer from halftone engravings. *Printing Inks and Color, Advances in Printing Science and Technology*, Pergamon Press, Vol. I, 303–11, 1961.
2. J. A. C. YULE and W. J. NEILSEN, The penetration of light into paper and its effect on halftone reproduction. *Taga Proceedings* 65–76, 1951.
3. F. R. CLAPPER and J. A. C. YULE, The effect of multiple internal reflections on the densities of halftone prints on paper. *J. Opt. Soc. Amer.* **43**, 7, 600–3, 1953.
4. K. H. SCHIRMER, Zur messung der gedeckten Fläche von Rasterfilmen und der bedruckten Fläche von Rasterdrucken. *Fogra Mitteilungen* **33**, 6–10, 1962.

DISCUSSION

MME BENEDITE: I wish to stress the elegance of the method described by Dr. Calabrò which enables, for a given print, the simultaneous determination of the actual dot area and printed ink thickness by means of reflectance measurements only. Of course a calibrating graph, corresponding to a set of prints made under known conditions with exactly the same ink and paper, must be prepared and the method is only valid for coloured inks, and not for black.

It can, nevertheless, be very useful where the weighed shell technique cannot be used (as in the case of stereotype printing for instance).

TOLLENAAR: What is the cause of the low ratio of the printed area to the printing area?

CALABRÒ: It is due to insufficient contact at small ink film thickness.

LARSSON: What kind of load cell did you use? It would also be very interesting to know the dimensions of the gauge, and whether you got first the maximum pressure from it or perhaps even the complete time-variation of the actual pressure.

CALABRÒ: The load cell we used has a diameter of about 4 cm and a thickness of about 1 cm. Small deformations proportional to the load applied result in variations of the electrical resistance.

This cell was placed at one of the three points of support of the rigid base on which the plate was fixed. It was thus possible, after appropriate calibration, to ascertain the actual pressure at each zone of the plate, at the very instant it was under pressure from the cylinder.

WALKER: I note that one of your printing plates had a dot area of only one per cent. This must have been a very difficult plate to prepare and use.

CALABRÒ: In fact, a plate with such a small dot area is far from easy to use, but we found it very necessary, in the course of our work, to have such a value so close to zero, in order to minimize extrapolation of the results.

GINMAN: How is the absorption factor defined and how do you calculate it?

CALABRÒ: This absorption factor is the one defined according to the C.I.E. definition. It was directly calculated from the reflection factor given by the Elrepho instrument (i.e. 1 − Reflection factor).

STUDIES ON THE TONE REPRODUCTION OF CURVED PLATES IN SHEET-FED ROTARY LETTERPRESS PRINTING

by J. ALBRECHT and K.-H. SCHIRMER
Institut der Deutschen Gesellschaft für Forschung im Graphischen Gewerbe, München, Bamberger Haus

Abstract—In the course of a "round robin" test of wrap-around-plates for sheet-fed rotary letterpress the tone reproduction in single-colour halftone printing was studied. The test series included one-piece wraps (etched as flat or curved plate) as well as some so-called combination-wrap-around-plates containing individual plates on a carrier foil.

The different results in tone reproduction produced on an art paper, are compared. The tone reproduction curve to be expected when the density range of the point is smaller than that of the original is discussed. The preference of the light and middle tones as opposed to the shadows, that will become necessary in such a case, is explained, and it is referred to the characteristic curve required for this kind of tone reproduction.

IN the quality assessment of prints from wrap-round plates in single-colour rotary letterpress, the tone reproduction of the print is of major importance Tone reproduction in this context means the reproduction of tones of various density of an original (photographic image) by means of halftone printing. It is influenced by the characteristic halftone curve of the original, the printing-down and etching procedures, the printing process, and also by the selection of printing inks and printing paper.

In the following, the problems of tone reproduction are dealt with in the following stages.

(1) Which grade of tone reproduction is attained in practice and considered as good, fair or bad?
(2) How is ideal tone reproduction supposed to appear in print?
(3) Which are the requirements of ideal tone reproduction in the halftone negative and how can these be realized?

In 1962 and 1963 the FOGRA-Institute conducted a "round robin" test with wrap-around plates that had been produced by various photo-engraving plants from identical originals. The original, among others, contained two photographic continuous tone images and corresponding gray scales one of which was to be reproduced in 120, the other in 135 screen rulings. The wrap-around plates were produced by the firms in their usual manner and printed in the FOGRA-Institute on a Heidelberg two-colour flat-bed letterpress under constant conditions. The paper was coated art paper having some wood fibre content, the black ink was a type specially suited for printing from these plates, and of a consistency to allow a maximal density of 1.4 to 1.5 on the chosen paper. Most of the plates provided by the photo-engraving plants were one-piece plates of zinc (0.8–1 mm thickness), but they also delivered magnesium and Dycril plates. Furthermore, so-called combi-wrap-around plates were used. These consist of an aluminium plate of 0.3 mm thickness onto which curved printing plates are mounted. Materials used for printing plates were zinc, nylon, and plastic (duplicate).

Etching of the one-piece zinc plates was done partly on curved plates and partly on flat plates which were curved after the process. Thereby the halftone and line portions were either etched simultaneously or separately. Finally, there were also plates whose halftone portions had been etched in the conventional manner.

WHICH GRADE OF TONE REPRODUCTION IS ATTAINED IN PRACTICE AND CONSIDERED AS GOOD, FAIR OR BAD?

For examination of the tone reproduction obtained from various printing plates, density measurements were made on the steps of a gray scale reproduced simultaneously and the density of the print compared with that of the original. Likewise, the reproduction of the image was visually judged in comparison with the original and assessed as either good, fair or bad.

Visual judgment of the prints is influenced mainly by such characteristics as become obvious from a too narrow density range of the printed image due to the printing areas of the printing plates being too small in the shadow parts. The impression of the image is then of poor contrast. But also if the light parts lack contrast, i.e. if the reproduction of detail in the light portions is insufficient, the reproduction of the image is disturbed. In some cases insufficient details in the shadow portions may also be observed.

On five of the fourteen tested wrap-around plates the image reproduction of halftones of 135 screen ruling which were given particular consideration, showed a strong decrease in contrast. Figure 1, shows examples of tone reproduction curves of the prints from powderless etched plates. Whereas

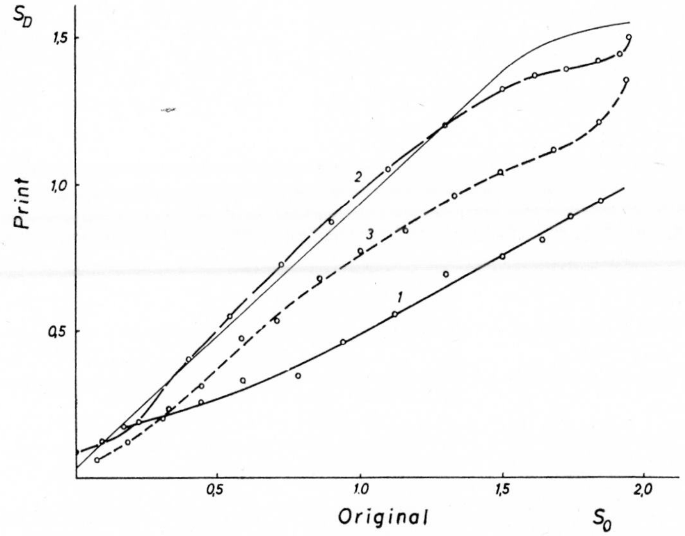

Fig. 1. Tone reproduction with powderless etching (135 lines/in.).

the tone reproduction curve for plate 2 may be regarded as good, plate 3 and particularly plate 1 show a loss in the density range of the print.

An essential disturbance of tone reproduction occurs whenever, as in the case of plate 6 (Fig. 2), there is an additional loss of detail in the light portions.

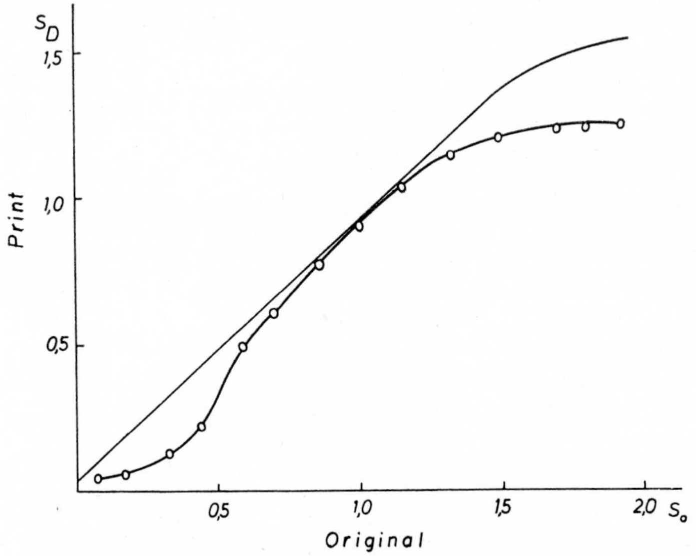

Fig. 2. Tone reproduction Plate 6.

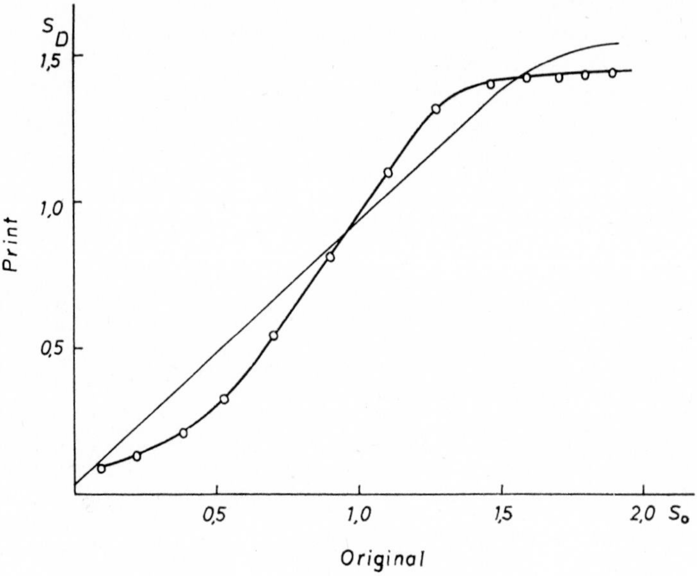

Fig. 3. Tone reproduction Plate 8.

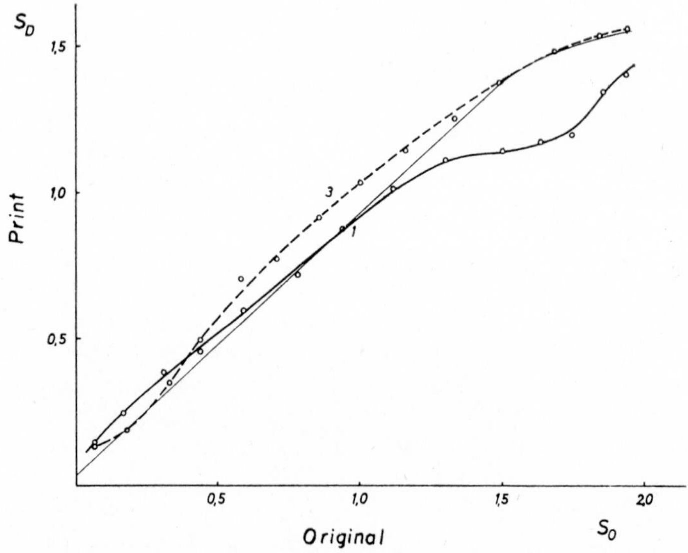

Fig. 4. Tone reproduction with conventional etching (135 lines/in.).

This could be observed in two cases. Tone reproduction will be rated poorly also when, as in the case of plate 8 (Fig. 3), apart from unwanted alteration of light details together with an increase of contrast in portions of medium density, shadow reproduction experiences a strong flattening making the shadows appear to lack detail.

Tone reproduction of conventionally etched plates may be regarded as good, as becomes evident from the two examples shown in Fig. 4. This, in particular, applies to the plate numbered 3, whereas the plate numbered 1 has a small loss in the shadows which can be seen from the distinct curvature of the tone reproduction curve in that region.

In summary, tone reproduction under prevailing conditions is considered good only if tone reproduction curves in light and medium portions run straight with a curving in the shadows as an indication of flattening. The curving may, as in the case of plate 3, Fig. 4, follow a constant trend or, as in the case of plate 2, Fig. 1, be associated with another increase in the regions of highest density.

HOW IS IDEAL TONE REPRODUCTION SUPPOSED TO APPEAR IN PRINT?

Supposing the density range of a print coincides with that of the original, ideal tone reproduction curves may be considered as linear. If, however, the range of the original is larger than that of the print, it must be reduced for the print. Such are the conditions in the example to be considered. It is the reproduction of a photographic glossy paper image whose density range extends from a density in the high lights at approximately 0.1 to that in the shadows at approximately 1.8, thus covering a range of 1.7. This original is to be reproduced in a print with a density in the lights of from 0.05 to 0.10 and a density in the shadows of approximately 1.5, i.e. a range of 1.4. In printing on uncoated paper, the density range in reproduction is further reduced to from 1.1 to 1.2.

In such a case, with the density range of the print not coming up to that of the original, the print will show less luminance steps than the original.

When the original possesses a range of 1.7, approximately 80 steps can be recognized. In a print of a range of 1.5, however, only about 70 steps can be distinguished and, when printing on uncoated paper, the number is further reduced to 60 steps. The question arises as to how the reduction in the number of steps should be handled. One could think of reducing at a constant rate, i.e. assume linear tone reproduction as before. This does not, however, produce favourable results, as in the high light areas it is necessary to minimize diminishing luminance differences in order to maintain the detailed structure of the light portions. Insufficient reproduction of details in light portions is generally considered undesirable. In areas of medium luminance, however, a loss in tone may be ignored. In the shadows, on the other hand, losses in tone may be undesirable yet this loss is not as noticeable as it is in the high light portions.

Similar problems occur in pictorial photography. R. Luther[1] has dealt with the question of how to reduce the luminance range in photography.

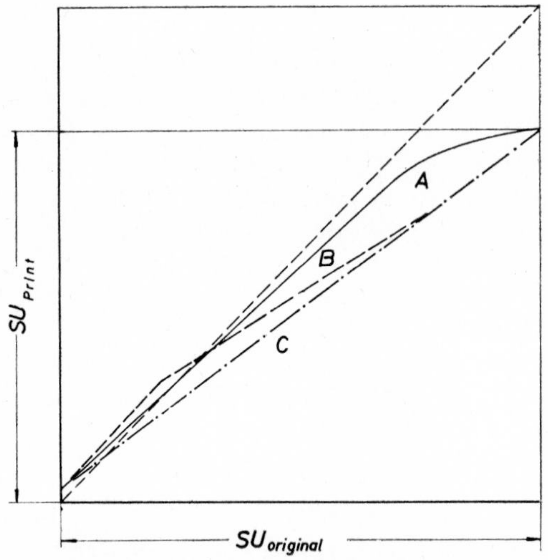

Fig. 5. Ideal tone reproduction of printed image (schematic).
SU_{print} = Density range of print
SU_{original} = Density range of original.

The problem there is the reproduction of the object's luminance steps in the image. According to R. Luther, the reduction of the object's luminance range to the density of the photographic image may be brought about in the following manner:

"One way is equally to distribute the reduction over the entire luminance interval. Experience shows, however, that other distributions may likewise result in a pictorial effect, i.e. make the picture appear to be genuine and in agreement with the original, despite objectively wrong reproduction caused by deviating distribution. The reason is that less details are noticeable in the shadows than in the light portions. It may be considered as a guide that in the light portions each step of the original should appear as an equal in the image. This will necessarily result in a loss of details in the shadows. The question of how far one can go without running the risk of getting shadows can be decided statistically only."

As the evaluation of the fourteen wrap-around plates in the test has shown, the tone reproduction in the print of a photographic image is regarded as good when the tone values run straight in the light and medium portions and are reproduced with practically no loss, and when there is but a negligible loss in the shadows. The degree of loss in shadow tones that is acceptable and thus may be considered permissible can be seen from a comparison of evaluations with tone reproduction curves. Whereas the flattening of curve 2 in Fig. 1 and curve 3 in Fig. 4 does not cause disturbing effects in the pictorial impression, plate 1 (see Fig. 4) and plate 8 (see Fig. 3) show distinct deviations in the tone reproduction in the shadow areas. It follows from the examples described above that in cases that require a reduction of the range in print as compared with the original, the ideal tone reproduction should have but a slight slope in the area of light and medium portions and moderate curvature in the shadow portions (case A, see Fig. 5).

For comparison, the descriptions following below will also contain the curve as proposed by R. Reuther[(2)], which further neglects medium and shadow portions in favour of the light areas (case B) as well as the proportional reduction of the range (case C), i.e. equal reduction of all tone values.

WHAT REQUIREMENTS DOES IDEAL TONE REPRODUCTION PUT TO THE HALFTONE NEGATIVE AND HOW CAN THESE BE REALIZED?

In order to determine the requirements, for ideal tone reproduction, of the halftone negative, the relation between the density of the halftone negative and the density of the print must be taken into consideration. This so-called transfer which can be represented by the characteristic transfer curve summarizes the effects of printing down, etching and the printing process.

Supposing an ideal transfer between the density, i.e. dot size in the half-tone negative, and density of the print then the characteristic transfer curve describes a definite curve (compare Fig. 6). It is computed from the fact that the dot size in print ϕ_D is related to that in the negative ϕ_N by ($\phi_D = 1 - \phi_N$), together with the relation

$$S_D = -\log \{1 - 10^{-S_N}(1 - 10^{-S_V})\}$$

in which S_N is the density in the halftone negative and S_V that of the solid in the print.

The characteristic transfer curves in practice are steeper, i.e. at equal density in the halftone negative they show a higher density for the print. The reason is the squeeze-out that occurs during the printing process even though initially, the etching causes a loss in dot size.

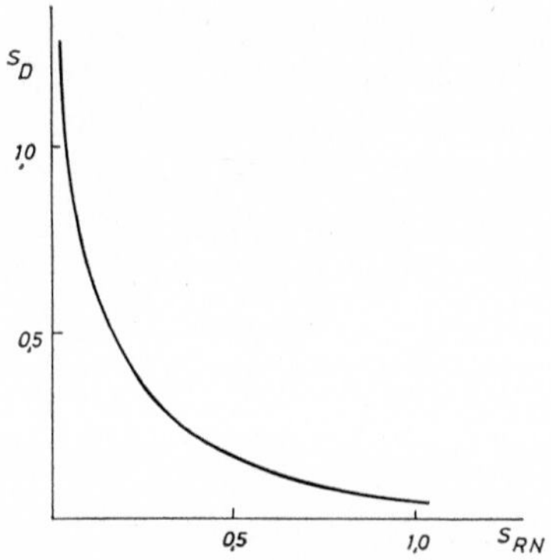

Fig. 6. Ideal characteristic transfer curve.

The reduction in dot size, i.e. the loss of dots in powderless etching at 135 screen ruling is demonstrated in Fig. 7, whereas Fig. 8 shows the enlargement of the printing area by the printing process. The final effect is an increase of

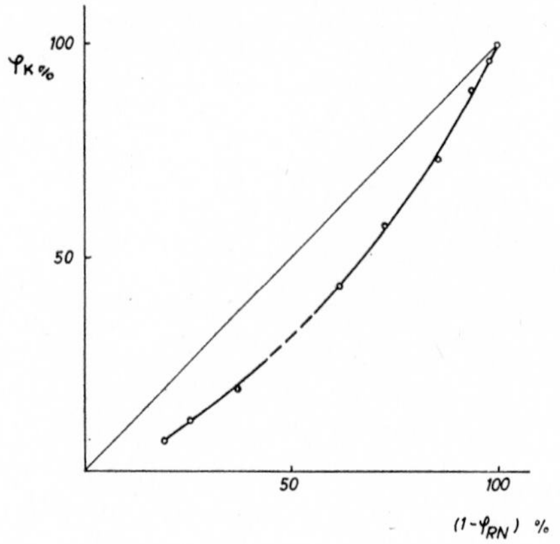

Fig. 7. Dot area loss with powderless zinc etching (135 lines/in.).

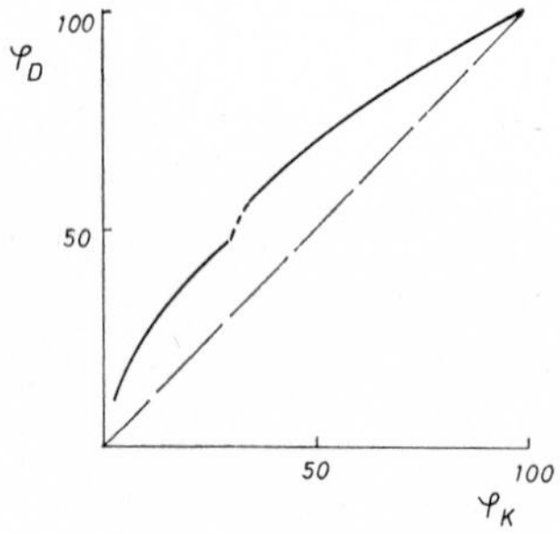

Fig. 8. Dot area of halftone plate and final print.

density in print as compared to ideal transfer, which may be attributed mainly to the squeeze-out effect and the resulting accumulation of ink in the squeezed fringe of the dot.

As Fig. 9 shows, uniform characteristic transfer curves cannot be expected if powderless etching procedures are applied under varying working conditions. Although the general course of the curve is maintained, the use of various etching machines, filming agents and etch conditions exercises some influence. This must be considered in determining the required characteristic half-tone curve.

In order to draw correct conclusions with regard to the halftone negative from the expected tone reproduction, the characteristic halftone curve corresponding to the transfer curve under definite etching conditions must be determined graphically. In this the Goldberg conversion diagram(3,4)* is of valuable assistance. In this diagram the single steps of dot plate production and of printing are plotted in the various quadrants of the diagram and comprise the relationship between original and halftone negative (characteristic halftone curve), halftone negative and print (characteristic transfer

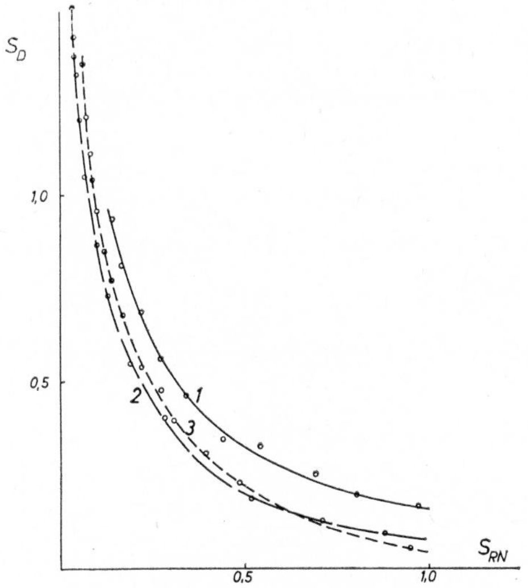

Fig. 9. Characteristic transfer curves with powderless zinc etching (134 lines/in.).

curve), original and print (tone reproduction curve). With this graphical method the medium of conversion is used for determining the contour of a halftone curve to ensure close and correct reproduction with wrap-around plates produced by a particular etching method. Figure 10 shows the construction of the required characteristic halftone curve corresponding to transfer curve No. 3 in Fig. 9.

In order to study the influence of various transfer curves on characteristic halftone curves, the conversion diagram was used to determine the required halftone curves for the two other transfer curves. Figure 11 shows the necessary variation in the characteristic halftone curve. It was interesting, too, to find out how the various definitions of ideal tone reproduction affect

* In English speaking countries, this diagram is frequently referred to as the Lloyd Jones' diagram—see Ref. (4). Editor.

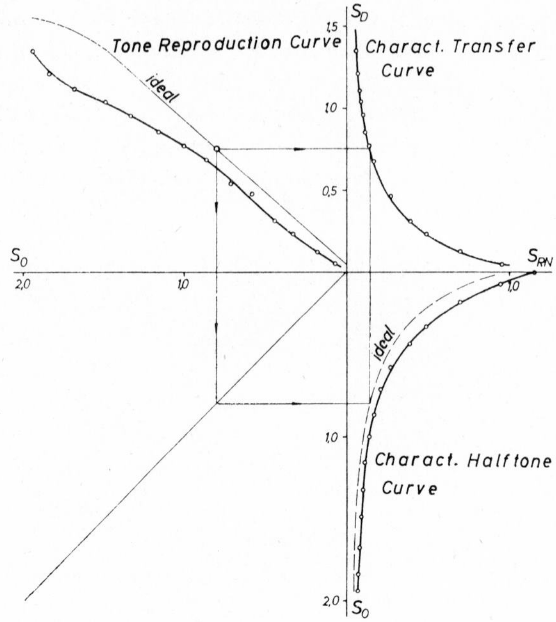

Fig. 10. Conversion diagram for powderless etching (135 lines/in.).

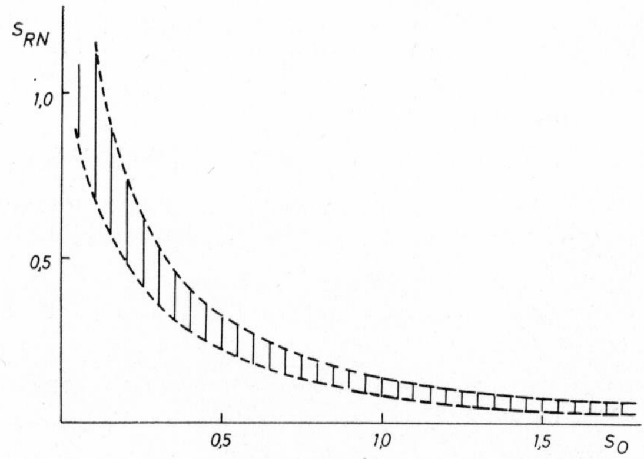

Fig. 11. Variation of characteristic halftone curve with different etching conditions.

the corresponding halftone curves. The result of this test is given in Fig. 12. Apart from the curve plotted in the conversion diagram it shows the characteristic halftone curves for cases B and C as applied to ideal tone reproduction.

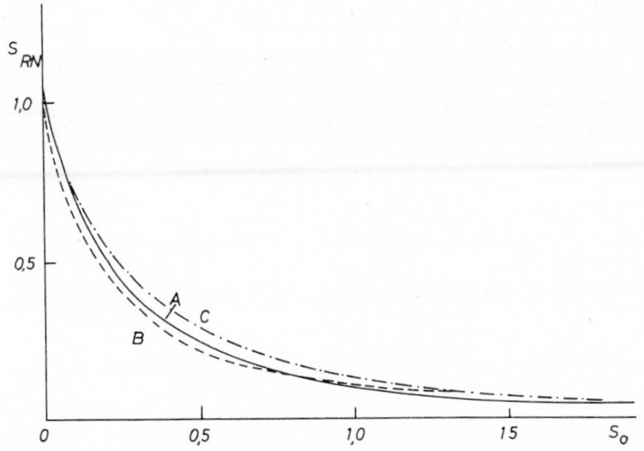

Fig. 12. Variation of characteristic halftone curve with different definition of tone reproduction.

Taking case A as an example of ideal tone reproduction, its characteristic halftone curve will appear as shown in Fig. 13, assuming that constant etching conditions prevail. This applies to the production of wrap-around

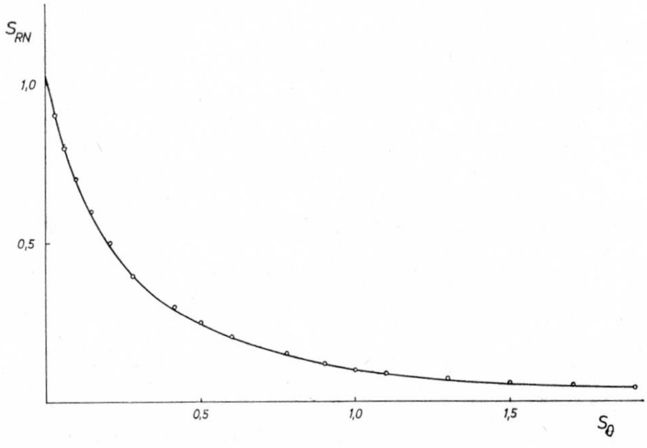

Fig. 13. Characteristic halftone curve for tone-correct negative.

plates in a 135 screen ruling. In the light portions the characteristic halftone curve will show a density of about 1.0, for an original density of 0.5 a corresponding value of approximately 0.25, and then will steadily fall until it reaches the maximal density of the original ($S_0 = 1.8$). Conducting an identical test with etchings of 120 or even coarser screen rulings the curve will be of a closely similar shape but just slightly less curved.

This bend in the characteristic halftone curve is not attained with common halftone transparencies. The proof is given in Fig. 14, curve 1 of which shows the usual form of cross line screen print. Even with common contact screens

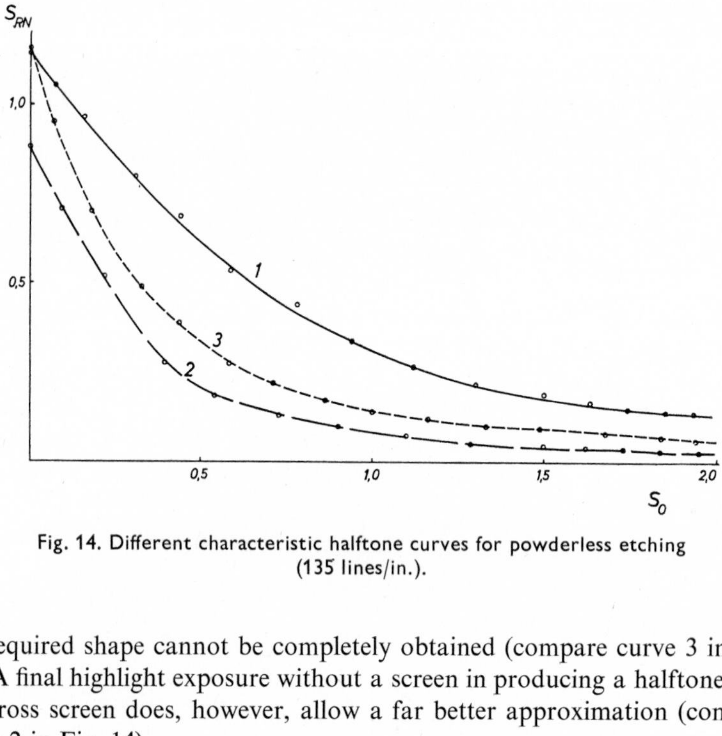

Fig. 14. Different characteristic halftone curves for powderless etching (135 lines/in.).

the required shape cannot be completely obtained (compare curve 3 in Fig. 14). A final highlight exposure without a screen in producing a halftone with the cross screen does, however, allow a far better approximation (compare curve 2 in Fig. 14).

In order to obtain the required characteristic halftone curves the test conducted in the FOGRA-Institute followed the scheme listed below:

(1) Use of pre-exposure, multiple stop system and highlight exposure without screen when producing halftones with a cross line screen.

(2) Use of a contact screen adapted to correct tone reproduction, e.g. IGT-PATRA-screen.

(3) Use of electronic engraving devices, as for instance the "Varioklischograph", whereby a halftone positive is cut from the original into a thin plastic film with a coloured surface. The halftone negative is produced photographically from the plastic film positive.

With the aid of these methods the characteristic halftone curve can be adjusted to any requirement as regards the transfer between halftone negative and print. This highly refined technique does, however, fill its purpose only if it is possible to keep etching conditions fairly constant.

REFERENCES

1. R. LUTHER, unpublished communication.
2. R. REUTHER, *Zur Helligkeitswiedergabe in der Schwarz-Weib-Photographie*, Photogr. Korrespondenz **7**, 103–110, 1956.
3. E. GOLDBERG, *Der Aufbau des photographischen Bildes*, Halle, 1922.
4. L. A. JONES, *J. Opt. Soc. Amer.* **5**, 232, 1921.

INFLUENCE OF INK RUB-OFF ON THE QUALITY OF HALFTONE ILLUSTRATIONS IN NEWSPAPER PRINTING

by G. E. Carlsson and L. Josefsson
The Graphic Arts Research Laboratory, Stockholm, Sweden

In 1962 a test-printing run of four different makes of newsprint was carried out in the printing plant of Dagens Nyheter in Stockholm under the auspices of the Joint Committee of Swedish Newsprint Mills and Newspapers Publishers on Newsprint Quality. This printing run was followed up by extensive subjective evaluations and trials and objective measurements of the print quality in the printed newspapers and the usual physical tests of the paper properties. The papers were then printed under various conditions with regard to speed and impression in the GFL laboratory rotary printing press.

The main purpose was to study the correlation between the relative print qualities produced under actual production conditions and on the GFL press, which is extensively used by most Scandinavian newsprint manufacturers.

PAPERS TESTED

Four papers manufactured on different paper machines and from three mills were printed in a quantity of four rolls of 7000 m length of each paper.

The paper properties tested are given in Table 1. As can be seen in this table, there is little difference between the apparent quality of the papers. It is true that paper B has a rather high smoothness number (low smoothness) for the wire side and that some difference exists for the oil absorbency values as well as for the luminance of the papers. It was not, however, possible to conclude from these tests that any major difference in print quality would show up in printing.

TABLE 1. PAPER PROPERTIES

Paper	Basis weight g/m²	Bulk cm³/g	Porosity Bendtsen 75 mm wc ml/min	Smoothness Bendtsen 150 mm wc				Surface oil absorbency 11.0 p. oil		Elrepho Printing Opacity filter FMY/C %	Luminance filter FMY/C %
				Load 1 kg/cm² ml/min		Load 5 kg/cm² ml/min		sec			
				Felt side	Wire side	Felt side	Wire side	Felt side	Wire side		
A	53.0	1.61	210	109	140	40	55	25	16	94.8	66.9
B	51.7	1.71	177	114	180	38	56	19	9	95.3	67.5
C	53.3	1.53	191	101	131	37	47	15	14	94.3	69.2
D	51.7	1.60	191	113	121	39	47	33	14	94.2	67.6

FULL SCALE PRINTING

In test-printing of this kind in a big newspaper rotary press several uncertain factors are present, which may influence the printing result, and it is necessary to eliminate these sources of error as far as possible. Such a source of error is the time factor. It is likely that the printing result will be different in the beginning and at the end of a long printing run because of temperature conditions as well as plate wear. Further when the printing is performed in different printing units of the press, it is not certain that they will give identical printing results.

In order to eliminate the influence of time and the printing unit the papers were printed according to the following scheme.

Unit No.	2	3	5	6
1st roll set	A	B	C	D
2nd roll set ..	B	C	D	A
3rd roll set ..	C	D	A	B
4th roll set ..	D	A	B	C

The papers were printed in double production and with first impression on the wire side.

Before the start of the test-printing, the press was warmed up by running without paper, and then the adjustments of impression and inking were made with an extra set of newsprint rolls. During the whole run the speed of the press was 16,000 cylinder revolutions an hour. The impression was kept constant, but after each change of paper the pressman at each unit made those adjustments in inking which he considered appropriate.

The copies later used for the determination of print quality were taken towards the end of a set of rolls.

Special page formes, containing solids, gray scales, selected halftone illustrations and resolution test objects had been made up.

EVALUATION OF THE PRINT QUALITY

Optical measurements of solids and gray scales in the printed newspapers did not show any significant difference between the papers, but revealed quite big differences between the inking level in the various printing units of the press.

Five different halftone prints on both the felt and wire side of the paper from every roll printed were chosen for the subjective evaluation. This makes a total of 160 specimens. The prints were cut out of the newspapers and fastened to pieces of paper board so that they would not be damaged by the observers. The specimens were marked so that the observers could not identify specimens of the same make.

Accordingly there were 16 prints of each object on the felt side and 16 prints on the wire side of the paper. The prints on the two sides were judged separately. It is considered practically impossible to rank as many as 16 prints by simple comparison, and the pair comparison method is the ideal. Such a procedure, however, would require no less than 120 comparisons for each object on each side of the paper, which means a total of 1200 comparisons for each observer, and of course, is impracticable.

There is, however, no difficulty in ranking only four prints, and the prints were then arranged in groups of four, each representing the prints made in one unit from the same stereo plate on the four papers.

Accordingly the observers then had 40 groups of 4 prints to rank. For each object and paper side, however, one extra group was included for the purpose of adaptation, when going over from one test object to another one. The observers also unknowingly had to repeat the judgment of one group of each object in order to make it possible to control the reproducibility of their rankings. The task of each observer then amounted to the ranking of 60 groups of four specimens.

According to the ranking the prints were given 1, 2, 3 and 4 points; number 1 for the poorest and number 4 for the best printing result.

The judgment was performed by 13 observers representing the following categories: printing research workers, newspaper printers, newsprint manufacturers, photo-engravers and advertising experts. From a rough unplanned examination of the prints it did not seem probable that any significant difference between the papers would come out of the subjective evaluation, in view of the small differences between them.

This proved to be the case as can be seen in Table 2.

As can be seen from Table 2 there was on the whole a very good correlation between the different observers' ratings, and the same result would have come out, if the evaluation had been performed only by the first four observers.

Significant differences between the papers were established for both the sides, with paper C best and then B and D about equal and A worst. The differentiation was, however, more pronounced for the wire side.

In Table 2 the score ranks are given as a total for each paper but it is also possible to sum up the ranking numbers for each of the 16 paper rolls printed. In Table 3 the sum of ranking points for each paper roll is given. For the sake of simplicity we only give the values from observer No. 8, whose judgment according to the control procedure applied was most reliable.

From Table 3 it appears that very good conformity existed between the print quality on the different paper rolls of each make. In the case of the wire

TABLE 2. SCORE RANKS FOR THE PAPERS FROM THE SUBJECTIVE EVALUATION

Observer	Felt sides				Wire sides			
	A	B	C	D	A	B	C	D
1	45	48	54	53	30	49	60	61
2	34	52	63	51	30	57	61	52
3	42	60	55	43	36	49	69	46
4	41	45	66	48	34	51	65	50
5	42	47	59	52	45	34	71	50
6	45	49	56	50	33	52	63	52
7	44	59	55	42	31	50	65	54
8	33	45	74	48	28	37	79	56
9	45	54	56	45	36	54	61	49
10	39	51	59	51	33	51	63	53
11	40	42	62	56	39	41	72	48
12	52	48	51	49	39	50	58	53
13	46	50	61	43	47	43	57	53
Σp	548	650	771	631	461	618	844	677
p	42	50	59	49	35	48	65	52
Standard deviation at 95% confidence limits ±	3	3	4	2	4	4	4	2
Ranking		B C A D				B C A D		

TABLE 3. SCORE RANKS FOR EACH PAPER ROLL FROM THE EVALUATION BY OBSERVER NO. 8

	Felt sides roll number				Wire sides roll number			
Paper	1	2	3	4	1	2	3	4
A	11	8	6	8	8	6	6	8
B	9	9	11	16	9	10	9	9
C	20	20	17	17	20	19	20	20
D	10	11	16	11	13	15	13	15

sides, every roll of each make fell into one of four clearly distinguishable quality groups.

The subjective evaluation of the print quality showed accordingly that a significant difference existed between the four makes of newsprint. Paper C was thus definitely best and paper A of lowest quality, which fact could not be derived from the physical tests of the papers.

LABORATORY PRINTINGS IN THE GFL PRESS

Test specimens of papers from every roll were printed in the GFL press. For each specimen printed, four areas with different amounts of ink were obtained. From the curves representing density as a function of ink on paper, the ink requirement of the paper for a density contrast of 1.00 was calculated.

The value of this parameter is generally considered as an important indication of the printability of newsprint. It is fairly obvious that a paper, which requires little ink to obtain a print density near the higher practical limit, should have good printability. A cleaner print, lower ink set-off and strike-through must be a result of a lower ink requirement. The laboratory printings were mostly performed with a standardized news ink, specially made for this press, but in some printings the ink from the full scale printing was used. Very similar results were obtained with the two inks.

The laboratory printings were carried out with two different printing speeds and impressions according to the following scheme.

Number of printing runs for each side of the paper		Printing speed m/sec	Pressure load kgf/cm
Standard ink	DN-ink		
2	1	1.5	6.0
2	–	1.5	15.0
2	1	4.6	6.0
2	–	4.6	15.0

Ten printing runs for each side of the paper were carried out. As four specimens of each of the four papers, one from each roll, were printed, the total number of specimens printed amounted to 320. Four areas with different amounts of ink were obtained on each specimen printed, and thus the numbers of printed areas, for which ink transfer and density were determined, amounted to 1280 (4 × 320).

The ink requirements of the papers obtained with the standard ink under the various printing conditions are shown in Fig. 1.

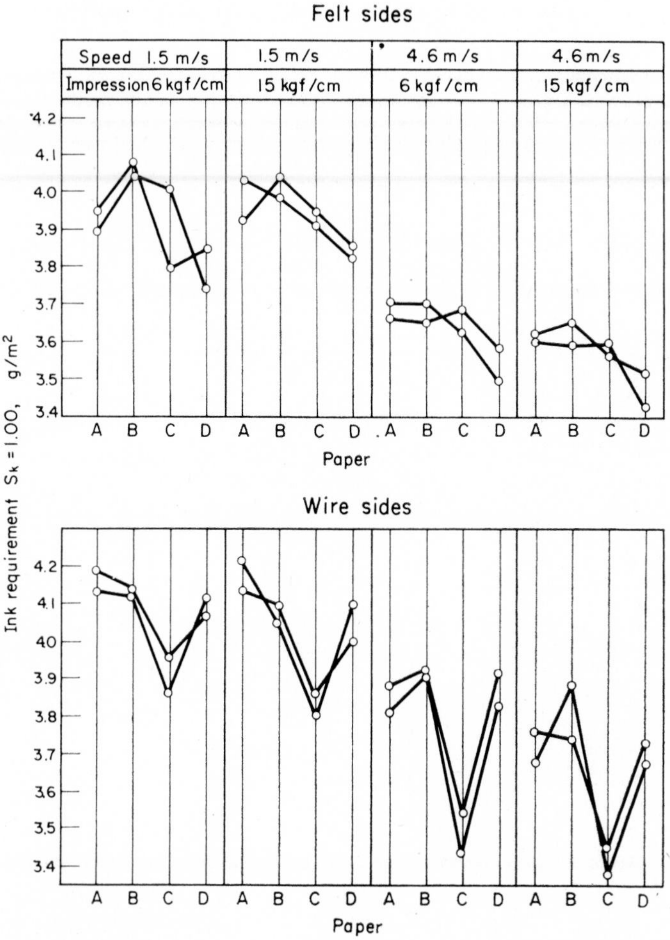

Fig. 1. The ink requirement of the papers for various printing conditions.

The mean values for the ink requirement of each make of paper under the various printing conditions are shown in Fig. 2, together with the mean values of the score ranks from the subjective evaluation of the prints from the full scale printing.

From Fig. 2, the following observations can be made. There are bigger differences in ink requirement for the wire sides than for the felt sides of the paper, which depends mainly on the fact that the wire side of paper C has much lower ink requirement than the wire sides of the other papers. Quite good correlation exists between the values obtained under the different printing conditions. Higher printing speed definitely causes a lower ink requirement. Higher impression gives only a small decrease of the ink requirement.

When comparing the results from the laboratory printing, expressed in this manner, with the score ranks from the subjective evaluation of the prints

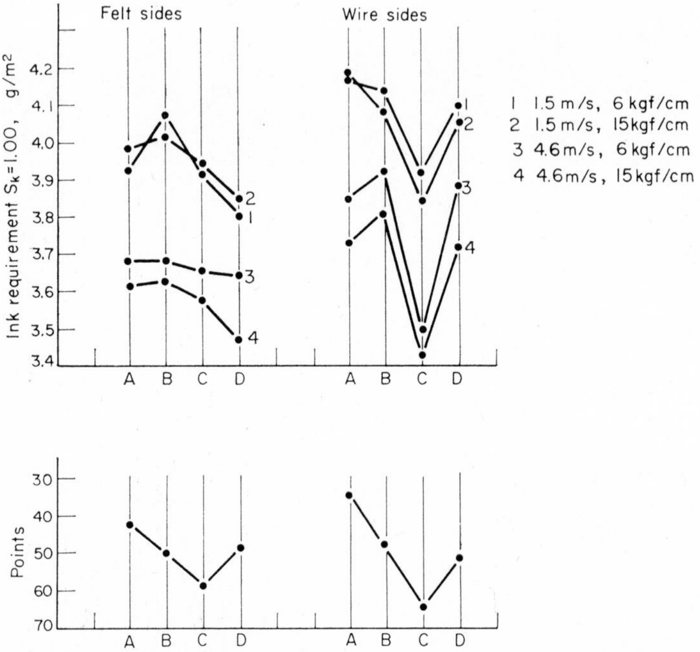

Fig. 2. Mean values of ink requirement at various printing conditions and of score ranks from the subjective evaluation of production prints.

from the full scale printing, it is seen that good correlation exists for the wire sides, especially for the values of ink requirement obtained at low speed and higher impression. For the felt sides, however, no correlation can be observed. Of the practical prints, paper C was judged best, but of the laboratory printings, paper D consistently showed the lowest ink requirement.

THE INK TRANSFER TO PAPER

The ink transfer to the paper was determined for all samples printed. Only small differences showed up, and they seem to be of no interest in this connection.

DISCUSSION OF RESULTS FROM PRACTICAL AND LABORATORY PRINTINGS

From a comparison between the results from the two printings, a very good correlation between the values of the ink requirement and the subjective evaluation of the full scale prints was thus achieved for the wire sides but not for the felt sides.

There are circumstances, which may have caused this discrepancy. In the full scale printing, both sides of the papers were printed, but in the GFL press each sample was only printed on one side. In the newspaper press the felt sides were always printed in second impression, and the paper had accordingly been subjected to compression during the first impression, and in consequence may have had an influence on the second impression. Such effects of a first impression were not observed when printing with the GFL press.

An essential difference between the two printing procedures exists, however, in that the print on the paper in the production press is rubbed against bars, folder and other paper webs, when still wet. The print quality is likely to be affected by this action, for the halftone prints will be smudged to some extent. In the laboratory press, the fresh print is not subjected to any rubbing or smudging action.

If now considerable differences should exist between the papers with regard to their ink absorbency properties, the print on a paper with low absorbency should be subjected to more ink rub-off and smudging than a paper with high absorbency. The quality of a halftone print might very well be better on a newsprint with high ink requirement but good ink absorbency than on a paper with low ink requirement but insufficient ink absorbency.

If a print on the felt side of paper D should cause considerably more set-off than a print on paper C, this circumstance could explain the discrepancy between the ranked print quality and the ink requirement of the papers.

It is thus of interest in this connection to study the set-off of fresh prints on the papers. This was possible with a new model of the GFL press, which makes possible a very accurate measurement of the set-off tendency of a print within a very short time after impression.

MEASUREMENT OF INK SET-OFF

The procedure to determine the set-off of a print can best be described with the aid of Fig. 3. In an ordinary printing test four inked steel plates (a) are placed on the plate cylinder (b) and in one printing operation four prints are obtained on the paper (c). When set-off is to be tested, only two of the plates are inked and placed in the positions 2 and 4 on the plate cylinder. Pieces of Kromecote paper board (d) with the same caliper and shape as the steel plates are fixed with tape in the positions 1 and 3. When the paper has been printed and the contact between the two cylinders is released, their relative position can be changed by a special mechanism. When the pressure

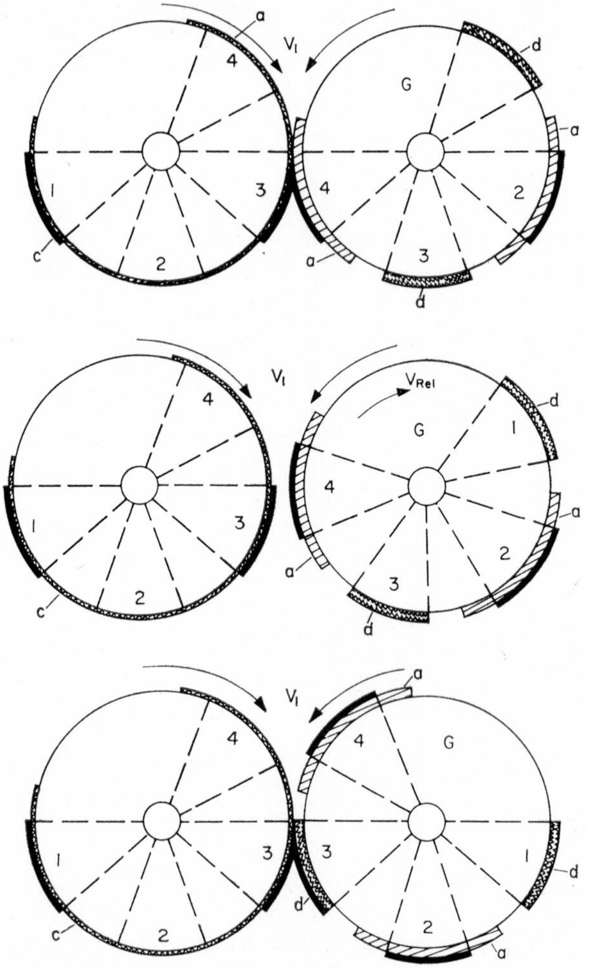

Fig. 3. Schematic drawing of the set-off testing procedure with the GFL press.

is again applied, the pieces of Kromecote come into contact with the two fresh prints. A certain part of the ink on the prints is then printed back on the Kromecote boards. The amount of this ink is closely related to the amount of ink not immobilized on the paper surface. The set-off can be measured at any time interval after printing from 0.6 sec and upwards.

Figure 4 shows how the set-off decreases with time for prints on newsprint with density contrasts of 1.00 and 0.85. The set-off is measured by measuring reflectance in the Elrepho-apparatus. The density values are then converted into film weights with the aid of a calibration curve.

In Fig. 5 a photograph is shown of the set-off prints obtained from the prints mentioned above at various time intervals. The set-off print gives not only a very accurate measurement of the penetration of the ink into the

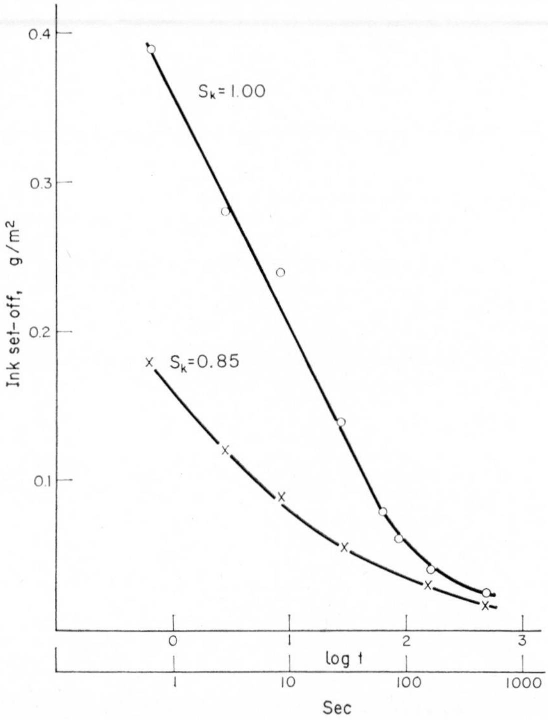

Fig. 4. Decrease of set-off with the time after printing four prints with density contrast, $S_K = 1.00$ and $S_K = 0.85$.

paper surface, but also a very good picture of the irregularities in the ink absorption over the paper surface. Figure 6 shows photographs of two set-off prints from samples of newsprint with quite different absorbency. In Fig. 7 photomicrographs from the same set-off prints are shown. The set-off print thus gives a very good replica of the paper surface and all irregularities in ink absorbency can be observed. In the case of newsprint the picture gives information on the distribution of the sulphite fibres in the paper surface, which is probably one of the most important factors with

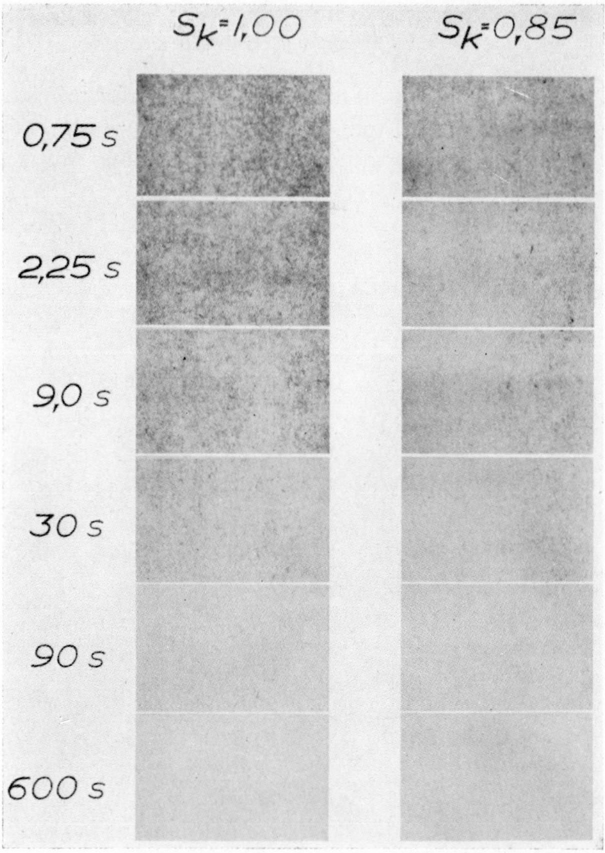

Fig. 5. Photographs of set-off prints from newsprint printed with density contrasts of 0.85 and 1.00, made at various time intervals after printing.

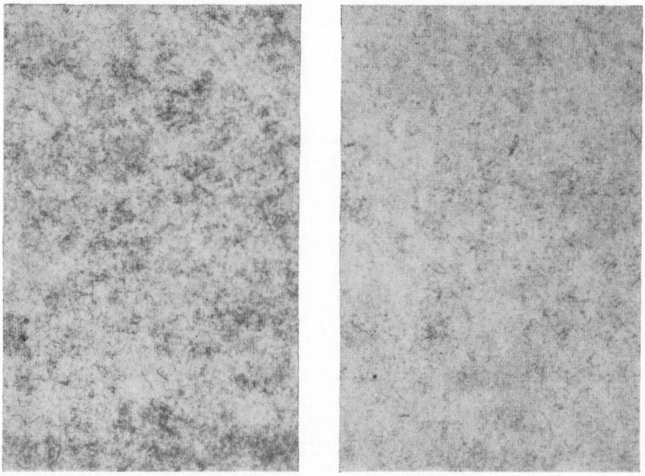

Fig. 6. Photographs of set-off prints from newsprint with different absorption properties.

regard to newsprint printability. Experience with this procedure at a Swedish newsprint mill has proved its value.

The set-off varies, of course, with the amount of ink printed on the paper, and when testing the set-off of prints on different papers, it is necessary that they be printed with the same quantity of ink on the surface.

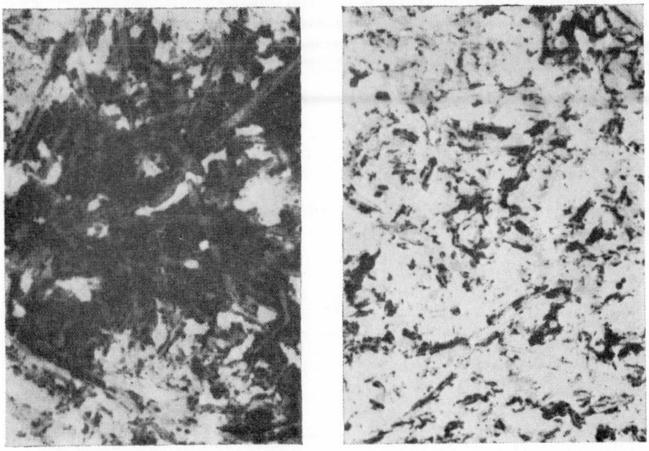

Fig. 7. Photomicrographs of areas in the set-off prints, shown in Fig. 6.

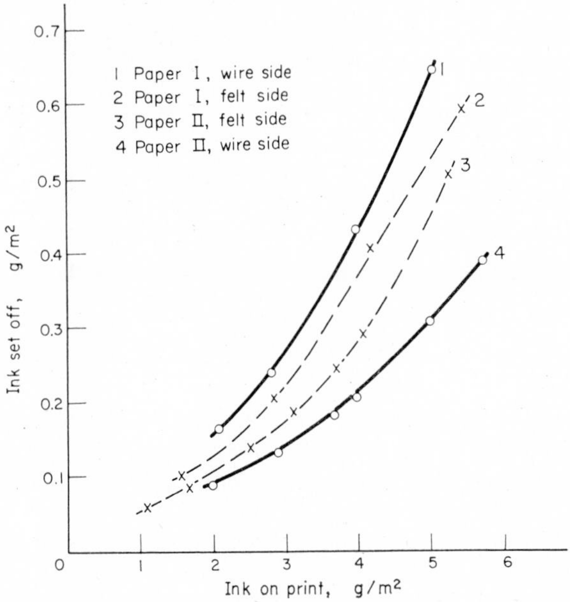

Fig. 8. Variation of the set-off with the amount of ink on the print for two samples of newsprint.

During the relatively short time we have used this device to study the set-off tendency of prints on different papers, it has been clearly established that great differences in this regard can exist between papers of the same kind, for example different makes of newsprint.

In Fig. 8 can be seen how the set-off varies with the amount of ink on the printed surface for two makes of newsprint.

MEASUREMENTS OF INK SET-OFF FROM PRINTS ON THE NEWSPRINTS USED IN THE TEST-PRINTING

When testing the set-off from prints on samples from all the rolls with 4.00 g/m^2 ink after a time elapse of 3.5 sec, the values given in Table 4 were obtained.

TABLE 4. THE INK SET-OFF IN g/m^2 AFTER 3.5 SEC FROM PRINTS WITH 4.00 g/m^2 INK

Felt sides	Roll number				Mean value
	1	2	4		
A	0.28	0.24	0.22	0.25	0.25
B	0.23	0.20	0.20	—	0.21
C	0.16	0.17	0.19	0.20	0.18
D	0.29	0.32	0.26	0.31	0.30
Wire sides					
A	0.18	0.16	0.18	0.17	0.17
B	0.18	0.16	0.17	0.16	0.17
C	0.23	0.21	0.21	0.28	0.23
D	0.19	0.22	0.22	0.21	0.21

This test showed accordingly that for the felt sides, paper D had a considerably higher set-off tendency than paper C, and also that there was little difference in this respect for the wire sides. This was just the condition required to explain the divergence between the ranking of the printability of the felt sides of the papers in the production and laboratory printing tests.

In Fig. 9 are, counting from the top, graphs drawn for the score ranks from the subjective evaluation (I), the ink requirement of the papers (II) and the set-off of the prints (III).

As it now seemed evident that the ink requirement values could not give good correlation with the print quality under actual production conditions without taking the set-off tendency of the papers into consideration, an attempt to introduce a correction for the set-off was made.

Without making a close study of the statistical correlations, it was easily found that by summing the ink requirement values and twice the ink set-off

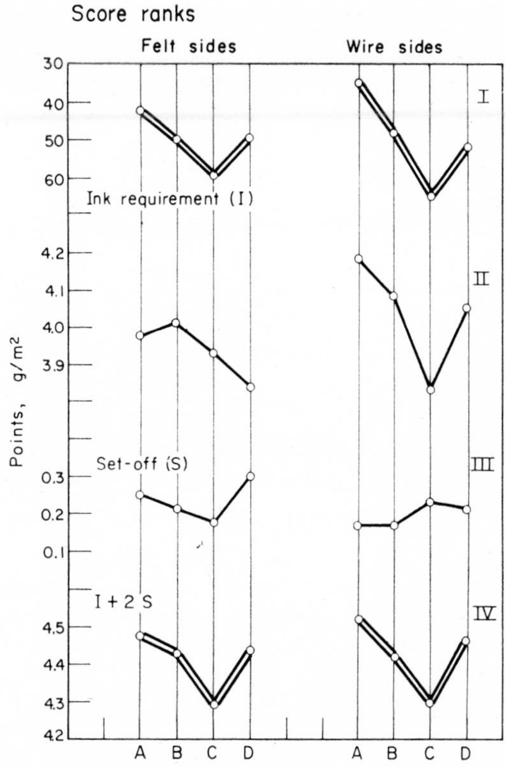

Fig. 9. Score ranks from the subjective evaluation (I), ink requirement for density 1.00 at 1.5 m/sec and 15 kgf/cm (II), ink set-off (III) and the ink requirement arbitrarily corrected for the ink requirement (IV).

values (graph IV), a very satisfactory correlation between the results from the laboratory and the production printing tests could be established.

The correction introduced is, of course, very arbitrary. It is based only upon this limited investigation and is closely related to the printing conditions existing in both the laboratory and production printing.

It may not, however, be incorrect to state that under the actual conditions in this investigation, the introduction of a correction for the ink set-off did establish a good correlation between the laboratory and production printing of newsprint with regard to print quality.

MEASUREMENTS OF INK RUB-OFF

The method of measuring the ink set-off described is based upon a true rolling contact between the print and the surface taking up the ink set-off, and when no rubbing takes place. The method enables a quantitative measurement of the set-off but does not give a picture of the extent of deterioration of a halftone print under rubbing action against the wet print. It may seem obvious that these two effects are closely related to each other, but we considered it to be of interest to demonstrate this fact.

We designed a device (Fig. 10) by which a pad of soft rubber (*G*) can be pressed with a light pressure (about 0.2 kgf/cm^2) against the printed surface,

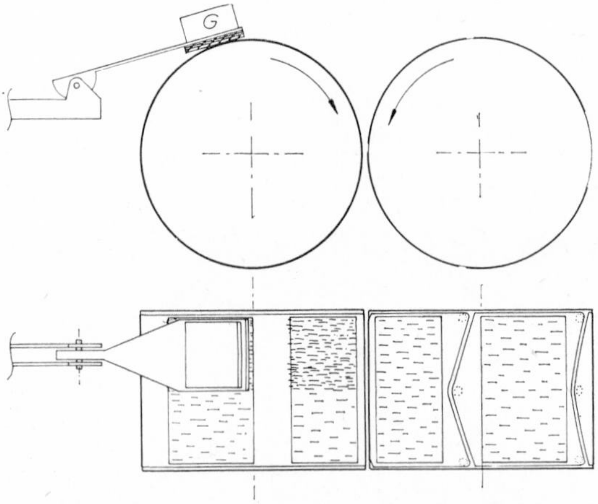

Fig. 10. Schematic drawing of arrangement for rub-off testing in the GFL press.

immediately after printing. It was arranged so that only one half of the printed surface was rubbed. In this way it was possible to study and also measure the effect of the rubbing.

Samples from two of the newsprint rolls, which in the set-off tests had shown the biggest difference, were selected for this test.

The rub-off was carried out only on the felt sides of the paper.

The papers tested were:

C_1 with a set-off on the felt side of 0.16 g/m^2

D_2 with a set-off on the felt side of 0.32 g/m^2

The new model of the GFL press is equipped with halftone printing plates of several tone values. It proved that the deteriorating effect of the rubbing was most marked in the lightest tones, which also would be expected.

In Fig. 11 photographs are shown of prints on the two papers with one half subjected to the rubbing action. In Fig. 12 photomicrographs of the same prints can be seen.

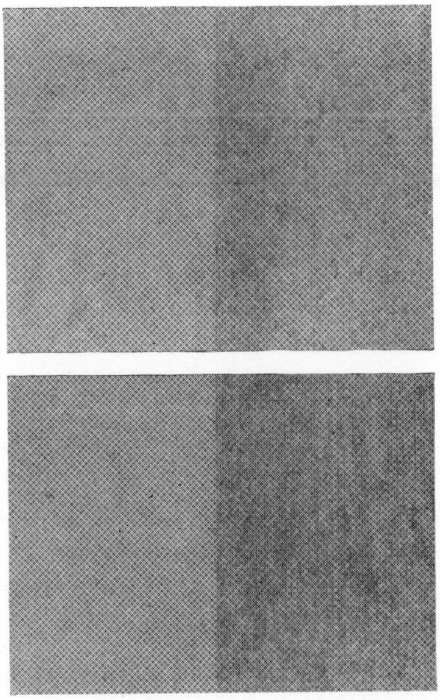

Fig. 11. Photographs of prints with the half part subjected to rubbing action.

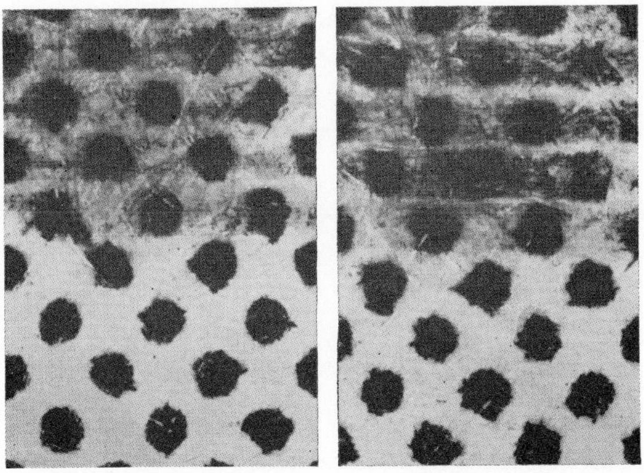

Fig. 12. Photomicrographs of areas in the samples, shown in Fig. 11.

On a subjective evaluation of the deterioration of the prints through ink smudging, by pair comparison methods, the result was that all samples of paper C were ranked better than the samples of paper D.

In measuring photometrically the increase of the density of the print caused by smudging, the values in Table 5 were obtained.

TABLE 5. INCREASE OF PRINT DENSITY IN RUBBED AREAS

Paper	C_1	D_2
Sample 1	0.097	0.132
Sample 2	0.081	0.120
Sample 3	0.081	0.109
Sample 4	0.075	0.100
Sample 5	0.075	0.099
Sample 6	0.062	0.131
Sample 7	0.079	—
Mean value	0.079	0.115

This test showed accordingly that a halftone print on paper D had deteriorated more than a print on paper C by a rubbing action against the wet print.

COMPARISON OF THE INK SET-OFF TENDENCY AND THE OIL ABSORBENCY OF THE PAPERS

The ink absorbency of the paper was determined by measurement of the surface oil absorption time.

It is, therefore, of interest to see how the ink set-off determined under printing conditions correlates with the oil absorbency values of the papers.

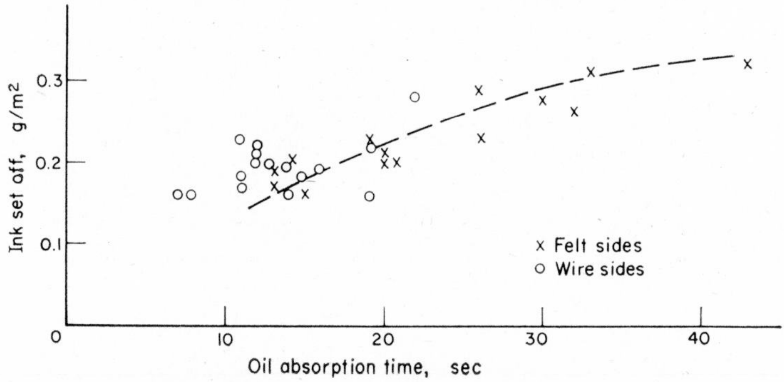

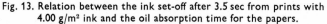

Fig. 13. Relation between the ink set-off after 3.5 sec from prints with 4.00 g/m² ink and the oil absorption time for the papers.

From Fig. 13, in which test values for every roll of newsprint are recorded, there is evidently a good correlation between these two parameters for the felt sides but not for the wire sides of the papers.

This observation is in good agreement with the opinion of some Swedish newsprint manufacturers, who have considered the oil absorption test valuable for the felt sides but of doubtful value for the wire sides of newsprint.

CONCLUSION

This investigation has indicated the fact that when newsprint is tested by laboratory printing, the general determinations of ink transfer, ink requirement and ink strike-through should be supplemented with a determination of the ink set-off tendency from a fresh print on the paper. As the behaviour of newsprint in this respect has a considerable influence upon the quality of halftone prints achieved under production printing conditions, no complete description of the printability of newsprint can be given without taking this effect into consideration.

The new model of the GFL laboratory press enables not only a very accurate measurement of the set-off of a print at time intervals from 0.6 sec after printing, but provides furthermore a very clear picture of the local distribution of absorbency irregularities in the paper surface, a fact of great value for the papermakers.

DISCUSSION

GINMAN: As you state, the ink requirement, defined as the amount of ink on the paper needed to give a certain blackness contrast, will influence the set-off and the print-through. Another print quality factor is the filling-in of the plate. The filling-in tendency most probably depends on the ink film thickness on the plate. If we would calculate the amount of ink needed on the plate to produce the blackness contrast chosen, this value could perhaps be related to the filling-in tendency of different papers.

CARLSSON: Your suggestion is certainly very interesting and I can say that we have recently tried to plot the blackness contrast as a function of the amount of ink on the plate. We have found that when doing so we get a more pronounced differentiation between various types of paper. Whether this procedure can give a better characterization of the printability of newsprint I do not know but the matter is certainly worth further study.

REIMANN: From many thousands of rub-off tests on newspapers with the Bendtsen rub-off tester two hours after printing, it is often found that an ink which is slowly absorbed by the paper will give good resistance to rub-off and vice-versa. Your test is really a smearing test.

FRØSLEV-NIELSEN: Further to Mr. Reimann's comment I would think that you would get a more definite assessment of smearing by turner bars by using a steel plate on your machine (Fig. 10) instead of a rubber plate.

CARLSSON: It might be possible but as our first trials with a rubber pad worked quite satisfactorily we have not tried anything else.

MISS PRITCHARD: You state in your paper that from a laboratory examination of the newspaper prints it did not seem that significant differences would be found. Was it not possible by microscopic examination to determine the fault on these prints? I am thinking that it is important to determine that the fault causing the difference between these prints is the same as that investigated on the printability tester, as in a machine run. Such things as varying misregister causing varying second impression set-off, or fluffing causing filling-in could occur, and these would not be expected to correlate with the paper properties investigated.

CARLSSON: After we had found the difference in ink absorbency and set-off tendency between the papers, we tried to see if the smearing of the halftone illustrations bore any relationship to the visual evaluation. It was not, however, possible to establish any correlation between any microscopic observations of the prints and visual ranking of them.

A CONTRIBUTION TO THE STUDY OF "PRINT THROUGH" IN NEWSPAPER PRINTING

by HÉLÈNE BENEDITE and JACQUES POUJADE
Sociétié Professionnelle des papiers de presse, Paris XVIe

INTRODUCTION

THIS study has been started because of the general complaint of the French Newspaper industry regarding the phenomenon called "Print Through" (P.T.).

By this term, we mean the blackening (or colouring) effect which a print, made on one side of the paper, is liable to give on the opposite side of the sheet.

It is well known that this effect may be due to a low opacity of the sheet (show through) and to a partial penetration of the ink into the paper (strike through), which is of course related both to the particular structure of the paper and to the specific properties of the ink used.

Our first aim was to supply newsprint manufacturers with objective and reliable information regarding the comparative behaviour of their production, so that they could in turn investigate possible ways of improving the quality of the sheet with respect to Print Through.

The value of Print Through is expressed by the density contrast of the back of the print. In our laboratory, we make all reflectance measurements with an Elrepho instrument. When a black ink is used for the printing, all density contrast measurements (for the printed areas as well as for the P.T.) are taken through a tri-stimulus green filter.

LABORATORY AND PRODUCTION PRINTING CONDITIONS

The first step was to produce a certain number of prints (on the newsprint under investigation) under well controlled and reproducible conditions.

Our present means of printing is a laboratory proof press (we expect to have a full-scale rotary unit equipped with proper instrumentation within the next three years).

We are using for our routine control of newsprint printability a G.F.L. rotary test press. This instrument and its performances have been described by Mr. Carlsson in several earlier publications. This press has the following advantages:

(*a*) the possibility to run it under reproducible conditions (pressure; speed; inking level);

(*b*) the speed is uniform at each possible speed level;

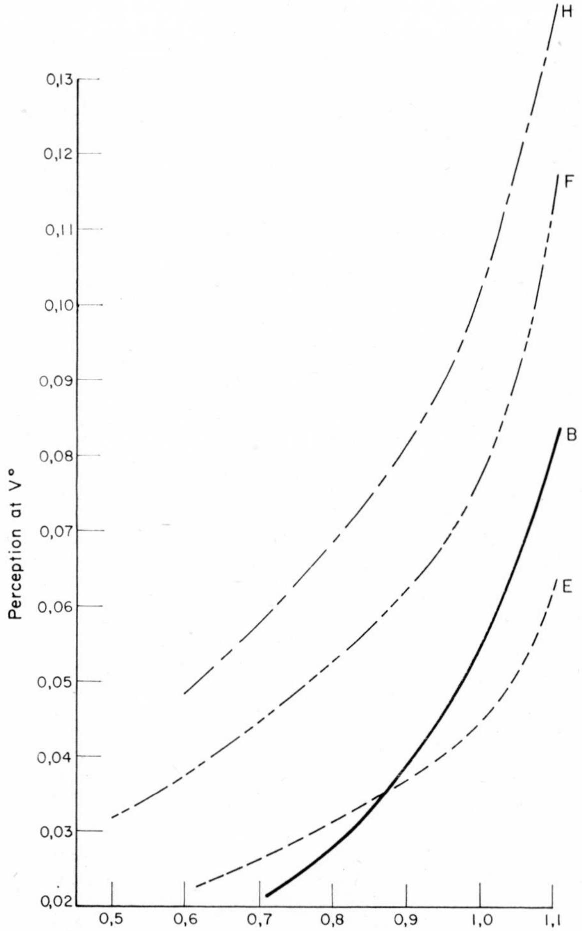

Fig. 1. Perception at the back of a flat tint, printed on G.F.L. press as a function of the contrast.
Felt side
Pressure: 15 kg/cm
Speed: 4.58 m/sec

(c) the "solids" obtained are of a reasonable size, so that three reflectance measurements can be made with the Elrepho;

(d) it is possible to get in *one* test run, four prints with a different inking level for each, all other conditions remaining the same.

With this test press, using the same ink, we can for instance "grade" the abilities of a set of various newsprint sheets to give rise to print through.

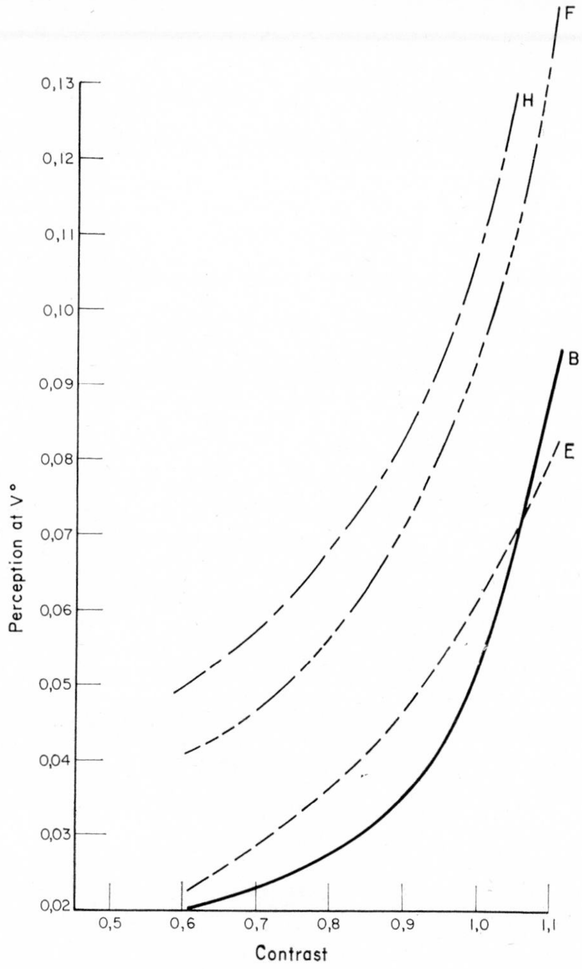

Fig. 1*a*. Perception at the back of a flat tint, printed on the G.F.L. press as a function of the contrast.

Felt side
Pressure: 15 kg/cm
Speed: 4.58 m/sec

We knew from previous experience that the differences thus ascertained were also exhibited with these same papers, when used under industrial conditions.

But we did not know

(1) whether the test printing could simulate well enough the result obtained on a rotary press, so that not only the respective ranking but also the actual value of the P.T. could be reproduced (with the same ink used, both on the test apparatus and on the rotary unit). In other words, we wondered whether our test apparatus was emphasizing or on the contrary minimizing the phenomena under study;
(2) to what extent the printing conditions (speed and pressure) which could not be kept under real control on the production press, were liable to affect the result.

Moreover, on our G.F.L. press, it was not possible to study the disturbances caused by the P.T. on halftones of various tone values when backed by a solid tone.

For all these reasons, we planned an experiment on the newspaper rotary press of one of our most important provincial papers.

PLANNING OF THE PRODUCTION TEST RUN

The unit used belonged to a conventional double size press on which an 8 page newspaper (42.5 × 60 signature) was produced. We had selected 8 different kinds of newsprint (1 American—1 Scandinavian—6 French makes)* which were to be studied on both sides. This meant 16 individual tests.

In order to avoid too drastic changes occurring during the test run, we decided to rewind "composite rolls"; each normal roll, of diameter (85 cm), having a length of about 8000 m of paper, we could have successive lengths of 1000 m of each newsprint on a same roll.

The winding was done in such a way that we had all top sides up on one roll, and all wire sides up on the next one. In this way, we were able to run 8 papers without any change or adjustment. The only stop of the press occurred between the two rolls, since this unit was not equipped with an auto-paster.

Our purpose being to print solid tones with various ink amounts on the paper, it was not possible to vary the inking during the run, as this would have resulted in unstable conditions during the 3 min required to print

* Among the 6 French newsprints, 3 were in fact produced by the same manufacturer on the same machine, but out of slightly different pulp furnishes.

1000 m of paper. As a consequence, we decided to vary the inking level crosswise, according to the sketch given in Fig. 2.

We had 4 plates across the width (in fact 8, as two similar plates are wrapped around the same cylinder). The first plate to the left was to be inked with a rather low level, slightly increasing from left to right. The two central plates were to be inked at the "normal" level of the newspaper; the last plate to

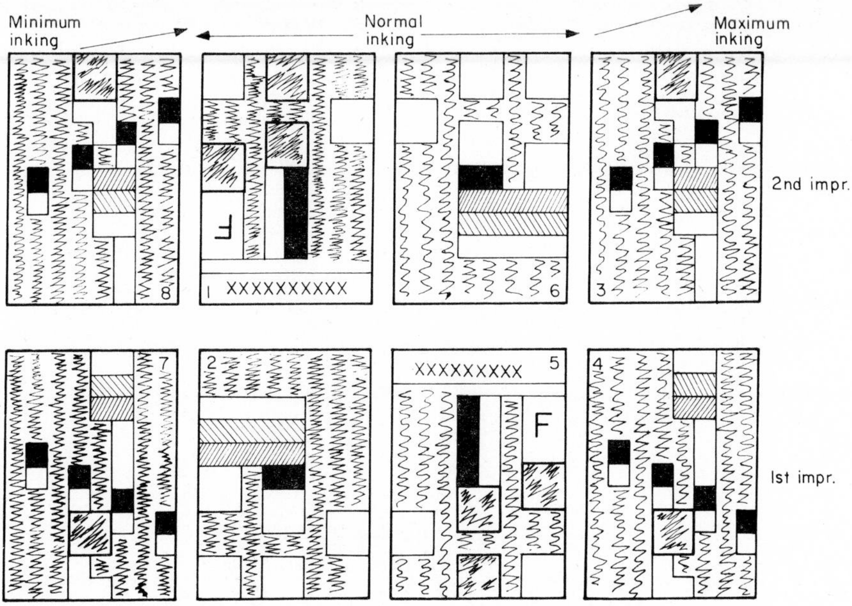

Fig. 2. Arrangement of printing plates on the rotary unit.

the right was to be "over-inked". In this way we intended to duplicate the variable inking which can be produced on the G.F.L. test press. Some solid square areas of each page were so arranged as to have no printing at all at the back, so that reflectance measurements could be made on both sides, and P.T. value be plotted against the corresponding blackness contrast.

The same curves (P.T. value against Blackness contrast) have therefore been established for each side of the 8 newsprint papers investigated, the printing being done with the same ink,

(*a*) on the laboratory test Press;
(*b*) on the rotary unit.

The newsprint sample used for the laboratory testing had been taken from a thick pad of paper, cut from each roll at the time of the rewinding of the composite roll, just after the winding of the 1000 m (and carefully wrapped and protected in between). The physical properties of each sample were determined in the laboratory, previous to the printing.

In the printing room, the test run was made during day time after a full week of careful preparation. Immediately after the run, the newspapers were taken to the laboratory and measured for blackness contrast and P.T. after 24 hr. The same schedule was kept between the laboratory printing and the optical measurements.

Other investigations made on the same run

Because this test run was a rather expensive and time consuming procedure, we have taken the opportunity to extend somewhat the original scope of our study. Therefore the various printing forms (shown in Fig. 2) were so designed and combined as to enable the study, of

(*a*) the effect of P.T. on the tone value of a continuous halftone printed at the back (these tone values, measured on the newspaper, were approximately of 39 per cent and 51 per cent dot area);

(*b*) the differences—with respect to P.T.—between first and second impression, with the aim of splitting the print through from the Second Impression Set-off;

(*c*) the quality of halftone pictures of various designs (landscapes—crowd pictures—portraits) which could be rated by subjective comparison. This last part of the study is not reported in the present paper.

EXPERIMENTAL RESULTS

I. PRINT THROUGH OF A SOLID TONE UNPRINTED ON THE REVERSE SIDE

(a) Comparison of test run with laboratory testing

The main conclusions can be summarized as follows:

(1) The test run has confirmed that the ranking of the 8 papers, for each side, were exactly the same under both printing conditions (i.e. in the laboratory and in the press room).

(2) The Print Through value, as determined on the G.F.L. press, for each blackness contrast level is systematically lower than the value resulting from the industrial printing. In other words, with the printing conditions adopted for the laboratory printing (nip load 15 kg/cm—speed 4.58 m/sec), we are minimizing the Print Through value as compared to what would be obtained in the newspaper itself.

An example is given in Fig. 3 where the 2 sets of curves are plotted on the same graph, for each side of two of the 8 papers investigated. Similar graphs were obtained for all other newsprints; but we thought that it would be sufficient to reproduce in this report only the extreme cases.

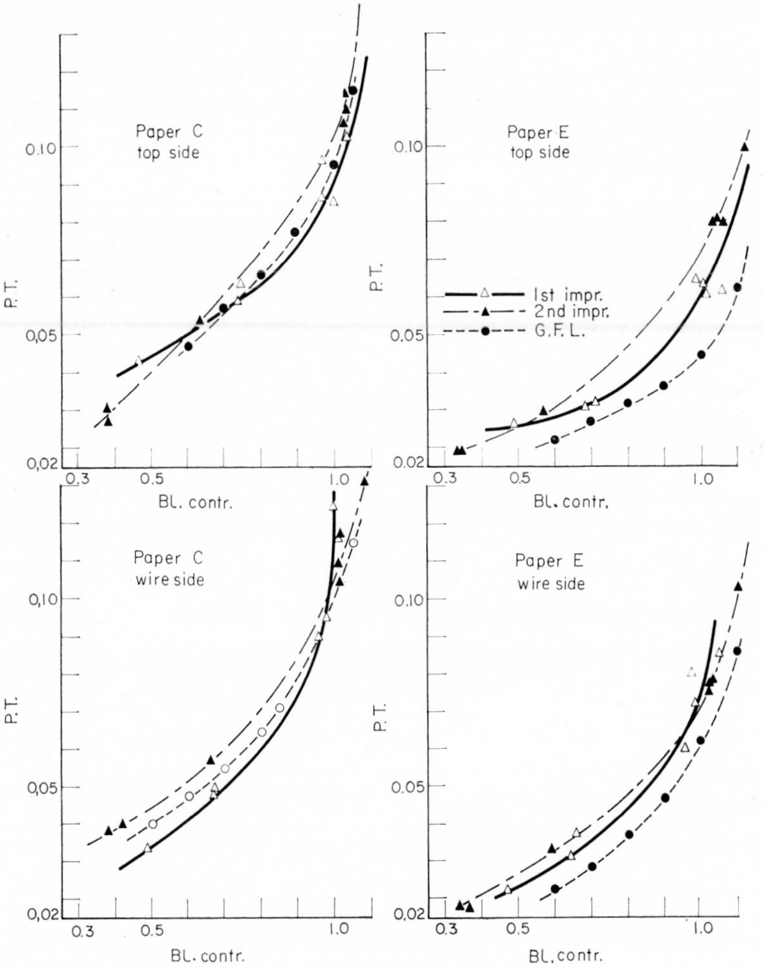

Fig. 3.

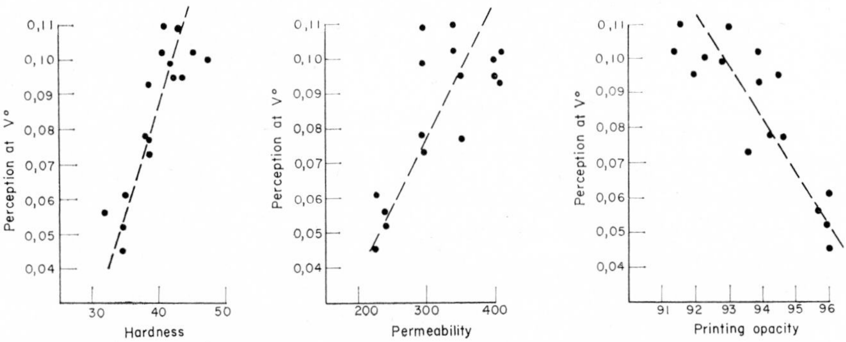

Fig. 3*a*. Correlation research between the perception at the back and certain physical properties of paper.

It should be noted that 7 out of 8 papers behaved more or less like paper E, whereas paper C can be considered as an exception in our case, since its G.F.L. curve lies in between the two curves corresponding to the rotary unit.

(3) In the industrial printing, the Print Through value (for the same side of the same newsprint) was different for each printing couple.

This was true in 15 cases out of 16. We thought it might only be due to a different nip load on each couple, since the speed was necessarily the same and the possible effect of a different inking being already taken care of in the blackness contrast measurements.

But we have no satisfactory explanation, yet, for the above mentioned exception, occurring only for one side of paper "C".

(4) In 7 cases out of 8, and for the wire sides of each paper only, the two graphs corresponding to each couple of the rotary unit cross for a blackness contrast value of about 0.95. This can also be noted on Fig. 3.

These last two considerations led us to the conclusion that the influence of the pressure needed further investigation which could—for the moment—be done only on our G.F.L. press, since the pressure could not be measured on the rotary press.

(5) It seems that the *differences* between Print Through values for the G.F.L. prints and the rotary press ones, for all papers, at each blackness contrast, are somewhat related to the Bendtsen hardness of the sheet, although no significant correlation could be established.

Whereas for the G.F.L. prints alone, some correlations do exist between Print Through value and printing opacity, porosity and Bendtsen hardness of the papers (Fig. 3a).

(b) Proof printing with the G.F.L. press under variable nip load

Some experiments were made on one of the 8 papers only, both for top and wire side, to see to what extent an increased nip load would affect the blackness contrast and the corresponding Print Through value. The results are given in Figs. 4, 5, 6, 7, 8 and 9. Four different pressure levels were used together with the same speed (4.6 m/sec).

From the curves given in Figs. 4 and 5, it can be seen that the effect of the pressure does not seem to be regular, especially for the top side of the paper. Figure 5 for the wire side, shows a particular point, corresponding to a blackness contrast between 0.9 and 0.95, for which the pressure does not seem to have any effect on the Print Through value. Figures 6 and 7 give, for both sides of the same paper, the variations of the blackness contrast (for various amounts of ink on the paper) as a function of the pressure. It might be noted that the blackness contrast (for each inking) corresponding to 12 kg/cm is (for the felt side) always lower than the blackness at 8 kg/cm.

We are investigating this fact, which is not quite clear to us, although it can be observed for the wire side, between 1.1 and 4 g/m^2 of ink on the paper.

The four preceding graphs are summarized in Fig. 8 where we have plotted the Print Through value against the pressure, for various ink amounts (continuous lines) and various blackness contrasts (dotted lines).

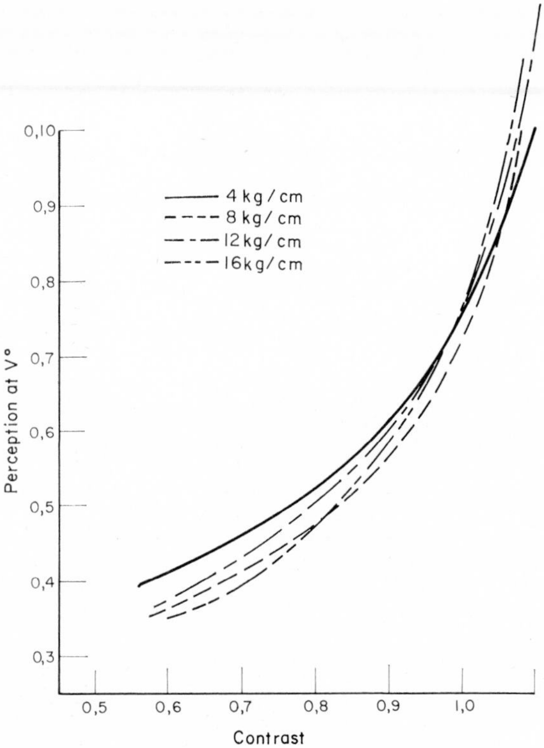

Fig. 4. Perception at the back of a flat tint printed on the G.F.L. press as a function of the contrast at variable pressures.

Paper: C
Felt side
Ink: G.F.L.
Speed: 4.58 m/sec

We have marked on this graph the zones inside which the top side of the sheet has a higher Print Through than the wire side, either for the same blackness contrast or for the same amount of ink on the paper.

It is seen in Fig. 3 that for the prints obtained from the rotary unit, the Print Through curves corresponding to the wire side of the paper, when printed on each couple, crossed each other at a blackness contrast of about 0.95. This fact supports our assumption that the difference between the two couples were mainly due to the pressure, since we have just seen that for that very contrast of 0.95, a pressure change does not affect the Print Through.

On the other hand, we have seen that the G.F.L. curves usually do not have any point in common with the rotary unit curves.

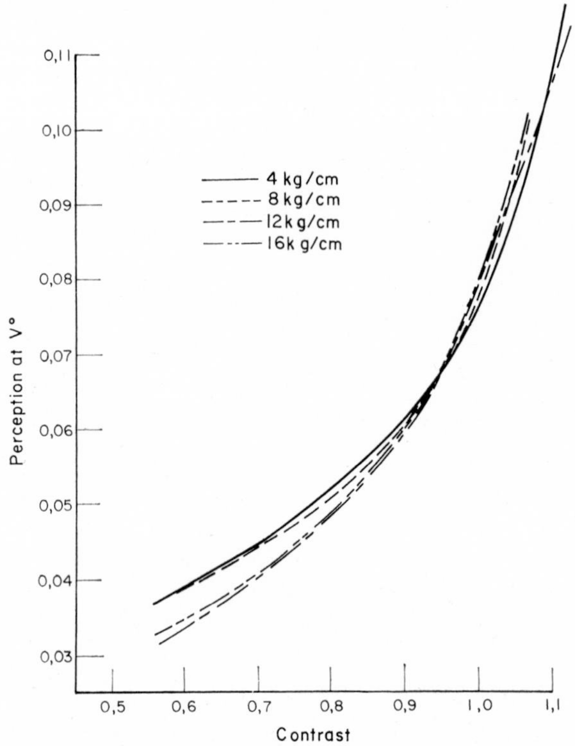

Fig. 5. Perception at the back of a flat tint on the G.F.L. press as a function of contrast at variable pressure.

Paper: C
Cloth side
Ink: G.F.L.
Speed: 4.58 m/sec

This could be explained by the fact that the "speed conditions" on the test press and on the rotary press are not similar (the G.F.L. being a small scale model) even though the nominal linear speed could be of the same order.

It could very well be that the actual printing conditions prevailing on the rotary press could be better simulated by running the small scale model (G.F.L.) at a lower linear speed.

This will be investigated further.

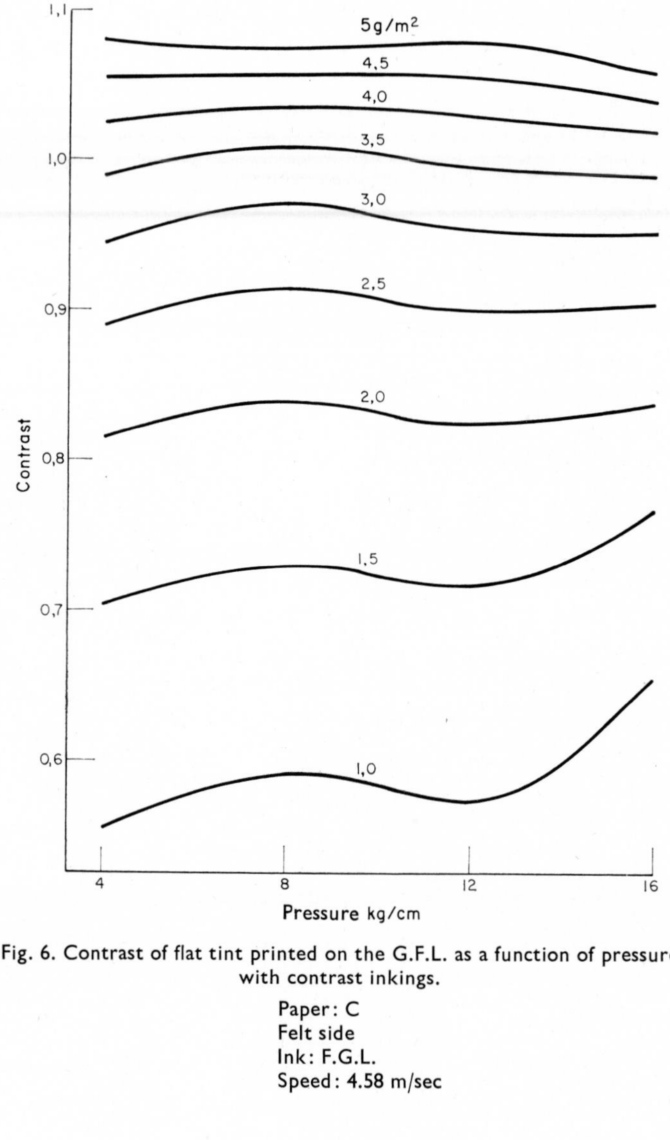

Fig. 6. Contrast of flat tint printed on the G.F.L. as a function of pressure with contrast inkings.

Paper: C
Felt side
Ink: F.G.L.
Speed: 4.58 m/sec

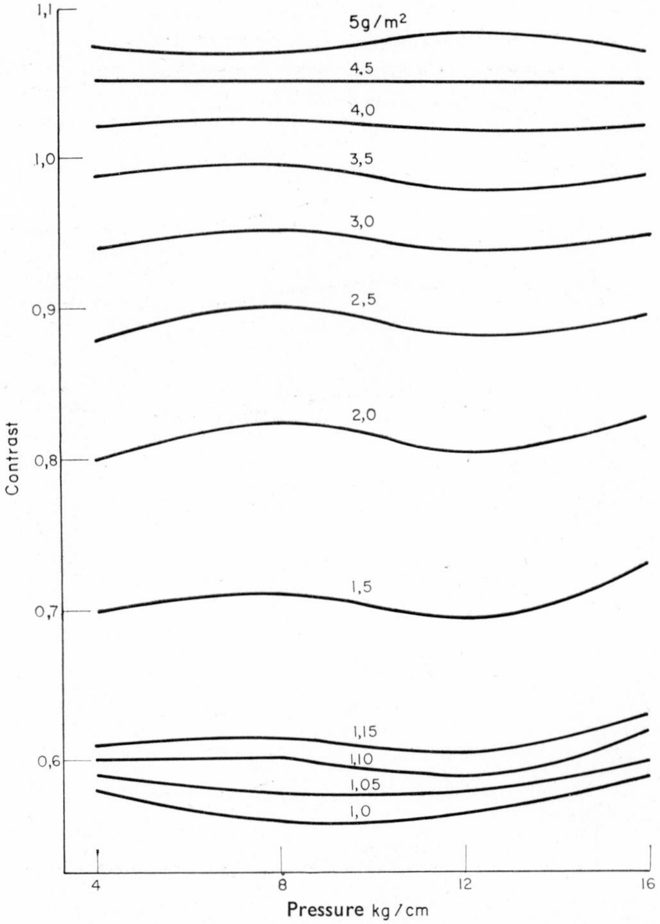

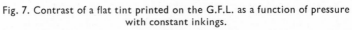

Fig. 7. Contrast of a flat tint printed on the G.F.L. as a function of pressure with constant inkings.

Paper: C
Felt side
Ink: G.F.L.
Speed: 4.58 m/sec

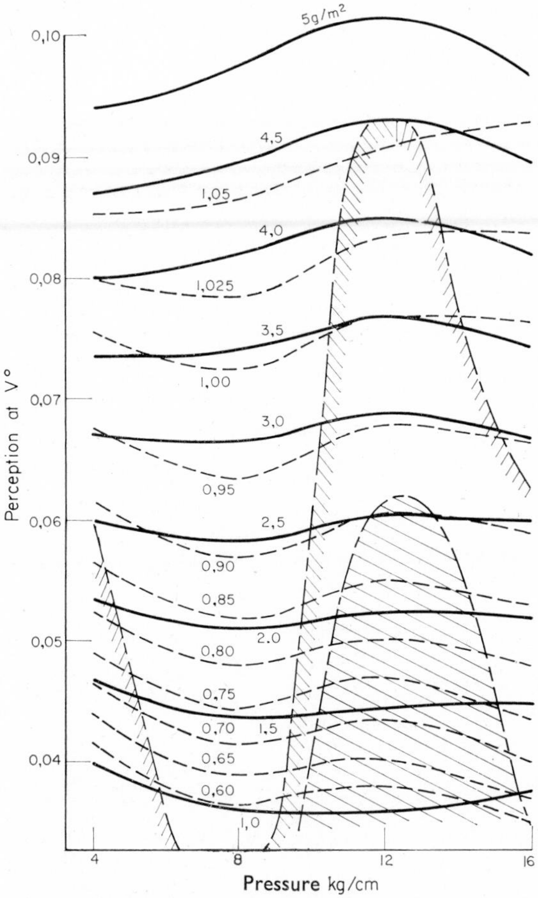

Fig. 8. Perception at the back of a flat tint printed on G.F.L. press as a function of the pressure.

——— With inking C   Corresponding zone relating to a same inking.

- - - - - Contrast C

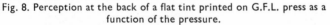

//// Zone for which the felt side prints through more than the cloth side for a similar flat tint contrast.

Paper: C
Felt side
Ink: G.F.L.
Speed: 4.58 m/sec

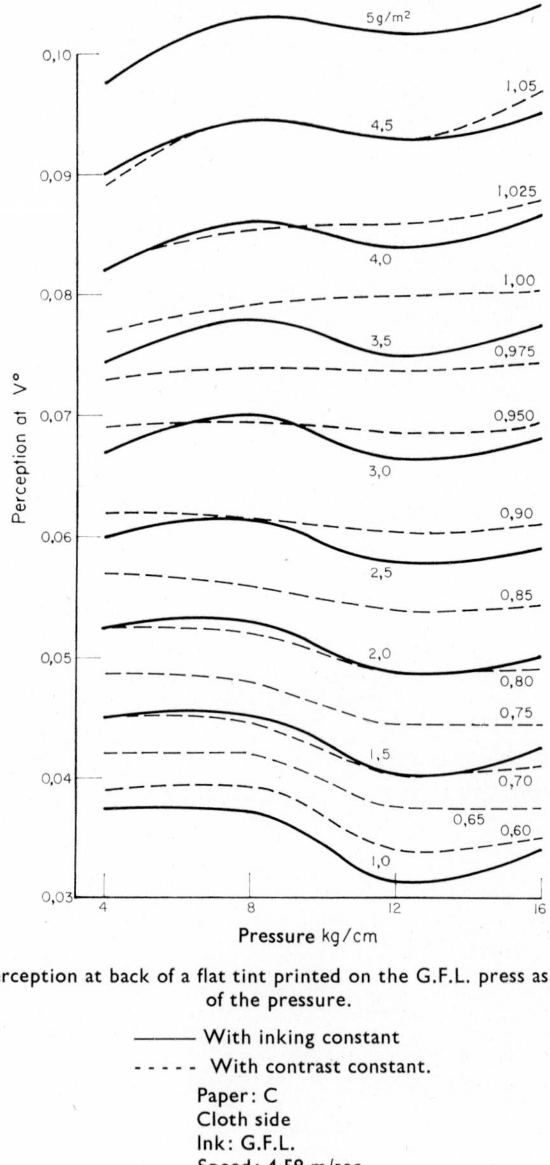

Fig. 9. Perception at back of a flat tint printed on the G.F.L. press as a function of the pressure.

——— With inking constant

- - - - - With contrast constant.

Paper: C
Cloth side
Ink: G.F.L.
Speed: 4.58 m/sec

(II) EFFECT OF PRINT THROUGH ON THE TONE VALUE OF A HALFTONE BACKED BY A SOLID TONE

We have already seen on the sketch given in Fig. 2 that the printing plates were so designed as to provide two continuous halftone areas (39 per cent and 51 per cent tone value) partly backed by another print:

(*a*) at the "normal inking" level, the prints at the back were a solid tone, a text and a line block;
(*b*) at "low" and "high" level, the print at the back was only a text.

In the case of text and line block, only subjective evaluation—followed by pair comparison ranking—could be made and will not be reported here. As for the effect of the solid tone at the back of the halftones, reflectance measurements were taken on both sides of eight different areas. We had, in fact, on one side of the print four areas each of tone value: 0, 39, 51, and 100 per cent, half of each area being backed by a solid tone whereas the second half remained unprinted at its back.

Taking the Print Through contrast (between backed and unbacked areas) at the 0 per cent tone value as reference point, our purpose was to see how the other tone values (full tone included) were affected by the Print Through of the same solid.

We found that the lowest tone value seemed to give rise to an *increased contrast* between the two areas, whereas the highest tone value was lowering the original contrast.

This appeared to be a general effect for both sides of the 8 papers.

But we felt that this first conclusion required further investigation for two different reasons:

(1) Since we had a markedly different behaviour for the two tonal values, we evidently needed a more progressive scale of tone values to see where the effect was reversed.
(2) It was not possible on the second couple to discriminate the Print Through from the effect of Second impression Set-off, since the printing pressure and inking of this second couple were most probably different from their respective values on the first one.

Therefore a second test run was made, with only one given make of newsprint. We prepared another set of plates, with 8 successive steps of tone values (including 0 and 100 per cent). This time, we kept the inking level constant, and from the experience gained during the first test run, we achieved a better control over the uniformity of the inking across the width.

We made two successive test runs, reversing the feed of the paper web into the unit, so as to get, on each couple in turn, separately the Print Through with and without Second impression Set-off.

The results of the corresponding measurements are given in Fig. 10. On these last two graphs, the optical densities of each half of the various half-tones (with and without a solid at the back) are plotted as a function of the percent dot area (measured on the negative).

Graph A refers to the density of the print, with and without Print Through (with *no* Second impression effect).

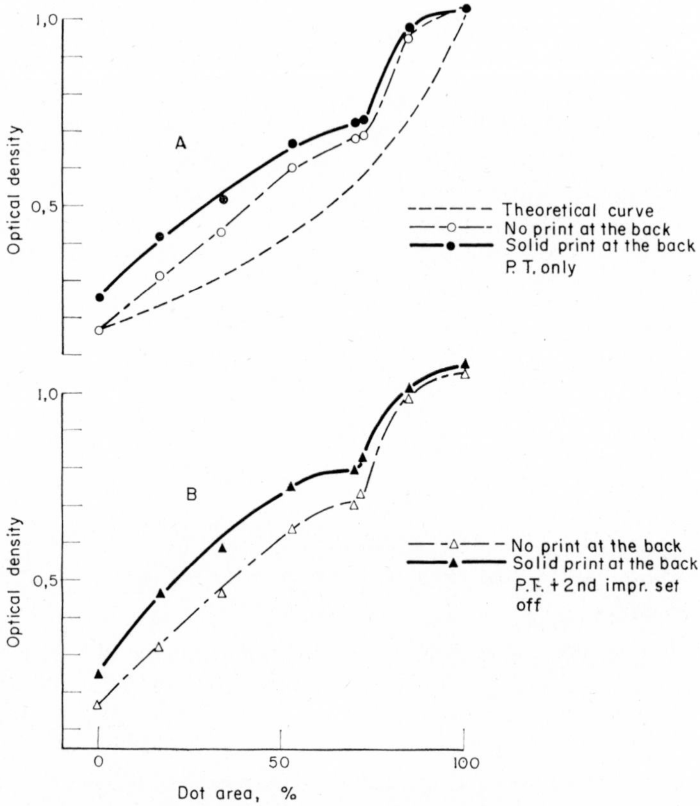

Fig. 10. Halftone optical density versus percent dot area on negative.

Whereas in graph B, the Second impression Set-off is superimposed on top of Print Through.

In spite of very many attempts at a mathematical treatment of the data, we have not been able to get our experimental results to fit with any theoretical or experimental law previously established by several authors (Yule, Poulter and Croney, etc.).

This could be due to the rather crude printing conditions prevailing on a newspaper press and to the low quality level of the newsprint surface as compared with the art coated paper used for instance by Yule in his experiments.

Newspaper printing conditions might result in:

a variable optical density of the dot, at various tone values;
an irregular variation of the squash of the dot.

As a consequence, we can only give our actual experimental results, which show the disturbance caused by Print Through on the density of a half-tone and the incidence of eventual Second impression Set-off, for the same couple on the same side (Top Side) of the paper.

It is to be noted that a rather steep rise occurs in the dark tones (similar to the one reported by Yule for offset printing), whereas Poulter found it for the light tones in letterpress. Finally, we can point out that the lower curve of graph B (neither Print Through nor Second impression Set-off) is slightly higher than the corresponding one in graph A, this being due to a certain amount of smearing because of the tight winding of the paper around the second impression cylinder; this is in some way a Second impression Set-off effect without any printing pressure.

CONCLUSIONS

The main conclusions of this first part of our study can be summarized as follows:

(1) Where no halftone is involved:

(*a*) the absolute amount of Print Through which may occur when printing, on a newspaper press, a solid at the back of an unprinted area, cannot yet be exactly determined by our laboratory testing;
(*b*) such testing gives, nevertheless, a correct ranking when various newsprints are compared, and can therefore already be successfully used for manufacturing control;
(*c*) it would be of still greater help if we could succeed in adjusting our laboratory testing conditions so as to simulate better the effect of industrial printing.

A real control over the printing conditions on a rotary press will only be possible with the full-scale experimental unit we have under study. But we hope that, in the meantime, it will be possible to go a step further by using the colorimetric technique described by Dr. Calabrò (this conference), to determine the actual printed area and ink film thickness on a print.

(2) Where a halftone is printed on the opposite side of a solid:

(*a*) the lightest possible tone value initially increases the contrast between backed and non-backed area.

(*b*) for increasing tone values, the contrast gradually decreases, as foreseen by the theory.
(*c*) where Second impression Set-off occurs on top of Print Through, the contrast steadily increases for higher tonal values than previously, up to a maximum slightly below 50 per cent tonal value.

We have up to now considered the measured values of Print Through. The next step must be to establish the correlations between such measured values and the corresponding visual perception, on the base of which ordinary observers usually express their appreciation of the phenomenon.

We wish to express our thanks to the Management and Technical staff of the Newspaper *La Voix du Nord*, in particular to Mr. Talpaert, Technical Manager, who has given us facilities; and to Messrs. Vincent and Paris, heads of Photoengraving and Production departments, who have kindly encouraged our study and given us invaluable assistance.

DISCUSSION

Carlsson: (1) You have established a difference in the actual amount of P.T. between the production and the GFL press. I believe that this difference is only valid for this special press and it seems very probable to me that you might have got quite a different result for another production press.

(2) You have found the same ranking between the papers with regard to P.T. in the two presses. The difference in the actual amount of P.T. may have been caused by the shorter impression time in the GFL press than in the production press. The fact that the hardest paper C behaves differently gives some evidence for this assumption as the ink transfer decreases considerably more for harder paper at increased printing speed.

(3) With regard to the abnormal rise of the density curve in Fig. 10 at about 70 per cent dot area I would like to know whether you were able to see if this was caused by the fact that the shadow dots began to be filled in at this point. When a shadow dot has been filled in with ink the result is that an area which earlier was unprinted now becomes covered with ink.

Mme Benedite: (1) It is true that the difference is only established on the very press we used in the experiment and would be somewhat different for other presses. But we thought it would be of interest to achieve an exact simulation of the actual industrial result even for one given press, so that we could afterwards use our GFL apparatus as a kind of "master instrument" to assess differences between various presses. Moreover, we believe we have shown that the main difference between the unit and the GFL Test press lies now in the speed conditions, and we propose to adjust our testing conditions in the laboratory in this respect.

(2) I do agree that the difference in actual values of P.T. between the two (GFL and unit) must be mainly due to the condition of contact at the moment of printing. Our experiments were made at the same linear speed (ωR constant); we now think it would be more suitable to perform it at a lower speed on the GFL, so that $\omega^2 R$ be constant.

(3) It is very probable that the steep rise is due to a sudden increase of density of the dot, due to filling in, but we have not really looked into it; we intended mainly to show on Fig. 10 the difference between the effect of P.T. alone and the P.T. plus second impression set off, on the same couple for the same inking level.

CHRISTENSEN: Why have you used dot areas of the negative as abscissa in Fig. 10 instead of the actual dot areas of the block? It would have changed the shape of the curves.

MME BENEDITE: Dot area is only plotted here as a reference scale. We measured it on the film because it was much easier than to do it on the curved stereo plate.

LARSSON: You told us that you had chosen a very good printing shop from a technical point of view for this investigation. Was the room air conditioned?

MME BENEDITE: The printing shop I chose was among the best in our country, but it was not that good as to have control of humidity and temperature of the atmosphere. However, we recorded the conditions and these were about 50 per cent r.h. and 20°C.

CLASSIFYING LINOTYPE SLUGS

by KÁLMÁN LOVÁSZ
The Experimental Plant and Laboratory of the
Printing Industry of Hungary, Budapest

HOT metal type is mostly produced on line composing machines. This method is of great importance in spite of the developments in other fields of text production.

The regeneration and handling of the type metal is, however, expensive. For this reason our Experimental Plant and Laboratory undertook to study the problem thoroughly. Several institutes and printing companies took part in this work. Some part of this work in progress will be reported here.

For evaluating the effect of changes in the different steps, in metal regeneration, metal handling and moulding, a relatively simple and quick classification of the slugs is necessary. We are unaware of such a method of classification in practical use. The information got from the users of the slugs is not entirely reliable since in use there are many other factors which have an influence but which are not measured objectively in every case. For example, the opinion of a machine minder as to the wear resistance of the slugs depends very much on the effective printing conditions as the state of the machine, cylinder dressing and so on.

Four indices were chosen for characterizing slugs: dimensional accuracy, surface smoothness of the type face, wear resistance and porosity.

Classification in terms of dimensional accuracy is a well-known one and it is an industrial practice in most countries.

The reason for choosing the other three additional characteristics is as follows.

The surface of a type face can be characterized by the micro- and macro-roughness. In micro-roughness there are elevations and depressions in a range of about 1 μ. This range is not quite critical in the printing technique. According to experience, this kind of roughness will be lost on most lino slugs after some thousands of impressions, irrespective of the initial condition of them, while a roughness of 1–2 μ develops as wear proceeds (see Fig. 1).

Macro-roughness involves essentially some discontinuities in which the surface of the type face is broken up.

These discontinuities cause non-uniform print, and to obtain a sharp impression it is necessary to increase the printing pressure and the amount of ink. The slugs set on line composing machines do not give a satisfactory printing quality mostly because of this macro-roughness.

The second characteristic is wear resistance, the importance of which does not need to be stressed. This problem occurs over 20,000 impressions, a limit shown by the measurements to be discussed later. Until now, wear resistance of slugs could be determined by practical printing. The method suggested by S. R. C. Poulter(1) is essentially such a method.

According to our measurements the wear resistance of the slugs is proportional to the Brinell hardness number. This fact is not immediately apparent since within a type form, the amount of wear depends on the distance and size of the other printing elements in the surroundings of the type under consideration. As for the wear, there are other factors making the situation more involved, e.g. accuracy of the printing cylinder, the printing pressure applied, the grain of the paper, the abrasiveness of the ink and so on.(2)

In our opinion the classification suggested could be employed on any printing elements made of type metal.

Compactness of the slugs, i.e. the volume of the holes inside the slug is suggested for the third characteristic. A quite porous slug will collapse at impression and it results in type failing and inclined lines. Similar troubles occur in matrix moulding.

A relationship between the above-mentioned troubles and the chemical composition was sought. Samples to the number of 292 were collected from several plants and composing machines.The samples were analysed chemically and spectroscopically. The chemical analysis gave the quantities of Sb and Sn while spectroscopic examination gave the impurities Cu, Bi, Ag, As and Zn. The comparison of the data with the three printing technique factors is still in progress. It can be stated, however, that changing the chemical composition within the standard (DIN 16512/1954) does not result in great differences in printing characteristics; the most important factors are those related to the adjusting and operating of the composing machine.

For studying linotype slugs and metal the works by the following authors among others are of interest: W. Hoffmann(3), I. Boreczky(4) and A. A. Semionov.(5)

MACRO-SMOOTHNESS

We did not find any means suitable for quantitative testing. Though micro-smoothness can be measured with an electronic roughness tester, this order of smoothness is, however, not so important for the printer. For checking macro-smoothness and type face faults a magnifying glass or a microscope with small magnification (60 ×) proved to be most suitable for this purpose.

In this way the slugs could be divided in ten classes on the basis of a subjective evaluation. After some practice two independent observers differed in opinion by not more than by one class. Values under 4 are unsuitable for printing, while slugs ranked into the classes 9 and 10 are suitable for printing even on art papers, as they possess continuous type faces.

The enclosed photographs serve as examples for classifying but for an effective judgment a whole slug must be taken into account.

According to experience to date the subjective classification of a type face approximately corresponds to the value obtained with the Courty spiral mould.[6]

WEAR RESISTANCE

For studying wear a text page was made up of slugs with different Brinell hardness set on different machines. This page ran on a flat-bed press for 100,000 impressions. An old type paper packing was used for cylinder dressing. At the start and after each 10,000 impressions some clean prints were put aside. The appearance of the 100,000th impression is shown in Figs. 1 and 2.

Fig. 1. Detail of a type in a linotype slug.

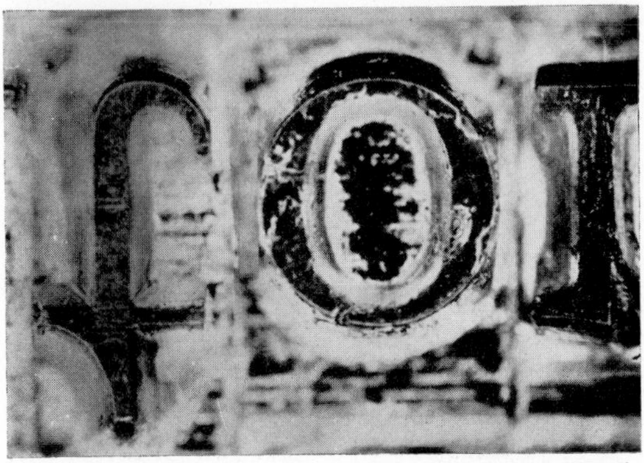

Fig. 2. Detail of a slug with a surface smoothness No. 5.

A subjective study of the prints shows that the amount of the wear depends especially on how much the other printing elements are spaced. The degree of overpacking (cylinder circumference ratio) is also to be taken in account.

Fig. 3. Detail of a slug with a surface smoothness No. 9.

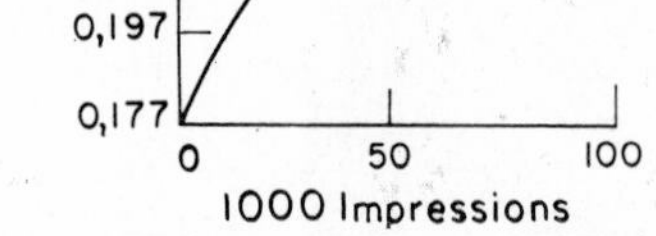

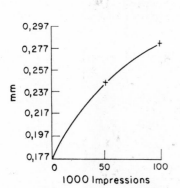

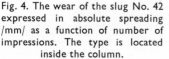

Fig. 4. The wear of the slug No. 42 expressed in absolute spreading /mm/ as a function of number of impressions. The type is located inside the column.

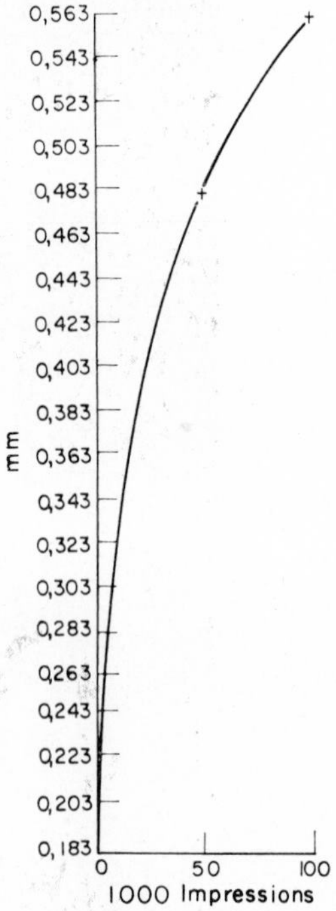

Fig. 5. The same type as in Fig. 4 out of the slug No. 42. The wear expressed in absolute spreading /mm/ as a function of the number of impressions. The type is located outside the column.

Figures 4 and 5 show the importance of the location of the type. The measured types were taken out of the same line. One of the *N*s is located within the column and the other in a part of the line protruding out of the column.

The nature of the wear is shown in the Schmaltz profile micrographs (Figs. 6 and 7).

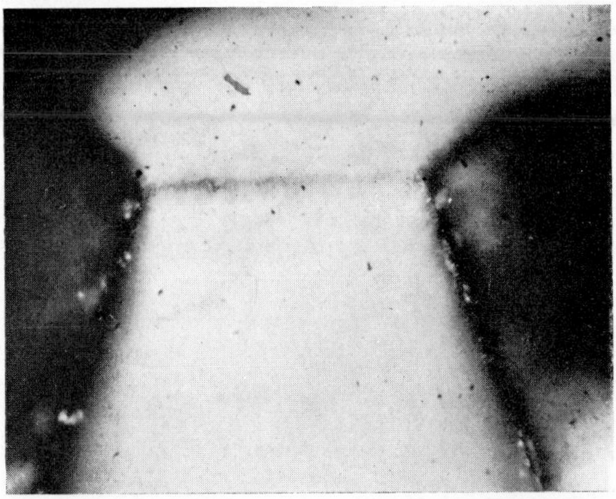

Fig. 6. A type profile before printing. The photograph was made on a Schmaltz light section microscope.

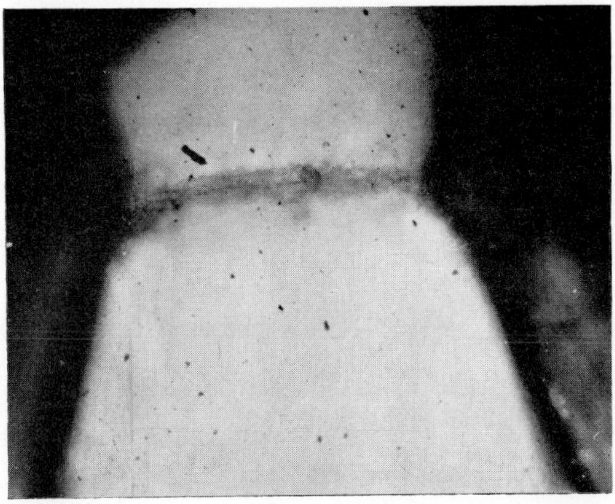

Fig. 7. The type in Fig. 6 after 100,000 impressions. Photographing conditions are the same.

These profile micrographs were taken from the same type before printing and after 100,000 impressions. The rounding-off of the type can easily be observed and has been discussed in detail in an earlier publication.[(2)]

To characterize the wear, the absolute spreading of the type was selected. It was measured, with a microscope, on prints made on art paper from the text page made up of the different lines mentioned above. Figures 8 and 9, show the absolute and the percentage amount of spreading as a function of the Brinell hardness. It should be noted that the lines consist of types of the same grade (8 and 10 Continental points).

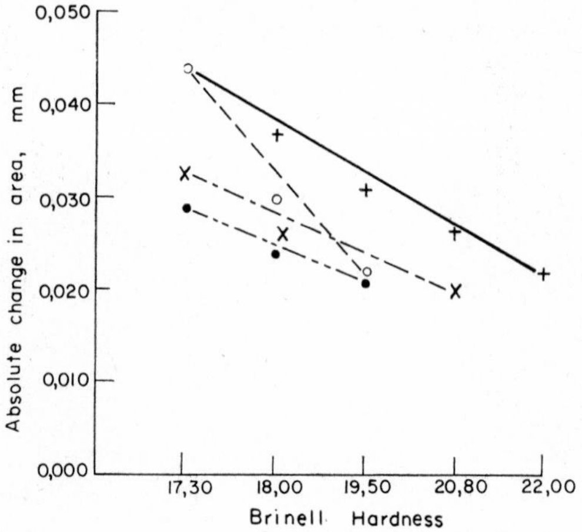

Fig. 8. The amount of wear (absolute spreading) on the different types is function of the Brinell hardness. The types were selected from slugs with different BH.

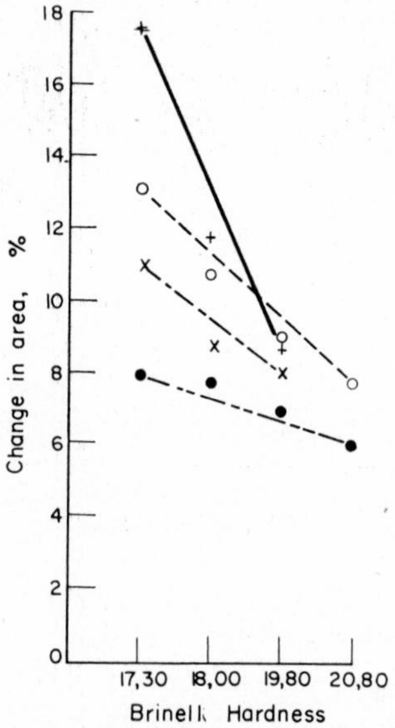

Fig. 9. Conversion of the data in Fig. 8 into percentage spreading.

Figure 8 can be interpreted as follows: there is a definite relationship between hardness and wear. The slope of the straight lines probably is caused by the "surrounding effect".

The development of the wear in terms of the absolute spreading is shown in Fig. 10.

The Brinell hardness measurements were made with a steel ball of 2.5 mm diameter loaded by 15.625 kg for 180 sec. The measurements were actually

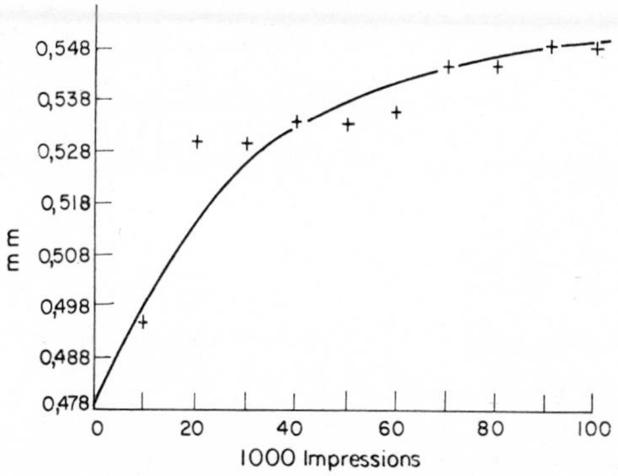

Fig. 10. The wear (absolute measure of the type face spreading) as a function of the number of impressions.

made on the type face side of the slug. An average of 4 to 5 measurements was taken at points by 2 mm.

POROSITY OR COMPACTNESS

The porosity of slugs was measured using Archimedes principle. From a weighing first in air (to within 0.1 g) a and then in water a_1, an apparent specific gravity is given by $a/a - a_1$. This we term compactness t.

The theoretical specific gravity of the standard type metal set on a Linotype composing machine (82 per cent Pb, 12.5 per cent Sb, 5.5 per cent Sn) was found to be 10.53 g/cm^3. According to our calculations the maximum of 1 per cent change in the composition of the alloying element affects the Sp. Gr. by a negligible amount.

Thus the difference between 10.5 and the apparent specific gravity of the alloy can be taken as a measure of the porosity.

The compactness of our samples was between 7.7 and 9.3. A compactness less than 7 makes doubtful in our opinion the suitability of the slug.

For investigating the distribution of the gas holes the slugs were planed off by light cuts (Figs. 11 and 12).

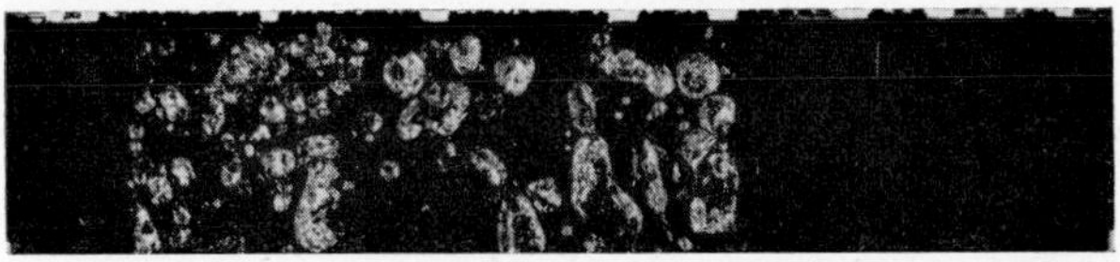

Fig. 11. A planed-off slug after inking. The holes look white. Compactness is 71.4 per cent.

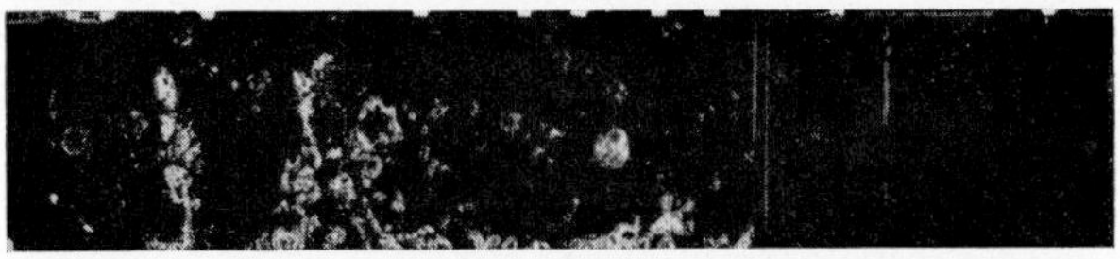

Fig. 12. A planed-off slug after inking. The holes look white. Compactness is 84.5 per cent.

szerencsétlen sorsú Charlesról.
ból . . .z-ból . . .
Pusztamonostor—Pusztamonostor elág. D
Tiszaug-Tiszafürdő mh. **Pusztamonostor** ....
Menettartam: — 6. 46 p.
.... **Pusztamonostor** ...... **Diósgyőri vasgyár**
Az íróemelőn írótű van elhelyezve. Ez alatt halad a
telessége vitatható.
...... **Diósgyőri vasgyár** Kavicsbánya keresztezés ...
— Némelyik napon nyolcvanan is meghalnak
ember szeme látja: itt hosszú **évek** óta nem **vágtatnak már**
Pusztamonostor—Pusztamonostor elág. D
wrh—?'y Y—Z—iAbm.GJú.o.1 vk, uűké KkóüZu,Z
cmfwyp cmfwyp cmfwyp m
Fülöp jól ismerte istállójának talán legszebb állatát, így gyöny
— Ez az én dédunokámrűzn
Menetidő — 6. 25 p. — Tartózkodás — 6. — p. — Menettartam — 6. 30 p.
VITÁNYI IVÁN: ÉRZELEM VAGY RENDƒ

De amikor becsukódik
képpen válaszol: „Tésztakiszaggatóm nincs . . . Nagy
az „el honor"-t, az ősi s tiszta, makulátlan vérrel való dicsek-
jelentkezéshez.
cmfwy cvmbfw cmfw cmfw cmfcmfw cmf cmfbb
hozzá. Pedig nem; nem ő alélt el, hanem ami rosszabb: a tözs-
nak a nagy nemzetközi utak, itt van az ország legnagyobb for-
Kobzos Tervgazdasági Értesítő Tárgymutató 19 pet.
etaoiÓh*etaetaetate tetaetaosnrdsn* snrdtaosnrdsnredaosnt nrnrdl
megfelelő értéket, ezért az oldalállító csavart mindig csak egy
vbgkqj ETAOIH SNRDLU CMYF WPVBGKQJ XZÖÜ— xzöü? cmwfpy
cmfwyp vbgkqj snrdlu cmfwyp etaoih snrdlu cmfwyp cmfwypnn
49. §. Tovább kell építeni és korszerűsíteni a közutakat. 46000
cmfwpy vbgkqj xzöü? vbgkqj snrdlu ETAOIH SNRDLU SNRD
cmfwyp snrdlu etaoih cmfwyp vbgkqj xzöü? vbgkqj vbgsnr
ha a légtérben süllyedő figurákat hajt végre, 500 m alá ne
megfelelő értéket, ezért az oldalállító csavart mindig csak egy
Kobzos Ügyészségi Közlöny 19 pet.
cmfwyp snrdlu snrdlu etaoih cmfwyp vbgkqj xzöü? vbgkqjcmn
cmfwyp vbgkqj snrdlu cmfwyp etaoih snrdlu cmfwyp cmfwypnn
cmfwpy vbgkqj snmrdlu etaoih d)—áws cmfwyp snrdlu cmfwyn
Ha nem enged, el vagyok szánva, elmegyek akárhová

Fig. 13. Original print from a forme made up of linotype slugs with different hardness, after 100,000 impressions.

We have found that gas holes are most numerous in the parts near to the foot of the line and the type face.

The three characteristics discussed in this paper should promote further research and development work. With sufficient data the relationship between printing characteristics and setting conditions—moulding temperature, pot temperature, setting speed, line body size, etc.—should emerge and make it possible to improve the quality of linotype slugs.

The three characteristics discussed above are applicable to all kinds of printing alloys.

REFERENCES

1. S. R. C. Poulter, Measuring forme wear. *Patra J.*, Jan., 1962.
2. K. Lovász, Letterpress forme wear. *Bulletins of Experimental Plant and Laboratory for Printing Industry*, A/1. Budapest, 1957.
3. N. Hoffmann, *Blei und Bleilegierungen*. Springer Verlag, Berlin, 1962.
4. J. Boreczky, Vliv medi, zinku, vizmutu a arsena na fizikálni vlastnosti pismovin. *Veda a vyzkum*, 7–26. Prague, 1960.
5. A. A. Semionov and V. A. Kogan, *Poligrafitcheskoie Proisvodstvo* **5,** 21–25, 1960.
6. E. Siebel, *Die Prüfung der metallischen.* Werkstoffe, 1955.

DISCUSSION

Christensen: (1) How did you distinguish between wear and breaking down of the edges of the type face?

(2) Does every value of hardness in Fig. 9 correspond to a different alloy composition?

Lovász: (1) We were able to make this distinction with the aid of the Schmaltz microscope.

(2) The sample variations were obtained by different compositions and 20 different machine settings.

SCREEN DOT FORMATION IN STEREOTYPING

by Olavi Perilá and Orvar Monni
Graphic Arts Research Institute, Helsinki, Finland

INTRODUCTION

The quality of tone reproduction is much poorer in newspaper printing than in most other printing processes owing to the shortage of time and of the poor grades of paper and printing ink employed. Also the short lifetime of the product has been one reason why so little serious work has been done to improve the quality of tone reproduction on newsprint.

Three stages of printing that influence tone reproduction may be distinguished: photo engraving, matrix moulding and stereotyping, and the actual printing. The main interest of the present study was to examine the second of these stages, and for this purpose investigations were carried out in a fairly large newspaper printing plant. One of the main objects was to define those factors whose variations in practice influence the properties of the finished stereo plates to such an extent that particular pains should be taken to keep them constant at optimal levels.

In order to avoid clogging the deep tone areas, the screen dots on the finished printing plate should always have a certain minimum depth. It is therefore necessary to take into account beforehand any losses in the depths of the dots that take place in matrix moulding and stereocasting.

Although tone reproduction is rather unsatisfactory in the actual printing stage, attention must be directed to ways of improving the reproduction already in the preparation of the matrix. For example, variations in the thickness of the ink layer influence tone reproduction in accordance with the following equation proposed by Laseur.[1]

$$\Delta p = (0.008R + 0.172)q.$$

In this equation Δp is the increase in the total printing area, R the total circumference of the dots in unit area and q the amount of ink applied to the plate. Since the edges of the screen dots giving moderate tones are the greatest in total length, their widening increases most as the amount of ink on the printing plate increases. Also the height levels may be different on stereo plates compared with ordinary letterpress printing plates, and for this reason the pressure on the paper is less evenly distributed even when the areas on the plates which transmit the pressure are equal.

RESULTS

The depth of the matrix dot in microns (μ) is shown as a function of the moulding pressure (kilo pounds/cm^2), the time and the temperature, and the moisture content of the flong in Figs. 1–4. The percentage tone values at different tone levels on a number of matrices are plotted in Figs. 5–8. Figures 9 and 10 show the variations of the depth and tone of screen dots on a cast stereo plate as functions of the pressure applied when making the matrix.

The distribution of screen dot depths on a matrix when different blanket combinations and grades of flong are used is shown by the column diagrams in Figs. 11 and 12. The corresponding tone values are given by the column diagrams in Figs. 13 and 14. The symbols in Figs. 11 and 13 designate the following blanket combinations (the material backing the matrix is given first); A, foam plastic: B, foam plastic + rubber sheet + foam plastic; C, foam plastic + rubber sheet; and D, machine felt + rubber sheet.

Figure 15 shows the depths to which the matrix was forced under pressure into holes or grooves as functions of the widths of the latter, and Figs. 16 and 17 show the depths when different blanket combinations and flong grades were used.

The contraction of the matrix as a function of the moisture content immediately after the matrix was dried and after it had first been dried and then air-conditioned is given in Table 1.

TABLE 1. CONTRACTION OF MATRIX AS A FUNCTION OF ITS MOISTURE CONTENT AFTER MOULDING

Moisture content	Change in length after drying		Change in length after air-conditioning	
	Machine direction	Cross direction	Machine direction	Cross direction
%	%	%	%	%
6.7	−0.35	−0.85	+0.1	−0.4
10.4	−1.0	−1.9	−0.45	−1.3
17.0	−1.6	−2.75	−1.2	−2.3
28.2	−1.15	−1.9	−1.55	−2.4

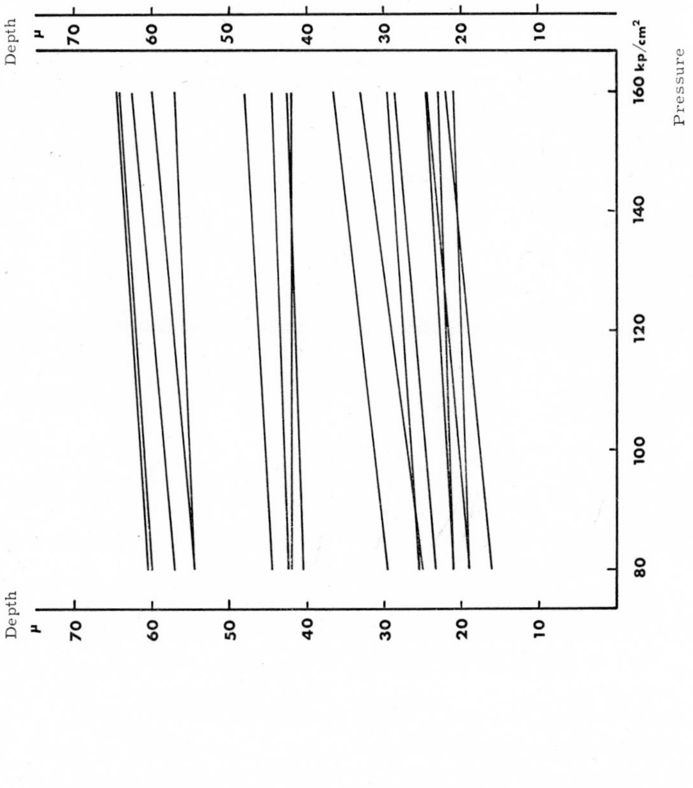

Fig. 1. The depth of the halftone dots of the matrices at various moulding pressures.

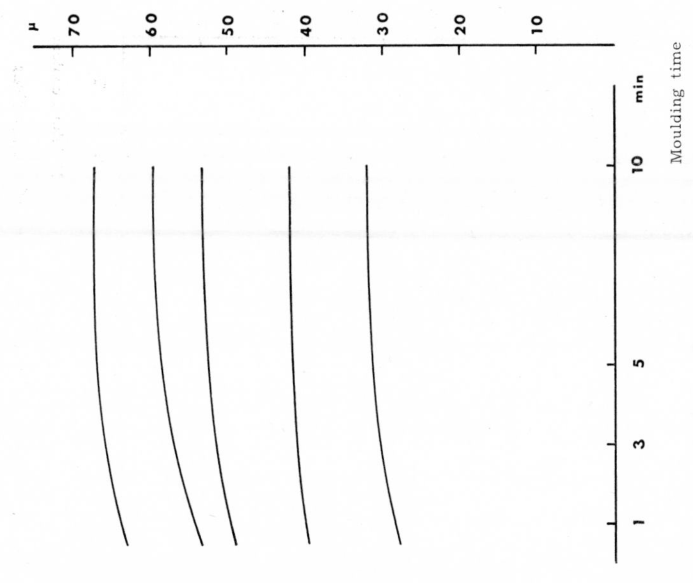

Fig. 2. The depth of the halftone dots of the matrices at various moulding times.

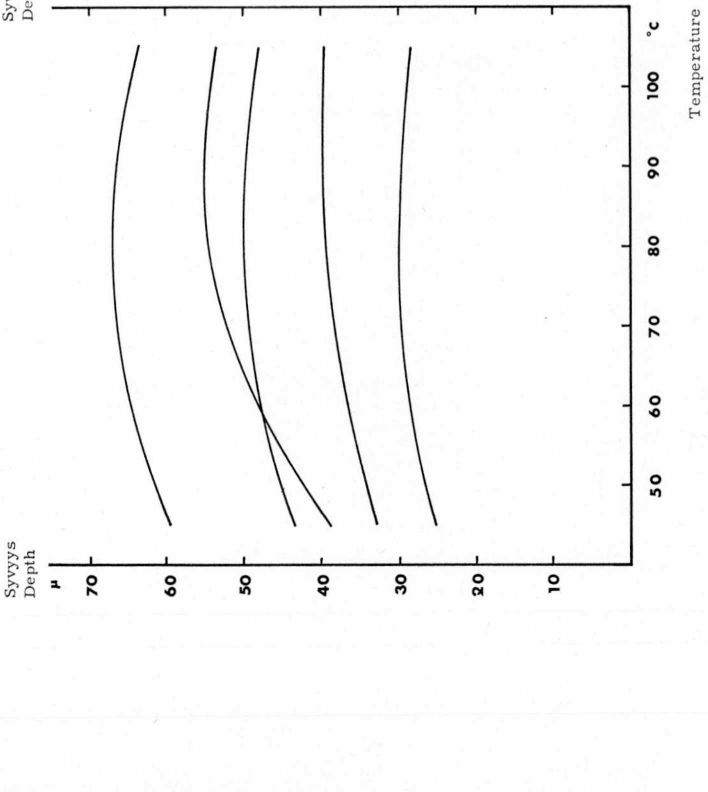

Fig. 3. The depth of the halftone dots of the matrices at various moulding temperatures.

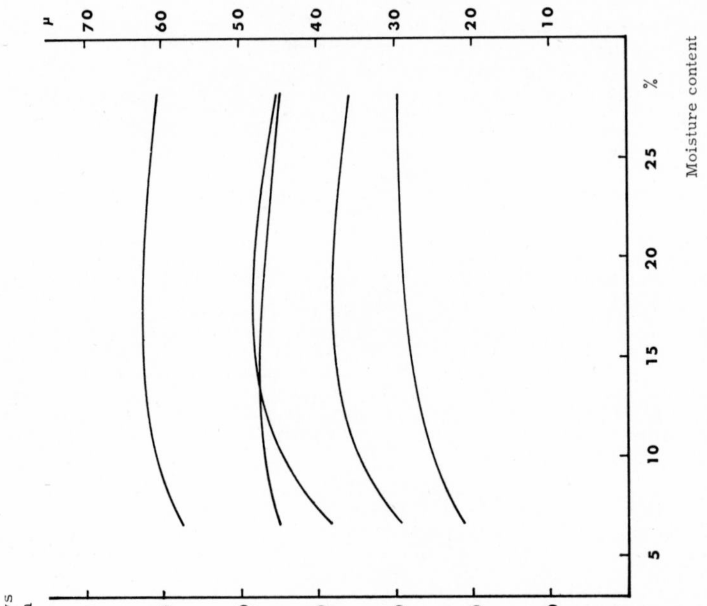

Fig. 4. The depth of the halftone dots of the matrices at various moisture contents.

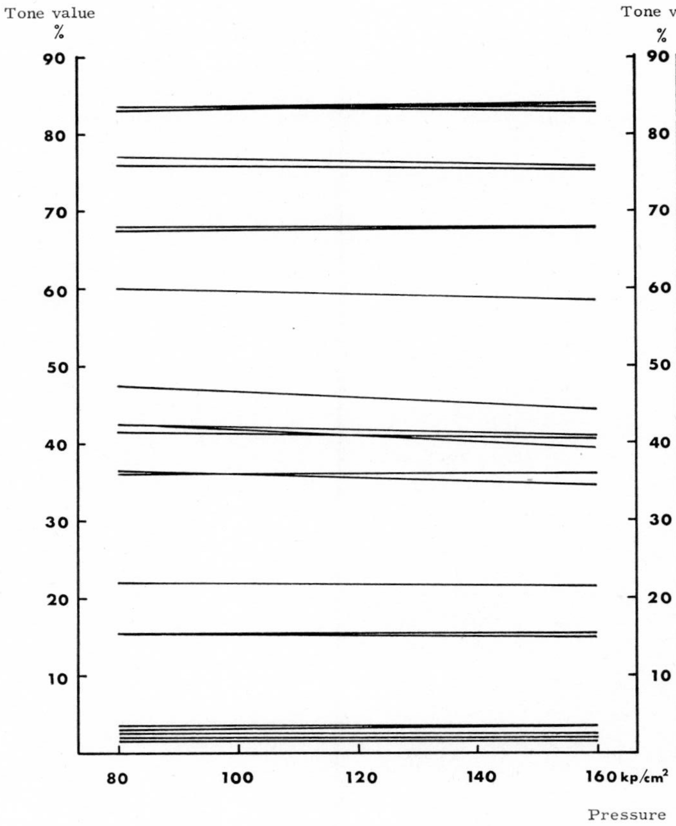

Fig. 5. The halftone reproduction of matrices at various moulding pressures.

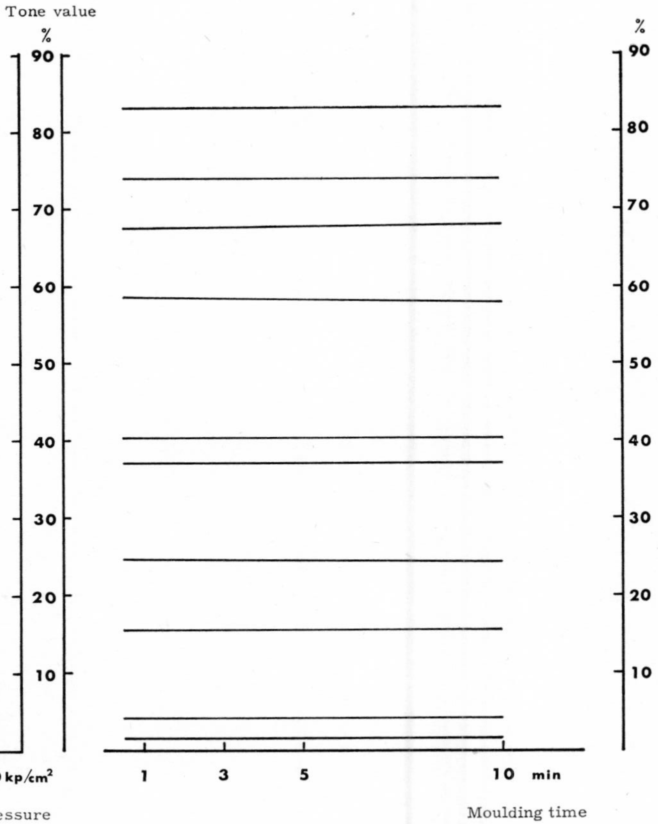

Fig. 6. The halftone reproduction of matrices at various moulding times.

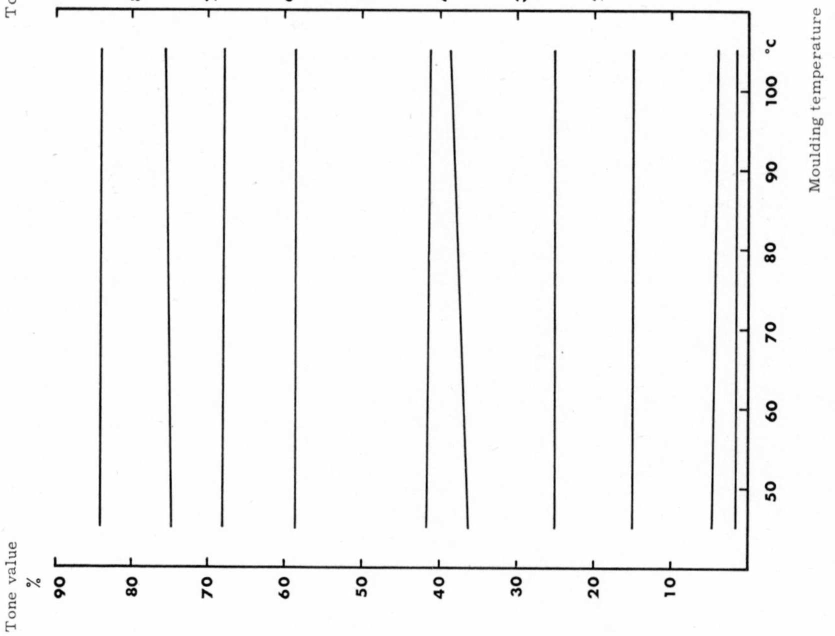

Fig. 7. The halftone reproduction of matrices at various moulding temperatures.

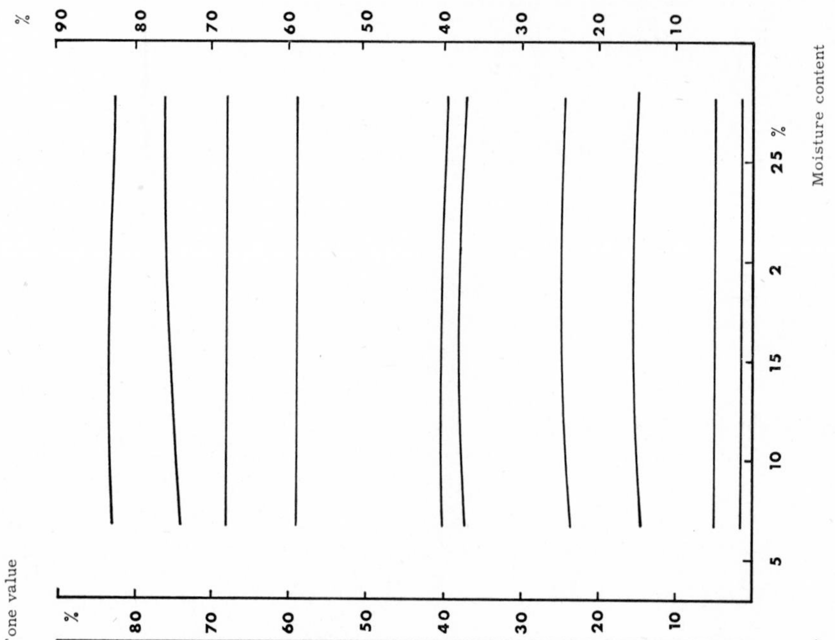

Fig. 8. The halftone reproduction of matrices at various flong moisture contents.

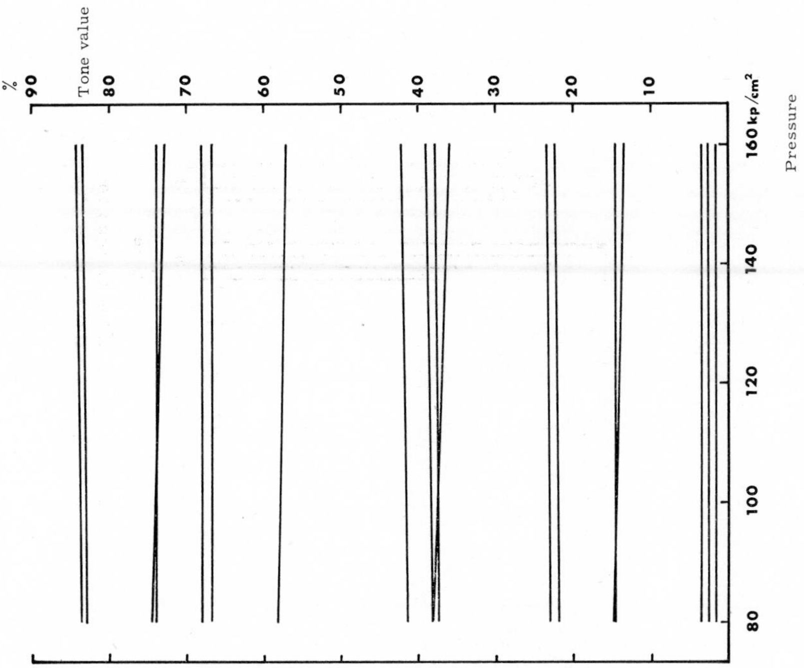

Fig. 10. The halftone reproduction of stereo plates at various matrix moulding pressures.

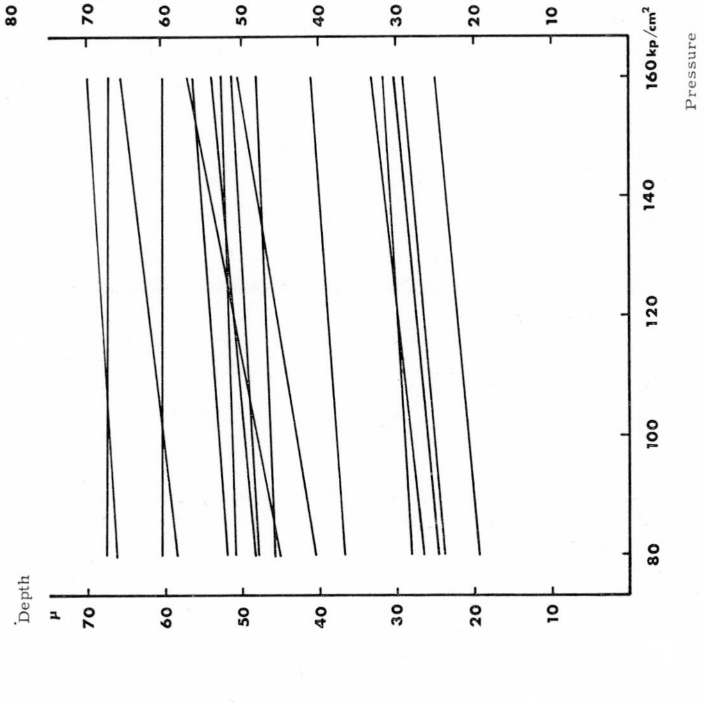

Fig. 9. The depth of the halftone dots of stereo plates at various matrix moulding pressures.

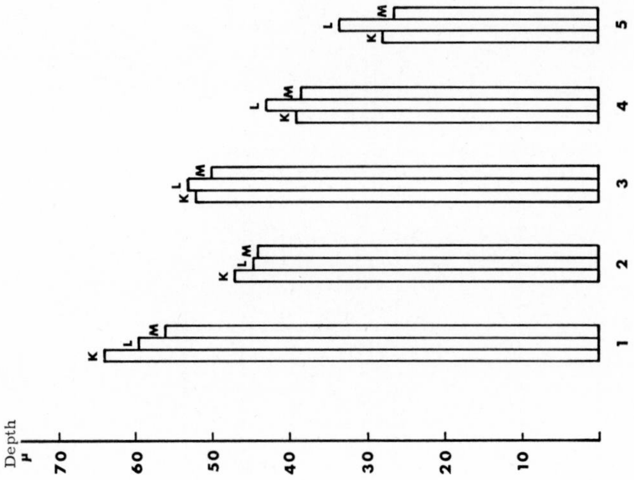

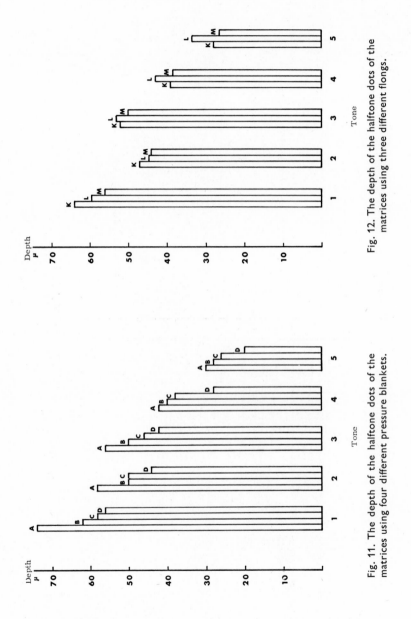

Fig. 12. The depth of the halftone dots of the matrices using three different flongs.

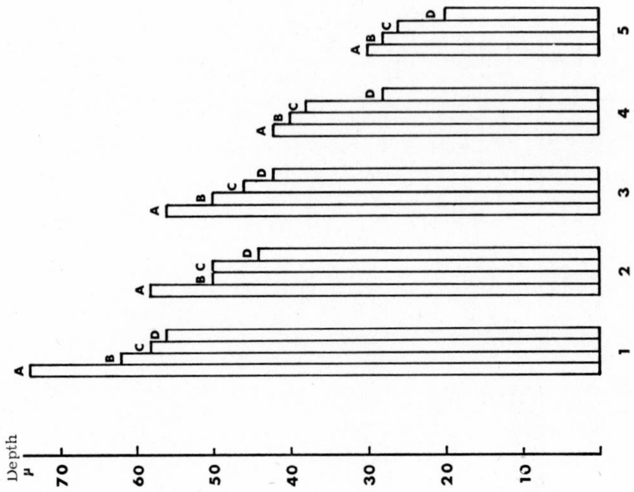

Fig. 11. The depth of the halftone dots of the matrices using four different pressure blankets.

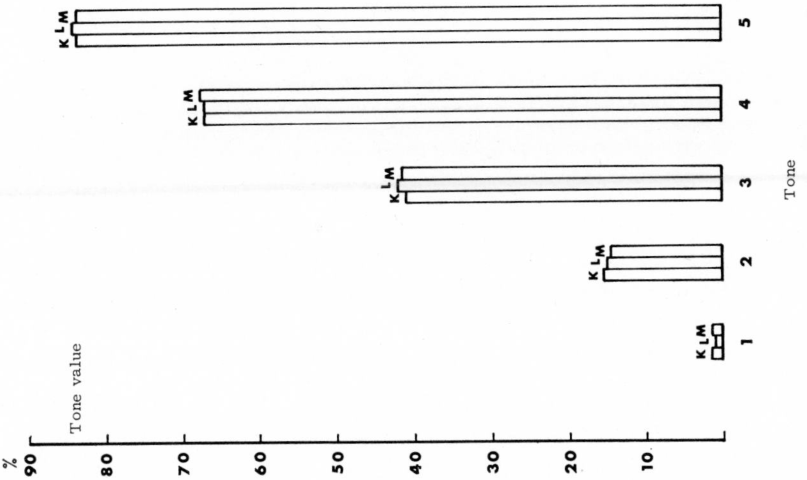

Fig. 14. The halftone reproduction of matrices using three different flongs.

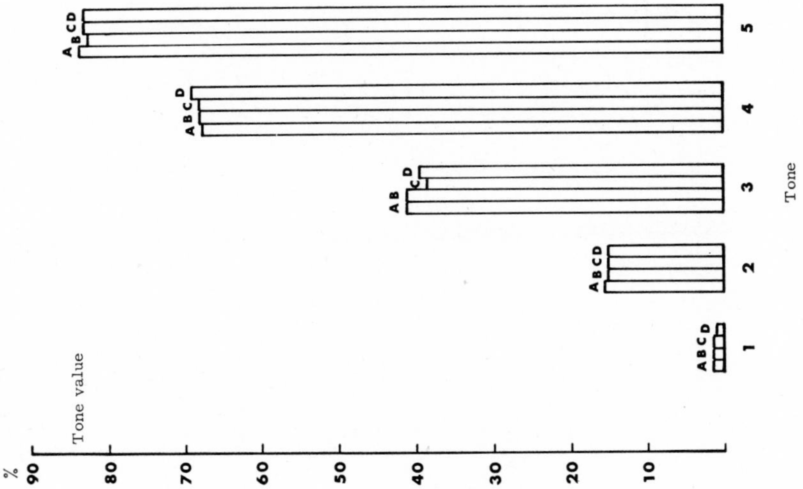

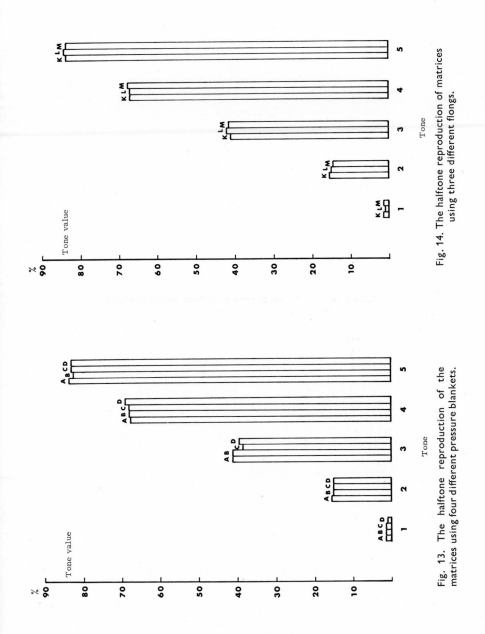

Fig. 13. The halftone reproduction of the matrices using four different pressure blankets.

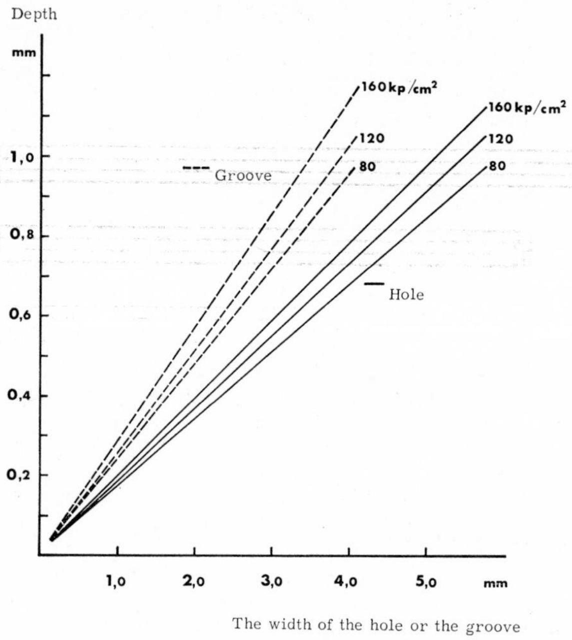

Fig. 15. The depth of the blind metal areas at various matrix moulding pressures and various widths of the blind areas.

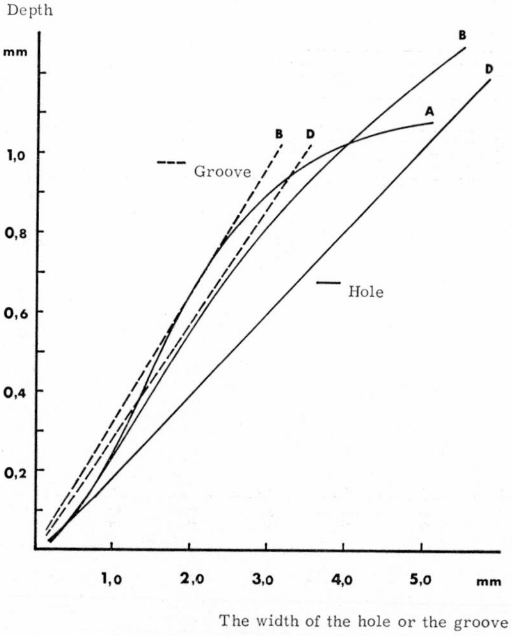

Fig. 16. The depth of the blind metal areas using different matrix pressure blankets at various widths of the blind areas.

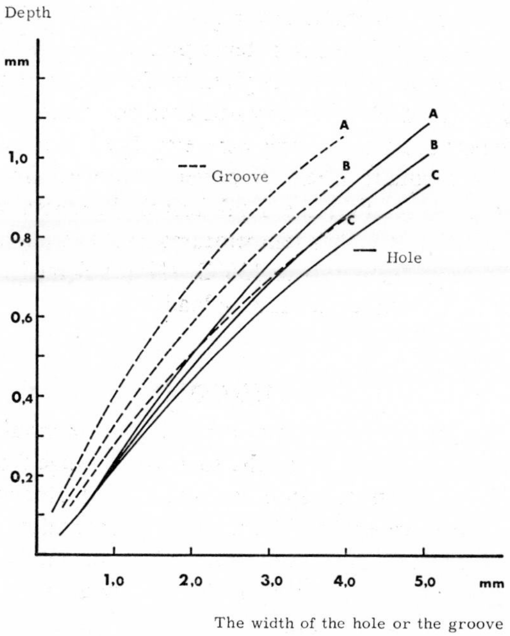

Fig. 17. The depth of the blind metal areas using different flongs at various widths of the blind areas.

The thickness of the underlays below the gray scale blocks in the forme varied from +0.3 to −0.3 mm. When curved stereo plates were cast with matrices and without using underlays, the heights of the gray scale blocks with underlays differed from the heights of blocks without underlays within

TABLE 2. THE EFFECT OF UNDERLAYS ON THE HEIGHTS OF FLAT STEREO PLATES

Underlay thickness	Differences in height	
	Exp. 1	Exp. 2
mm	mm	mm
+0.20	+0.001	+0.025
+0.10	−0.005	−0.01
+0.05	0	+0.005
−0.05	0	−0.02
−0.10	+0.01	−0.015
−0.20	−0.05	−0.075

the limits of ± 0.05 mm without any regular variation with respect to the thickness of the underlay. When flat stereo plates were prepared in a similar manner with the matrices, the results given in Table 2 were obtained.

The hardness of the plates after they had been cooled to room temperature in air when different rates of cooling were employed in the casting machine were approximately equal: when they were removed from the machine at temperatures of 40–110°C; the final Brinell hardness was about 23.5 kg/mm^2, but decreased at higher temperatures and was about 23 kg/mm^2 in the temperature range from 120 to 130°C. (Note: Brinell hardnesses were measured with a 5 mm ball under 125 kg load.)

DISCUSSION

According to Carlsson,[2] the loss of depth in matrix moulding is greatest, and of the order of 50 per cent, for the tone value range from 60 to 70 per cent. A dependence of loss of depth as great as that observed by Carlsson was not found in the present study although the maximum loss was in the same tone value range. This maximum loss was normally less than 40 per cent. The reproduction of the depth, as completely as possible, in the dark tones, however, is more important.

A higher pressure naturally increased the depths of the dots in the matrix (Fig. 1). Similar results have been reported by Carlsson,[2] Fischer[3] and others. It further seems that pressure had a greater effect at shallow depths (in dark areas) than at greater depths. In the range of pressures used, and which were the highest attainable in practice, the depth increased up to the highest pressures. The magnitude of the pressure did not appreciably alter the tone values of the matrix in the dark and light tone areas, but a slight decrease in value of the middle tone occurred with increasing pressure (Fig. 5). The explanation may be that the screen dots of the middle tones had to force away more of the flong material (Carlsson[2]) and the displaced material reverted to its original shape more rapidly with increasing moulding pressure during the following drying stage than in the other tone areas. The flong material forced into the holes and grooves of the plate increased fairly rapidly with pressure (Fig. 15).

The effect of pressure due to the matrix on the depth of the dots in the cast stereo plates was the same as the effect of pressure in the production of the matrix (Fig. 9). The reproduction of the tone values was not as good for the plates as for the matrices (Fig. 10). It should be noted, however, that the data employed to plot the curves was more limited in the case of the plates than in the case of the matrices.

The time of moulding, which varied from 30 sec to 10 min, was not found to influence tone reproduction (Fig. 6), although the depths of the dots increased with time (Fig. 2). In practice however, it is not possible to vary the time so much, the usual time range being 30 sec to 5 min. It will be seen from the figure that reduction of the time from the normal three minutes to half a minute did not lead to a greater loss of dot depth; a shorter time might be justified in urgent cases. A longer moulding time increased the depth to which the matrix penetrated into the holes and grooves of the plate; the depth increased 20 per cent when the time was increased from half a minute to 10 min. The effect of the moulding time may be divided into two parts, the increase in depth due to the plasticity of the matrix, which is restricted by the drying that occurs with time, and the decrease in the rate of reversion of the matrix material as the latter becomes drier.

Carlsson[(2)] observed that an increase in the moulding temperature from 20–100°C progressively increased the depths of the screen dots. From Fig. 3, it seems that the maximum depths were obtained when the temperature was in the range 70–90°C. The explanation for this may be the more rapid drying at the higher temperature and the attendant loss of plasticity of the matrix material. The temperatures recorded were maximum temperatures during matrix moulding and were measured at the matrix surfaces adjoining the form. These temperatures were attained 1–2 min after matrix moulding was begun (total time of moulding, 3 min) less rapidly when the moulding temperature was low, and more rapidly when it was high: this was due to the heat required to evaporate the moisture at the higher moulding temperatures. The moulding temperature had no appreciable effect on tone reproduction in the temperature range employed (Fig. 7). An increase in the moulding temperature from 45 to 105°C increased the depth to which the matrix penetrated into the holes and grooves of the plates by 10–20 per cent. It may be mentioned that raising the matrix moulding temperature diminishes the contraction of the matrix in the drying stage (Fischer[(3)]).

Carlsson[(2)] observed that a higher moisture content of the matrix leads to a greater depth of the screen dots, whereas Stanczak[(4)] noted an opposite trend when he studied high shrinkage matrices. The different results are probably due to different drying rates. In order to attain a large shrinkage, it is customary to choose a low drying rate so that relatively more time is available for the reversion of the penetration, but when ordinary matrices are used, the drying is effected so that the reversion is as small as possible. The data plotted in Fig. 4 reveal that the dot depths increased at first with increasing matrix moisture content, but then attained maximum values when the moisture content was in the range from 15 to 20 per cent; the drying procedure was that normally followed in the printing plant (gas oven, drying time 2 min). As shown by the data in Table 3, matrices of higher initial moisture content (28.2 per cent) were still fairly moist after drying, and as the drying at room temperature then took a longer time, more time was available for the reversion. A corresponding maximum was noted in the tone values when the moisture contents of the matrices were in the range of 15–20 per cent (Fig. 8). A higher moisture content facilitates penetration of the matrix into the holes and grooves of the plate. A greater penetration, of the order of 15–20 per cent, was clearly noted when the moisture content increased from 6.7 to 10.4 per cent, and the penetration was 50–60 per cent greater when the moisture content increased from 6.7 to 28.2 per cent.

TABLE 3. MOISTURE CONTENT OF THE MATRIX AT DIFFERENT STAGES

	Moisture content, %			
Before moulding	6.7	10.4	17.0	28.2
After moulding	5.4	8.6	15.1	17.9
After drying	0.4	0.2	0.4	6.5

As seen from Table 1, the shrinkage of the matrix is primarily determined by the moisture content before moulding (unless the drying is carried out under conditions promoting shrinkage). It has also been found that the degree of shrinkage decreases at higher drying rates (Fischer(5)) (cf. above). After drying, the matrix tends to take up moisture from the air and expand. As the data of Tables 1 and 3 show, the matrices of higher moisture content did not have time to dry enough under the standard conditions used, and as a result, both the drying and shrinkage continued during the air-conditioning stage.

Softening of the blanket clearly increased the depth of the screen dots as seen in Fig. 11. The best results as far as depth is concerned were attained when only a sheet of foam plastic was employed as the blanket, but the matrix was not sufficiently raised in blind metal areas. Furthermore, the edges of the block and the forme damaged the matrix at a pressure of 80 kg/cm^2. These defects were not observed when the foam plastic–rubber sheet–foam plastic combination was employed and the depths of the dots were still clearly better than when the ordinary machine felt–rubber sheet combination of the printing plant was used. The former combination gave better results at a pressure of 50 kp/cm^2 than the latter combination at a pressure of 120 kp/cm^2. The combination of foam plastic and rubber sheet had the same disadvantages as the foam plastic alone, although to a lesser degree. Carlsson(2) stated that a soft blanket gives shallower dots than a hard one, but the paper–felt and paper blankets he used were so much less elastic than the blankets we have used that the results are not comparable. The different blanket combinations did not influence tone reproduction to a noticeable extent

(Fig. 13). When foam plastic replaces the felt, the matrix is somewhat more moist after moulding, its drying proceeds more slowly and reversion is greater. Our measurements were made after the drying, and hence this effect was included in the results. The ability of the various blankets to raise the matrix is reflected in the depth to which the matrix penetrates into the holes and grooves of the plate (Fig. 16). The better properties of the foam plastic became evident at the smaller holes and at the narrow ends of the grooves, whereas the "ordinary" blanket was more effective when the hole diameter exceeded 5 mm.

Tone reproduction was approximately the same for all three flongs examined (Fig. 14), but the depths of the screen dots varied greatly (Fig. 12). From high light to shadow, flong M gave the smallest depths, but the properties of the grades K and L were such that grade K produced the deep spots better and grade L the shallow spots. As the depth of reproduction of the dark tone dots is the most important, the matrix grade L may be taken to have been the best of the three as far as depth is concerned. The depths of penetration of the matrices into the holes and grooves of the plates led to a similar conclusion (Fig. 17), although the depths mainly increased in the order $K > L > M$.

Similarly as in the printing stage, the form of the stereo plate surface determines essentially the pressure produced at each point in matrix. The magnitude of the pressure is influenced by the density of the forme face, the pressure being inversely proportional to the fraction of the printing area, and by the plasticity of the matrix and blanket. In addition, the form of the dot or type and the elasticity of the matrix and blanket determine the direction of the compressing forces. For these reasons it is customary to overlay large printing surfaces, such as halftone blocks, so that the pressures on them become as large as those acting on the type. As mentioned earlier, variation in underlay thickness within the limits of $+0.3$ and -0.3 mm to the type height led to no notable differences in the curved stereo plates. Different underlays did have an effect when flat stereo plates were prepared, although the variations between duplicate casts were also fairly large (Table 2). The explanation of the unsatisfactory results with the curved plates may be that the underlay primarily effected uneven displacement of the matrix into the blanket and did not produce the desired compression. The relatively large casting pressure in the preparation of the curved plates prevented the uneven displacement of the matrix, whereas the pressure was appreciably smaller and hence the forces straightening the matrix much smaller when flat plates were cast.

The stereo plate is cooled as rapidly as possible to obtain a fine-grained, hard and smooth surface (Goggin[6]). Slow cooling leads to the formation of large metal crystals that make the surface less smooth and less hard.

The results can be most easily evaluated by measuring the hardness of the cooled cast metal surface. As mentioned above, the surface was softer when the temperature of the plate, on removal from the casting machine, was 110°C or higher in our experiments. Because of the danger of later deformation, a plate should not be removed from the casting machine before it has been cooled down to 60°C (Schmidt[(7)]) and because the cooling should be effected as rapidly as possible to reduce porosity, there is evidently no risk that the surface will become weaker because of too low a rate of cooling in practice.

EXPERIMENTAL

For the most part the matrices were prepared in a MAN (720 t) matrix moulding machine and the stereo plates were cast in a MAN semi-automatic casting machine in one printing plant. A number of control experiments were carried out in machines of the same make in a second printing establishment.

The standard moulding conditions were those normally employed in each plant for formes of the type in question: moulding time 3 min, the temperature of the lower plate of the moulding machine 65°C. The temperature of matrix at the final stage of moulding was 55–60°C and its moisture content about 15 per cent. The hydraulic pressure of the pressing machine was 120 kp/cm^2, which corresponds to a pressure of about 85 kp/cm^2 with a solid forme. The printing surface was about 25–35 per cent of the area of the forme, and hence the average standard pressure was about 300 kp/cm^2. The pressure values used above are always hydraulic pressures. The same or a similarly composed forme was employed in all mouldings (Fig. 18). The standard blanket consisted of a machine felt about 3 mm thick and a triple corded rubber sheet about 1 mm thick.

The test block was of copper, containing five screened tones of 30 lines/cm, and a solid area. The depths of the dots in the plates, matrices and stereo plates were measured with a microscope. For the determination of the tone value, the printing area and the corresponding area on the matrix were photographed through a microscope, the film was projected at a high magnification on a screen, and the tone areas on the image were measured relative to the total printing surface. The tone values and the corresponding dot depths on the plate were 1.5 per cent, 66 μ; 15.8 per cent, 52 μ; 40.9 per cent, 62 μ; 68.9 per cent, 48 μ; and 83.3 per cent, 38 μ. Also two solid plates were placed in the forme; one of these had drilled holes 0.3, 0.5, 0.7, 1.0, 1.5, 2.0, 3.0, 5.0 and 10.5 mm in diameter, and the other uniformly-expanding machine-made grooves 125 mm long and increasing from 0 to 3.85 mm in width.

The temperature of the matrix during the moulding was measured with a thermo-electric resistance. The size of the sensitive area of the thermo-resistance was 11 × 28 mm and its thickness 0.12 mm. The unit was placed at the level of the type height in the forme. The measuring bridge was calibrated at a series of temperatures in a thermostat.

The flongs were moistened by immersing them in water and placed, separated by moist paper sheets, in a cupboard. The flongs were stored at least one day to allow the moisture to become evenly distributed. When the effect of moisture content was studied, and in some other tests, the wetting

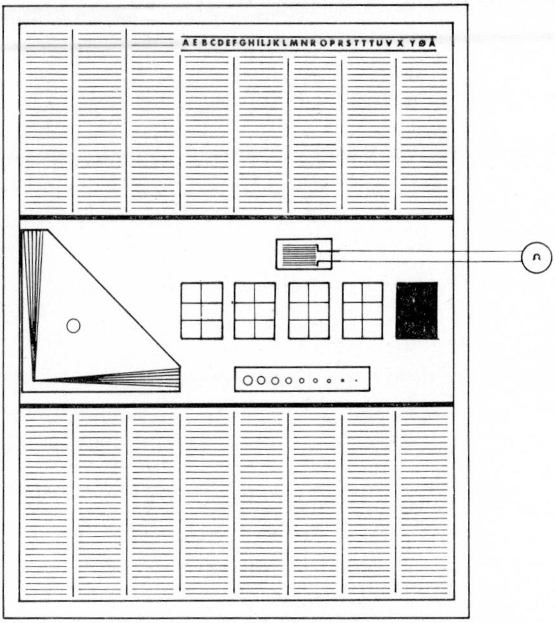

Fig. 18. A schematic drawing of the proofing form.

was done by spraying a known amount of water on the flong; they were then sealed in a plastic bag, and kept at constant temperature until the moisture had been evenly distributed.

When different blanket combinations were studied, the machine felt was about 3 mm thick. The 1 mm thick rubber sheet was made of three cloth and two rubber sheets, the foam plastic sheet was 12 mm thick.

The flongs were of commercial grades. The German grade *K* and the French grade *M* were 0.95 mm thick and the English grade *L*, 0.80 mm thick. When the flongs were compared, the mouldings were normally carried out at 15 per cent moisture content, but in this instance at 20 per cent.

The differences in height effected with underlays were measured relative to the surface of the block without any underlay.

The rates of cooling of the cast stereo plates were varied by changing the time of cooling (30–15 sec) and the rate of flow of the cooling water. The temperatures of the plates were measured immediately after the latter were removed from the casting machine and before they were left to cool in air. The Brinell hardnesses of the printing surfaces were determined by forcing a tempered steel sphere 5 mm in diameter into the surface with a weight of 125 kg, and measuring the surface area of the impression. The hardness was calculated by dividing the weight imposed upon the sphere by the area of the impression.

SUMMARY

The formation of screen dots in matrix moulding and stereo plate casting has been studied under conditions prevailing in newspaper printing plants. Most attention was paid to the depths of the dots and tone reproduction. The factors varied were pressure, time, temperature, moisture content of flong before moulding, blanket combination, grade of flong, thickness of underlay during moulding, and rate of cooling of cast plates. The collected data are compared with previously reported data.

The depth of the dots was found to increase with pressure, time of compression and softness of the blanket over the ranges where factors could be varied. The best results were attained at moulding temperatures between 70° and 90°C. The most advantageous flong moisture content was 15–20 per cent. Tone reproduction was not influenced by a change in moulding time or temperature, by the nature of the blanket, or by the flong quality. The middle tones became lighter with increasing pressure, and the tone values rose to a slight maximum when the flong moisture content was in the range of 15–20 per cent. Underlays did not produce any changes in the printing surface height of cast curved stereo plates. The surface of the cooled cast plate was slightly softer than normally when the rapid cooling in the casting machine was interrupted before the temperature had fallen below 110°C.

REFERENCES

1. G. M. W. Laseur, *Printing Inks and Colour, Adv. in Printing Sci. and Tech.*, Pergamon Press, Vol. I, 1961.
2. G. E. Carlsson, *GFL Meddelanden* **22,** 3 (1949).
3. M. G. Fischer, *Zeitungstechnik* **10,** 18, (1958).
4. F. J. Stanczak, *ANPA Mechanical Bull.* **124,** 744 (1961).
5. M. G. Fischer, *Zeitungstechnik* **9,** 14 (1958).
6. J. Goggin, *Graphic Arts Monthly* **12,** 36 (1960).
7. W. Schmidt, *Papier u. Druck*, Druck u. Reprod. 115 (1961).

DISCUSSION

CARLSSON: We have found the same relation between the loss of depth and the tone value of the block as Mr. Perila. In a very extensive investigation we made about 15 years ago we found almost the same depth in the matrix, as in the block in the extreme highlights and shadows, but a large loss in the middle tones with a maximum at a tone value of about 60 per cent.

CHRISTENSEN: Investigations we have made show that you cannot take the loss of depth in the matrix as a percentage of the depth of the block dots. Only in the extreme highlights is there a correlation between depth in block and depth in matrix. The depths in the matrix are, among other things, functions of the dot areas in the block, and the curve for the loss of depth as a function of dot size in the block has no maximum point in the neighbourhood of the middle tones. Another point is that inking-up in the highlights is very sensitive to the depths of the dots in the block when the dot areas are below 10 per cent. In the middle tones and the shadows it does not matter if you increase the depths in the block from a certain minimum depth.

PERILÁ: The loss of the depth in the matrix calculated as a percentage of the depth of block dots as a function of the dot size has been calculated for the purpose of comparing it with the results of Carlsson(2). We did find the same maximum (tone value range from 60 to 70 per cent) as he did.

SOME EFFECTS IN THIN LAYERS OF INKS

by GEORGE GÁTÍ
Hungarian Printing Ink Research Laboratory, Budapest

ONE of the important tasks in our printing ink development work is to continue improving the qualities of offset and letterpress inks so as to minimize technical uncertainties in the printing process.

In our work we found that the deviation of the properties of thin printing ink films from the bulk character is an important effect in the paper/ink/printing forme system during the printing process. This gives a new aspect to the interpretation of the physical phenomenon of ink transfer and of the equations derived from it. Thin layer effects are important.

ADAPTING HOLE THEORY TO DISPERSE PRINTING INK SYSTEMS

The mechanism of thin layer effects in printing inks can be understood from an application of defect lattice theory.

Taking a crystal model as a starting-point, defects and holes exist in crystal lattices. In case of N particles and m holes the number of possibilities arising from the distribution of the particles, i.e. the thermodynamic probability of the configuration distribution is

$$W_{kf} = \frac{|N+m|!}{N!m!} \tag{1}$$

Expressing it by Stirling's formula we obtain

$$\ln W_{kf} = -\left(N \ln \frac{N}{N+m} + m \ln \frac{m}{N+m}\right) \tag{2}$$

Differentiating this for the number of the holes gives

$$\frac{\partial \ln W_{kf}}{\partial m} = \ln\left(1 + \frac{N}{m}\right) = \ln \frac{N}{m}; \quad \text{if} \quad m \ll N \tag{3}$$

The energy of hole formation per lattice element is ε; in case of m holes $m\varepsilon$. In an adiabatic rearrangement this energy is covered by the thermal energy of the crystal in which case the decrease of the thermal component of the thermodynamic probability per particle is

$$\partial \ln W_{kf} = -\frac{m\varepsilon}{kT} \tag{4}$$

For a constant total energy the equivalence is characterized by the maximum value of ln W, when the number of the holes is

$$\ln \frac{N}{m} - \frac{\varepsilon}{kT} = 0, \text{ i.e. } \frac{m}{N} = \mathrm{e}^{-\varepsilon/kT} \tag{5}$$

When an adjacent lattice element passes into a hole, it has to cross a potential barrier separating the two equilibrium states requiring activation energy u'.

The probability of a lattice element getting new activating energy at successive moments, or of the same with numerous lattice elements at the same moment is proportional to

$$\mathrm{e}^{-u'/kT} \tag{6}$$

The average time necessary for the particle to get activation energy is t'; if $u' = 0$ the frequency of changes of places will be determined by t_0.

$$t' = t_0\,\mathrm{e}^{-u'/kT} \tag{7}$$

The t' is thus the average length of time for the particle keeping its place even if it has an empty place near itself. When the lattice element has filled in the hole it is only able to pass on if a new hole migrates beside it and that is in proportion to the relative frequency of the holes (5). The time necessary on average for the displacement (δ) of a selected particle between two points is the relaxation time (t) which is inversely proportional to the probability of the rearrangement.

$$t = t_0\,\mathrm{e}^{-(u'+\varepsilon)/kT} = t_0\,\mathrm{e}^{-u/kT} \tag{8}$$

The average displacement speed is

$$w = \frac{\delta}{t_0}\,\mathrm{e}^{-u/kT} \tag{9}$$

The relation to the macroscopic diffusion speed is

$$\mathrm{d}n = -D\frac{\mathrm{d}c}{\mathrm{d}x}\,\mathrm{d}t$$

$$D = \frac{\delta^2}{2t_0}\,\mathrm{e}^{-u/kT} \tag{10}$$

Extending the hole theory to liquids, we cannot consider a crystal lattice, and the order may generally be limited only to small parts of space characterized statistically as a fluctuating state of near order. In liquids there are no lattice points, accordingly holes represent gaps arising from the surrounding molecules not being in close packing. In liquids the number of holes is considerably higher because of the looseness as compared with the crystal and much less activation energy is needed for the passing-over of molecules. According to Frenkel the average displacement speed of liquid molecules is to be handled in a statistical way analogous to that of the crystals, and the equation (10) can be written for the diffusion constant in case of liquids too. The relation between the mobility of the molecules, v_m, and the diffusion constant D derived by Einstein is

$$v_m = \frac{D}{kT} \tag{11}$$

The fluidity Φ is the product of the mobility v_m, and of the distance δ of the molecular layers

$$\Phi = v_m \delta \tag{12}$$

From (10), (11), (12) we obtain

$$\eta = \frac{1}{\Phi} = \frac{2t_0 kT}{\delta^3} e^{u/kT} \tag{13}$$

The dependence of η on the external pressure p is given by

$$\eta_p = \eta_e^{pv_0/kT} \tag{14}$$

As the activation energy u is composed of the energy u' necessary for surmounting the potential, and of hole formation energy ε, it is necessary to do work not only against cohesion forces but also against external pressure in the making of a hole. If the size of a hole is v_0 the excess-work per hole is pv_0.

In a liquid unaffected by shear-force the passing-over of molecules is statistically the same in all directions.

External deformation forces reduce activation energy in the direction of the force, the statistical frequency of the passing-over will thus increase in the deformation direction. When the deformation force is large as compared with the u, then flow starts in the direction of deformation. With a very large u, and a small shear force, the mobility of the particles does not increase in the force direction to a sufficient extent in comparison with other directions, in which case no flow but at most an elastic deformation takes place.

Taking (8) into account, a flow can be originated by small shear forces over a long time. If within a relatively short time a small force encounters a permanent set, we can still refer to viscous flow. A liquid showing viscous flow can behave as elastic material against very short time force effects. Viscous liquids, i.e. materials with short relaxation time, behave as elastic materials if the loading period is less than the relaxation time.

The behaviour of viscoelastic materials can be described by the relation of external time t_e (loading time) and of internal time t (relaxation time). Thus

When $t_e \gg t$ we have liquid flow

when $t_e \ll t$ we have elasticity, solidity and solid like behaviour

The hole theory can be adapted to the micro-Brownian motion. This makes possible its application to disperse systems like printing inks and this has been confirmed by infrared absorption spectrograms.

We studied the absorption spectra of a polyester type oil-base disperse film-forming agent. The same film-forming agent was pigmented with 18 per cent phthalocyanine blue, the characteristic and well-estimable absorption maxima of which did not shift. For some new experiments our film-forming agent was pigmented with 25 per cent aluminium hydroxide, and even this pigmentation influenced only to a small extent absorption maxima characteristic of hydrogen bridges.

These results are shown in Figs. 1, *a, b, c.*

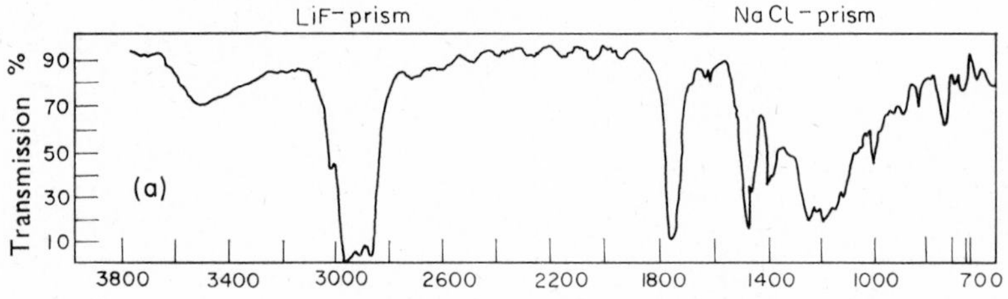

Fig. 1*a*. Polyester type oil base.

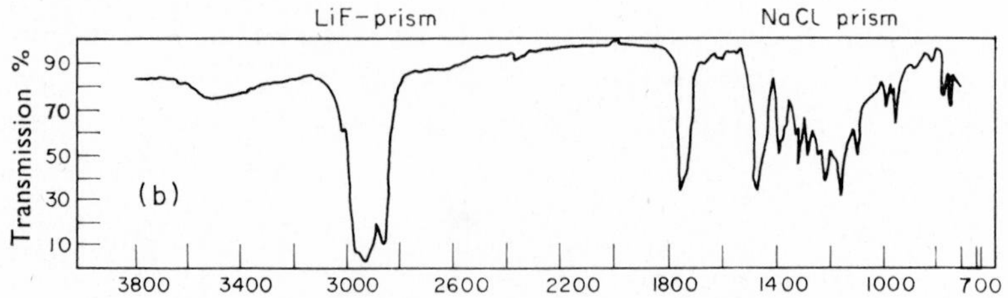

Fig. 1*b*. Polyester type oil base pigmented with 18 per cent phthalocyanine blue.

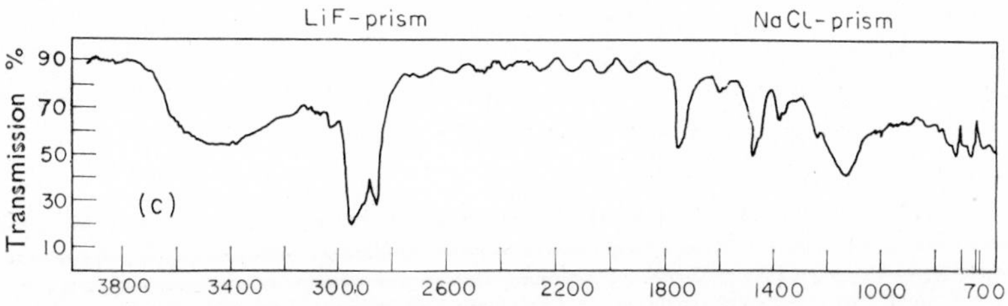

Fig. 1c. Polyester type oil base pigmented with 35 per cent aluminium hydroxide.

THE THIN LAYER EFFECT

In the most important phases of printing the film thickness used for offset and letterpress inks generally is under 25 μ. This film thickness is, in relation to the size of the pigment particles (0.2–1 μ) of nearly the same order as the structure of the system.

This thin layer undergoes a structural change in the field of force of the boundary surface. The dispersion and orientation effects considerably increase the activation energy necessary for molecular migration because of additivity, thus increasing relaxation time, and viscosity, Eq. (8), (13). This phenomenon is analogous to the effect of the external pressure on viscosity. For the formation of a hole it is necessary to do work against not only cohesion forces but also surface forces.

Viscosity and relaxation time thus substantially increase exponentially with interfacial forces. Taking (14) into account, changes in viscosity—in analogy with the effect of the external pressure—must depend very much on hole volumes also in the field of interfacial forces. Regarding relative looseness of printing inks, this effect is considerable. The structure-changing effect of surface forces is still increased by linkage of the macromolecules of the film-forming agent with the solid boundary surface. (The layer fixed in case of molecules with the same structure but different chain length is formed above all by the shortest and most mobile molecules for they are able to orientate most easily.) In a thin film, the relaxation time and the viscosity increase in the direction of the solid boundary surface. At the surface, a greatly structured state with a solid gel character results which is not disturbed by forces operating over long periods.

The thickness of this coherent layer extending upwards from the boundary is determined by the duration of the applied force.

EXPERIMENTAL PART

The thin layer effect derived from the hole theory is supported by the fact that viscosity values measured in ink layers of 10–50 μ on a Bekk viscosimeter deviate from the bulk viscosity values.[1,2]

On a NPIRI BAND Viscosimeter the higher viscosity values as compared with the rotation viscosimeter were presumably found because of considerably smaller layer thicknesses.[3]

In the present work structural changes in thin layers applied to solid surfaces were studied by means of X-ray diffraction obtained by a 5 hr exposure, through a Ni filter, to monochromatic CuKα, rays. The materials examined are summarized in Table 1 and the X-ray diffraction diagrams are given in Fig. 2. Figure 3 shows the intensity distributions of the diffraction rings, in which the dotted lines represent the boundaries of diffuse rings.

TABLE 1. MATERIALS EXAMINED

Number	Material	Comment
386	A-401 vehicle (polyester type)	In a thickness of 30 μ on polyvinyl acetate surface
394	A-401 vehicle (polyester type)	In a thickness of 800 μ in a metal ringlet without applying to a surface
384	Benzidine yellow pigment	Debye–Scherrer's powder diagram
382	A-401 vehicle pigmented with 18% benzidine yellow	In a thickness of 30 μ on polyvinyl acetate surface
393	A-401 vehicle pigmented with 18% benzidine yellow	In a thickness of 800 μ in a metal ringlet without applying to a surface
385	Hansa yellow G	Debye–Scherrer's powder diagram
381	A-401 vehicle pigmented with 18 per cent Hansa yellow G	In a thickness of 30 μ on polyvinyl acetate surface
395	A-401 vehicle pigmented with 18 per cent Hansa yellow	In a thickness of 800 μ in metal ringlet without applying to a surface

The diffraction diagrams show considerable structural changes in a printing ink film applied in a thickness of 30 μ to a polyvinyl acetate surface as compared with a thick ink layer in contact only with the air. This probably reflects changes in orientation within the molecules of polymeric chains. The widening of the diffuse rings in crystalline polymers refers to a shifting of the ratio of crystalline and amorphous phases. The crystalline and amorphous phases are not separated, there are no developed boundary surfaces or symmetrical faces; under different influences the amorphous-crystalline ratio changes within wide limits.

The interaction between benzidine yellow and vehicle proves stronger than between Hansa yellow and vehicle. The structural change effect appears to be more definite in the benzidine yellow/vehicle system showing a higher interaction.

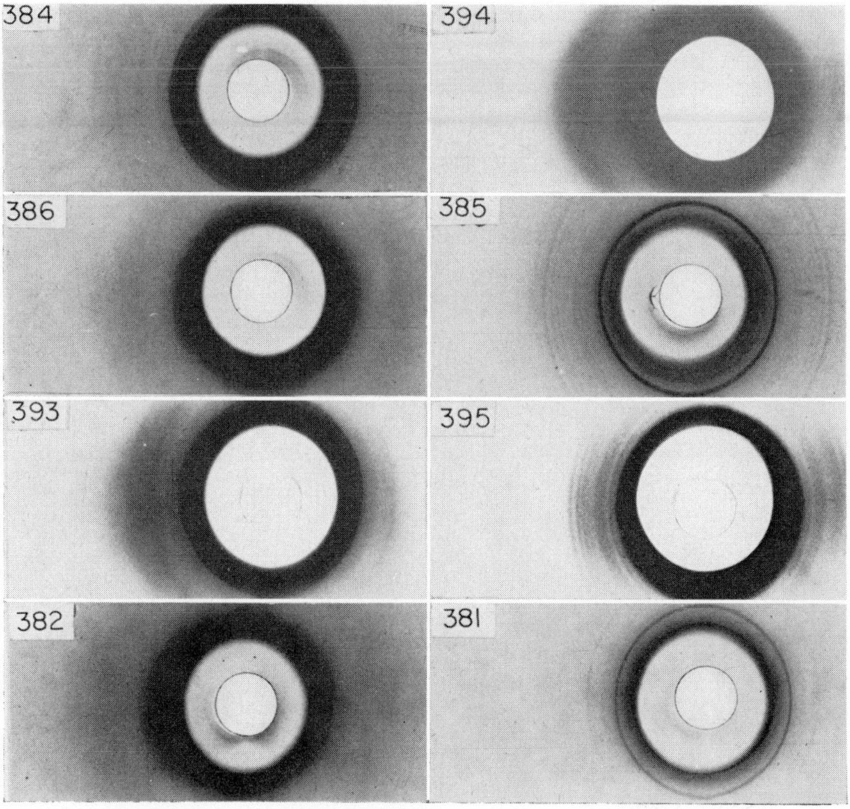

Fig. 2.

THE ROLE OF THE THIN LAYER EFFECT AND THE ABSORPTIVE EFFECT OF PAPER IN INK TRANSFER

Ink transfer curves are well expressed by the formula derived by A. C. Zettlemoyer and his collaborators,(4,5,6) i.e.

$$y = (1 - e^{-kx})\{b(1 - e^{-x/b}) + f[x - b(1 - e^{-x/b})]\}$$

E. Rupp and K. Rieche(7) set up a similar equation in which roughness and absorptivity are very important factors and this takes the form (using the customary symbolism):

$$p = (1 - e^{-a^2m^2})\{w_0(1 - e^{-m/w_0}) + \alpha[m - w_0(1 - e^{-m/w_0})]\}$$

According to the ink transfer curves, ink distribution number increases to a certain maximum with the amount of the ink on the printing forme, and then decreases and tends towards a constant value.

Regarding the factors influencing transfer, Pihl[8] found that neither ink

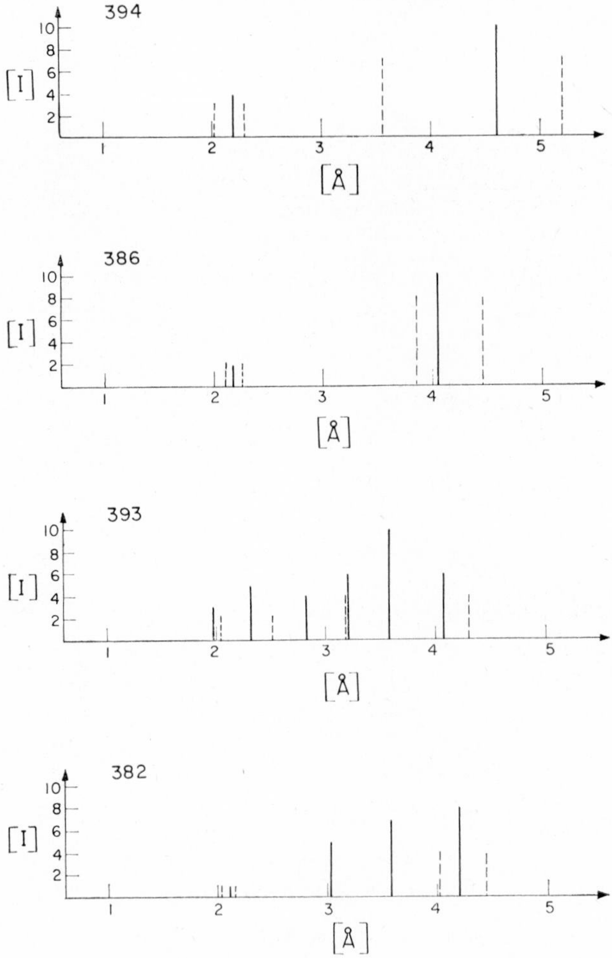

Fig. 3.

absorptivity of paper nor smoothness can be critical factors. The fact namely that the transfer curve of the coated paper has shown a higher maximum with smaller film thicknesses than that of the natural papers led Pihl to conclude that the absorptivity of paper does not entirely control ink transfer.

The parchment did not give any maximum, consequently smoothness also cannot be a decisive factor. Two papers showing the same measured smoothness and oil absorptivity (one a clay-coated, the other a calender roll paper containing sulphite pulp) also had curves of different type.

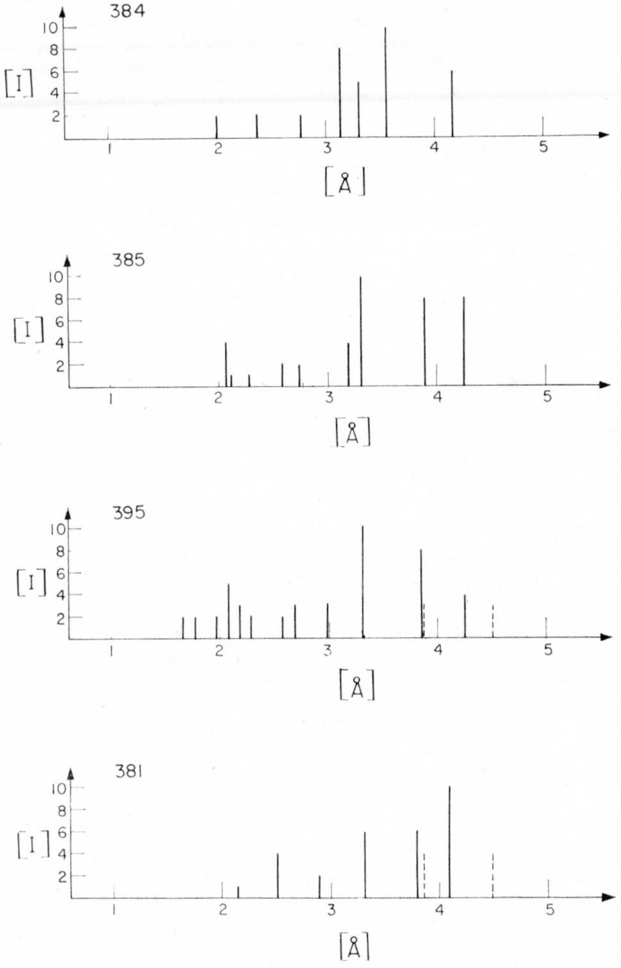

Fig. 3*a*.

Now let us consider the printing forme–ink–paper system in the printing process. If the thickness of the ink layer on the printing form does not or hardly exceed the coherent zone at the printing speed applied, the layer behaves as an elastic body, and no ink transfer occurs. In the case of a layer thicker than the coherent zone, a sandwich like system exists when considering the paper in contact with the forme. Coherent layers extend inwards from both the printing forme and the paper. Coated paper surfaces show a selective effect in ink absorption. They absorb the free film-forming agent much more speedily than the pigment–lyosphere system. This selection phenomenon is the filtration effect. Natural papers also show this effect but it is much smaller as compared with coated papers. Depending on the degree of filtration an ink layer of uneven thickness having a more compact structure as compared with bulk structure is formed within the same time. This film on the printing form surface is undoubtedly more compact and contains less holes (defects) compared with a layer affected only by surface forces owing to the actual changing pigmentation of the ink, by loss of some of the vehicle.

The ink separation which is facilitated through the cavitation effect according to the investigations of Banks, Mill,[9,10] and Strassburger[11] occurs in the less ordered layers between the paper and the printing forme. The holes or the defects are concentrated namely in this region after coherent and greatly orientated layers have been formed on the surface of the printing forme and on the paper. The external tension is concentrated at the defects between the two coherent and orientated layers, and it becomes, naturally, the cavitation zone. In brief, ink transfer appears to be determined first of all by the ratio of thickness of the two coherent and orientated zones being produced between printing forme and paper during the printing process.

Let us consider the thin layer effect in the physical picture of ink transfer. In the case of a small amount of ink on the printing forme, a higher maximum occurs on art paper than on natural papers because of the greater degree of filtration. Increasing maximum values occur with increasing pressure or decreasing printing speeds as a consequence of increasing filtration. This is verified by the fact that the ink distribution number remains invariant beginning with a relatively small amount of the ink on the printing forme, and that this cannot be influenced even by changing the pressure. There is no filtration on a non-absorbent foil. On the surface of the foil a coherent and orientated layer is formed as on the printing forme. The ink splitting number, however, is not independent of the printing speed even on the foil surface. With increasing force-time effect the thickness of the coherent zone decreases and therefore ink transfer increases. With increasing amount of ink on the printing forme, the ink transfer curve becomes flat and tends to a constant value. The reason for this is that an increasing amount of ink reduces the significance of the thickness of the coherent and orientated layers formed on the printing forme and on the paper surface as compared with the total layer thickness. Separation by cavitation takes place in the centre of the "free" layer of loose structure.

Summarizing then, the factors determining ink transfer and the total amount of energy needed to separate the ink film, are as follows:

(*a*) filtration effect of the paper;

(*b*) sensitivity of the ink to filtration which can be expressed by the relation between the change in concentration of the vehicle and the change in relaxation time caused by it;

(*c*) interaction between the surface force field and the structure of the ink that determines the amount of thin layer effect;

(*d*) time factor.

BULK RHEOLOGY OF INKS

From what has been said it is inferred that the rheology of inks in bulk is not entirely relevant.

In the critical phase of the printing process it is rather the thin layer effect of the ink that is of importance.

The role of bulk rheology gradually comes to an end after the printing ink has passed through the first distributors in the printing machine. On high-speed printing machines the deformation rate of the ink can reach even a value of 10^4 sec^{-1}, and this brings about the maximum decomposition of the structure of the ink.

The experiments of Gudkova, Kosarovitsky and Mikhaylov[(12)] clearly verify that the choice of velocity gradient is of decisive importance from the stand-point of a meaningful description of the viscosity of printing inks. It is not sufficient to use for characterizing rheological features of a structural system, the method in which characteristics are examined at a given shear stress and at arbitrary velocity gradients, i.e. at different degree of the structure.

When the ink is fully broken down structurally by shear the full rheological curves have no longer any role. A printing ink with a destroyed structure shows linear (Newtonian) flow characteristics.

SUMMARY

Printing inks undergo a structural change owing to the surface forces in a layer-thickness of 20 μ. This phenomenon is analogous with the effect of the external pressure on viscosity.

In a thin layer on a surface, the structure of the printing ink departs from bulk structure. As a consequence of this, relaxation time and viscosity considerably increase.

Through the filtration effect of printing papers a layer of uneven thickness and constitution—and having a solid gel structure (coherent and orientated), is formed on the surface.

By means of this thin layer effect, ink transfer curves can properly be interpreted. In the printing process the splitting of the ink occurs in the layer between the coherent layers because defects are concentrated here. The external tension thus exerts its influence on a much smaller region than the cross-section, and a cavitation promoting splitting action takes place in this zone. Bulk rheology in the case of printing inks seems to be of decreased relevance. For studying thin layers X-ray diffraction, infrared spectroscopy, and magnetic resonance are important methods.

REFERENCES

1. A. Voet, *Ink and Paper in the Printing Process*, Interscience, New York (1952).
2. A. Voet and C. F. Geffken, *Ind. Eng. Chem.* **43,** 1614 (1951).
3. NPIRI Bulletin, No. 53, 1959.
4. W. Walker and J. Fetsko, A concept of ink transfer in printing. *Am. Ink Maker* **33,** 12 (1955).
5. J. Fetsko and W. Walker, Measurements of ink transfer in the printing of coated papers. *Am. Ink Maker* **33,** 11 (1955).
6. J. Fetsko, W. Walker and A. Zettlemoyer, Techniques for controlling laboratory printing conditions. *Am. Ink Maker* **33,** 10 (1955).
7. E. Rupp and K. Rieche, Beiträge zur Bedruckbarkeit von Papier und Folien. *Leipzig Inst. Graph. Tech.* (1959).
8. Pihl, The ink transfer to paper in the printing. *Svensk Papperstidning* **55,** 358 (1952).
9. Banks and Mill, *J. Colloid Sci.* **8,** 137 (1953).
10. Banks and Mill, *Proc. Roy. Soc.* **A223,** 414 (1954).
11. Strassburger, *J. Colloid Sci.* **13,** 218 (1958).
12. Gudkova, Kozarovitsky and Mikhaylov, K voprosu o vliyanii strukturno-mekhanicheskikh svoyistv pechatnikh krasok na ikh povedenie v pechatnom protsesse.

DISCUSSION

Hsu: (1) Your mathematical treatment is for liquids in general, yet all examples quoted refer to polymers. Do you regard your argument of viscoelasticity equally valid for simple liquids, such as simple mineral oils or water?

(2) Are you able to give an estimate of the relaxation time of a printing ink, say, a mineral oil based ink?

Gáti: (1) The hole theory is valid for simple liquids. The relaxation times of simple liquids are very short. We are talking about viscous flow, where a small force operating for a very short time will respond to a permanent set.

(2) In my estimate the relaxation time of a mineral oil based ink is 10^{-5} to 10^{-7} sec.

Zettlemoyer: I have had the opportunity, with the aid of Madame Benédite, of discussing Mr. Gáti's concepts with him. His idea of the ink micelle composed of pigment particles closely spaced with polymer molecules interacting and connecting two or more particles appears to be quite useful and reasonable to explain structure. However, it seems unreasonable to me to believe that surface forces extend to 20 μ. If this were so, we would expect that, for example, ink transfer from metal plates would differ from that for plastic plates. No difference is in fact found as is shown in the paper which I have given at this conference.

Gáti: The additivity of the forces from layer to layer increases the extension of the field of intermolecular forces. The structure changing effect is enhanced by fixation of the macromolecules of vehicle in direct contact with the solid boundary surface.

In a thin ink film, the relaxation time and viscosity increase in the direction of the solid surface. Immediately at the boundary surface a predominantly structured state with a solid gel character (i.e. a coherent state) results.

The thickness of this coherent zone is determined by the duration of the external force.

WALKER: The way your X-ray diagrams support the picture of molecular orientation in thin ink films was not quite clear to me from your paper. Would you care to describe this more fully?

GÁTI: The X-ray diagrams show generally a considerable change in the atomic density in the field, when comparing a thin layer with a thick layer of same ink. Verification of this is seen in the change of line intensity and position. This probably reflects changes within the molecules comprising polymer chains.

The widening of the diffuse ring (Fig. 394, 386) in crystalline polymers refers to a shifting of the ratio of crystalline to amorphous phases.

INTERFACIAL TENSION MEASUREMENTS OF OFFSET-INKS RELATED TO HALFTONE-PRINTING IN OFFSET

by R. LARAIGNOU
The Graphic College of Denmark

INTRODUCTION

IN the offset printing process the correct water–ink balance is vital to obtain a good printing result. In particular the sharpness of dots in half-tone-printing and the possibility of keeping clean dots in shadow areas are dependent on the behaviour of water and ink with each other; the water tends to emulsify with the ink, making it short and buttery. If too much water is picked up, the ink starts to pile up on the rollers and greasing or scumming may occur. The tendency of the ink to emulsify is related to a number of factors, among which the interfacial tension between the ink and the water is one of the most important.

Until now no easy method has been developed to determine the interfacial tension between offset ink and water, due to the consistency of the inks.

J. H. Bitter[(1)] measured the interfacial tension of offset inks against water by making measurements on 0.1 per cent ink solutions in benzene. This percentage is too small to provide reliable information concerning the interfacial tension of the undiluted material.

This work describes a relatively simple method which has been developed to determine the interfacial tension between water and ink, making use of a Lecomte de Noüy balance. This method is based on the dilution of the ink in an appropriate solvent (benzene) in different concentrations, making it possible to extrapolate the measurement for the pure ink.

THEORETICAL CONSIDERATIONS

Several factors influence the good working properties of an offset-ink. Among these factors are: the rheological properties, the interfacial tension ink/water and the affinity to the metal plate.

The rheological properties

The ink must possess a viscosity sufficiently high to withstand the action of the water compatible with requirements of the paper in its ability to resist picking at the speed of operation.

The pigment must be well wetted by the vehicle. The wetting of the pigment by the vehicle must be preferred to wetting by water so that the latter cannot enter the pigment surface–vehicle interface and displace the vehicle.

The interfacial tension ink–water

It would seem apparent that ink having high interfacial tension against water will have better working properties on an offset press, all other conditions being equal. Liquids with low interfacial tensions against water will emulsify easily, since low values of interfacial tension mean that only little work has to be done to increase the interface. If the interfacial tension is high the two non-miscible liquids will emulsify with greater difficulty; more energy has to be put into the system to create new interfaces. Thus, if the interfacial tension of the ink toward water is high, the ink will have less tendency to emulsify. It is a well-known fact that all offset inks emulsify to a degree with the fountain solution. Prior investigations have shown that the amount of water picked up by an average good ink will be somewhere between 10–20 per cent by volume.

The emulsification of water into the ink will give the ink a shorter body and the tinting strength of the ink will go down. If too much water is picked up, the ink can become so short that the distribution suffers and the ink starts to pile.

The affinity to the metal plate

The ink must also possess sufficient affinity to the metal plate and more especially to the printing areas. This affinity is in our opinion related to certain polar-materials which in most cases have the effect of lowering the interfacial tension against water.

No method has to our knowledge been developed to measure these "attractive" forces between the ink and the metal plate. It is only known that most fatty acids possess this affinity to a greater or lesser degree.

From this it follows that a satisfactory offset ink while requiring that its interfacial tension toward water be high, requires that other properties be taken into account, such as viscosity, pigment wetting, affinity to the metal plate.

EXPERIMENTAL

The method is based on the fact that when two materials, *A* and *B* are mixed together the resulting interfacial tension against water is particularly influenced by the one having the lowest interfacial tension. This phenomenon is shown in Fig. 1.

Let us suppose that *A* has a rather high interfacial tension of about 30 dyne/cm and *B* an interfacial tension of about 10 dyne/cm. Only small

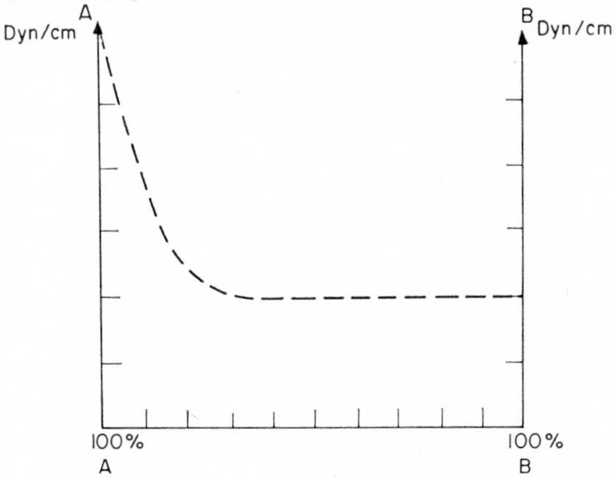

Fig. 1.

amounts of *B* in *A* will give a value which is very near to the interfacial tension of the pure product *B*.

In all cases where it has been possible for us to study the whole concentration curve of interfacial tension values against water (solutions where *A* was benzene and *B* various liquids) we have shown that for a 25 per cent concentration of substance *B* the values were very close to the values of the pure product *B*. In no cases were they higher than 3 dyne/cm over the values of pure *B*. See Figs. 2 and 3.

It is often very difficult, especially with viscous inks to make a measurement with sufficient accuracy at a concentration higher than 25 per cent in benzene. This is due to too high a viscosity difference between the water and the benzene solution, and also in many cases the benzene solutions are thixotropic. Both factors will lead to too high a value in the determination.

In any case, it is often of interest to make measurement at a concentration different from 25 per cent, for example 15 per cent. If the value obtained at 15 per cent concentration is very near that at 25 per cent (within 1 dyne/cm), this indicates that the curve has flattened out and that the value obtained at 25 per cent is very close to the value of the pure product. If the difference is significant it might be necessary to try to make a measurement at a higher concentration than 25 per cent, for example 30 or 35 per cent. At this high concentration, as mentioned above, the interfacial tension measurement becomes difficult to make with great accuracy.

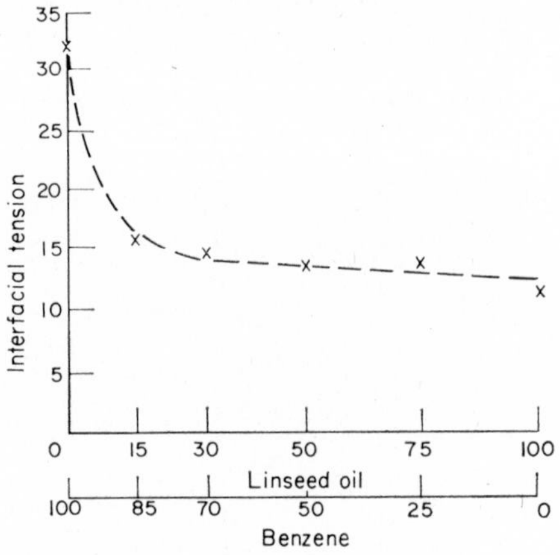

Fig. 2.

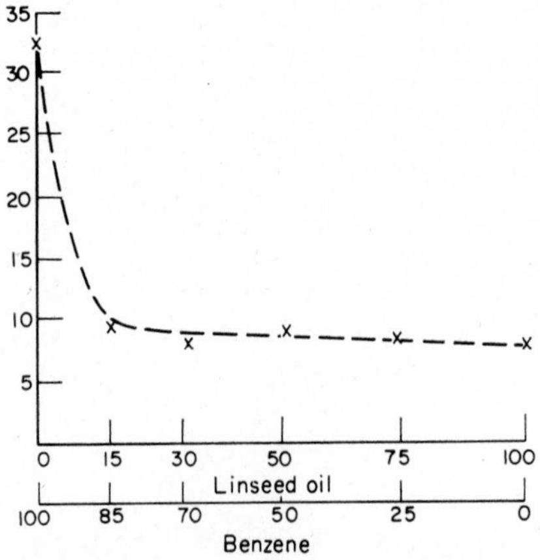

Fig. 3.

Benzene was selected as a solvent for these ink solutions because it possesses a low viscosity and a rather high interfacial tension higher compared with most of the materials contained in the ink. It has sufficient solvent power, so as not to precipitate the resins and the more complex oils entering the ink formation and further, is readily obtained in a pure state.

Carbon tetrachloride also qualifies. Benzene has an interfacial tension against water of approximately 30 dyne/cm and carbon tetrachloride a value of approximately 40 dyne/cm (measured at 25°C). Since, when using this method, one is interested in getting a curve which flattens at low concentrations of ink the benzene will be used for products having interfacial tension values under 30 dyne/cm, and the carbon tetrachloride for those having interfacial tension values between 30–40 dyne/cm.

Experimental details

Since the values obtained depend on the temperature all the measurements are made in a room at a constant temperature of 25°C. The product to be measured is diluted or dissolved in benzene (or carbon tetrachloride) to the desired concentration. This dilution must be done very carefully to assure homogeneity.

The container is now filled halfway with pure tap-water having a pH of 6.5 and a surface tension of 72.5 dyne/cm. If the tap-water has a lower surface tension, due to some surface-active grease, this can in most cases easily be eliminated by cleaning the surface of the water with a piece of filter paper. The paper will absorb the surface-active agent and the surface tension of the water will rise to approximately 72 dynes/cm.

The platinum ring of the du Noüy apparatus is now placed on the bottom of the vessel in the water phase. The benzene solution, whose specific gravity in practically all cases is lower than that of water, is then poured on the water surface in a thickness of approximately 1 cm. The vessel is covered with a piece of paper to prevent evaporation and is placed for a minimum of 20 min in the constant temperature room before the measurement is done.

Tap-water was selected instead of a well defined fountain solution, or even distilled water. This is because no noticeable difference was found in the interfacial tension values when using tap-water of the above characteristics, distilled water or a fountain solution of pH 5.5 (with phosphoric acid).

Since fountain solutions used by printers vary both in composition and in pH, and since there were no reasons to select one fountain solution instead of another, it was decided to use tap-water. Moreover in many printing plants only tap-water is used.

The accuracy of the measurement

The accuracy of the measurements was controlled by repeating each measurement several times on the same solution. It was observed that the interfacial tension decreased during the first 20 min after having poured the ink-solution on the water surface.

Figure 4 shows the interfacial tension values obtained at various time-intervals after having poured a 25 per cent varnish–benzene solution on the water. To get a constant value and attain equilibrium it is therefore necessary to let the benzene–ink-solution stand with the water for a minimum of

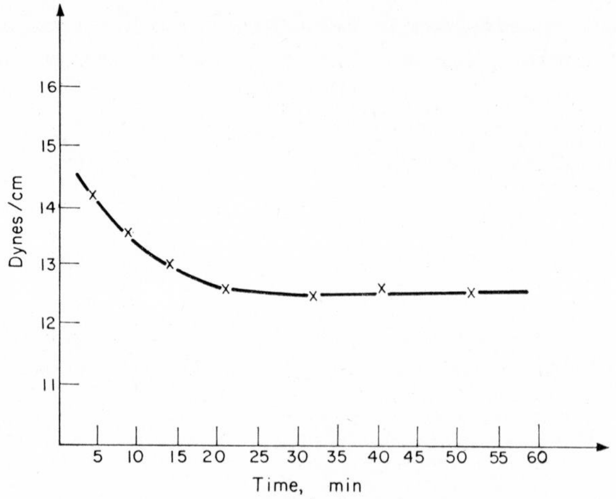

Fig. 4.

20 min before the measurement is done. The reason for this is that the surface active components in the ink must have time to orientate themselves at the interface.

The reproducibility of the measurement

To control the reproducibility of the measurement, several inks and raw materials were measured five times under the same conditions and the following results were obtained:

TABLE 1

Ink A (15% concentration)	Ink B (15% concentration)
15.7 dyne/cm	13.2 dyne/cm
15.6 dyne/cm	12.8 dyne/cm
15.4 dyne/cm	12.8 dyne/cm
15.7 dyne/cm	13.0 dyne/cm
15.3 dyne/cm	12.9 dyne/cm

The results above show a very good reproducibility.

Our work on the interfacial tension measurements of inks and the different raw materials entering the ink formulation, has demonstrated that the interfacial tension of a well ground mixture of pigment and vehicle will depend on the vehicle and on the pigment in different ways.

The free polar groups in the vehicle, those which are the main cause of low interfacial tension, might be partly or completely adsorbed by the pigment surface, thus increasing the interfacial tension compared to the original vehicle, or be of such a nature that no absorption will occur and with practically no change in the interfacial tension compared to the original vehicle.

Polar materials may on the other hand be increased in number due to their having been brought into the system by pigments on whose surface there exists surface active materials. In this case the interfacial tension will be decreased.

The following measurements show these facts very well. Two inks were compared under the same conditions (same concentration, same vehicle), but with different pigments:

TABLE 2

	Benzene solution 15%	Concentration 25%
Varnish (coal tar resin in mineral oil) ..	17.0 dyne/cm	16.5 dyne/cm
20 per cent Lake Red C (resinated) in coal tar-varnish	14.8 dyne/cm	14.5 dyne/cm
20 per cent furnace black in coal tar-varnish	22.2 dyne/cm	22.0 dyne/cm

The Lake Red C pigment has lowered the interfacial tension of the original varnish whereas the carbon black pigment has increased it.

It is interesting to note from Table 3 values for the raw materials that the alkyd resins generally show a very low interfacial tension. This explains why the alkyd resins have excellent wetting properties towards most pigments. On the other hand, mineral oils possess very high interfacial tensions; they show poor wettability of pigments. Most phenolic resins possess interfacial tensions lying in the region of 12–17 dyne/cm. Their wetting properties toward organic pigments are generally low. Most raw linseed oils have a rather low interfacial tension (3–5 dyne/cm). By rapidly heating up the raw linseed oil to about 270°C and then cooling it down, the interfacial tension goes up very markedly. The heat-treatment destroys the surface-active materials in the oils, such as phosphatides. Lecithin is a very strong wetting agent often used by ink manufacturers to improve the flow of the ink as it gives better wetting of the pigment. Due to the very strong action of lecithin in lowering the interfacial tension, one has to determine the right amount to be used in each case. This method provides a means to control this problem. Many products, like flushed pastes, may contain surface active agents which will give inks with too low an interfacial tension. This surface agent in the flushed paste often comes from the flushing aids, such as amines or amine salts, that have not been washed away sufficiently. The right paste to use can be selected by this method.

There seems to be a certain relationship between the above interfacial tension values of ink and their performances on the offset press.

Inks having rather high interfacial tension have performed well, whereas inks with low interfacial tensions have worked badly. It is actually too early to state what should be the limits of interfacial tension for good running of an offset ink but further investigation is being undertaken. But as we already have noted, factors other than the interfacial tension influence the behaviour and the performance of an offset ink.

TABLE 3. INTERFACIAL TENSION VALUES OF SOME RAW MATERIALS ENTERING THE INK FORMULATION

Benzene solution	15%	25%	50%	100%
Wood rosin FF	14.6	14.5	—	—
Rosin modified hard phenolic resin	12.3	11.9	—	—
Gilsonite select	20.7	20.3	—	—
Long oil soya alkyd	5.2	5.3	—	—
Long Talloil alkyd	5.8	6.2	—	—
Long oil isophthalic alkyd	6.8	6.0	—	—
Aliphatic hydrocarbons 210/230°C	—	—	—	26.8
Aliphatic hydrocarbons 230/260°C	—	—	—	31.2
Aliphatic hydrocarbons 260/290°C	—	—	—	35.5
Thin spindle oil 2° Engler/50°C	—	—	—	25.5
Aromatic (residual) oils	—	5.6	—	4.8
Xylol	—	—	—	35.5
Raw linseed oil	—	—	3.6	—
Heat-treated raw linseed oil	—	—	10.3	—
Alkyd linseed oil	—	—	12.1	—
Heat-treated alkyd linseed oil	—	—	17.0	—
Blown linseed oil	10.1	10.2	—	—
Standard 2 poises/25°C	—	—	16.2	—
Rosin oil	—	—	—	8.5
Dehydrated castor oil	—	—	—	10.3
Lecithin	0	0	—	—
Cobalt naphthenate 6%	22.5	21.1	—	—
Flushed alkali blue A	13.8	13.7	—	—
Flushed alkali blue B	12.8	12.6	—	—
Flushed alkali blue C	11.6	11.4	—	—
Flushed alkali blue D	6.4	—	—	—
Flushed alkali blue E	3.0	—	—	—
Flushed alkali blue F	13.4	13.1	—	—

TABLE 4. INTERFACIAL TENSION OF SOME INKS

	15%	25%
Transparent white offset DF	21.2	19.6
Black offset LB	20.8	18.6
Red offset DL	—	23.5
Black offset DR	18.0	17.7
Black offset GM	13.0	—
Black offset RD	15.6	15.4
Black offset HS	13.7	13.2
Red offset NT	18.1	19.0
Black offset TL . ..	9.5	8.3
All the above inks were said by printers to have good working properties, whereas the following inks were said to show a tendency to greasing and piling.		
Black offset LC	7.9	7.9
Black offset LN	7.2	7.2
Yellow offset RL	11.5	10.9
Black offset VA	5.1	5.0
Black offset RO	4.1	—
Black offset BA	2.3	1.9

REFERENCES

1. J. H. BITTER, Emulsification of offset inks. *Int. Bull.*, Jan. 1956.

INDEX